New York City 5 Borough Atlas

FIFTH LARGE SCALE EDITION

Copyright 1998 Hagstrom Map Company, Inc.
46-35 54th Road, Maspeth, New York 11378
www.hagstrommap.com
Printed in Canada

Cover Photo of Lower Manhattan from Queens by Battman

Legend for Street Maps

Main Highways/ Limited Access

Main Through Roads

Vehicular Tunnels

State ⟨24⟩ U.S. ⟨1⟩⟨9⟩ ⟨278⟩ Interstate — Highway Symbols

16 — Interchange Numbers

Subway-7th Av Lines 1,2,3,9 *(formerly IRT West Side)*

Subway-Lexington Av Lines 4,5,6 *(formerly IRT East Side)*

Subway-Flushing Line 7 *(formerly IRT Queensboro)*

Subway-Lines A,B,C,D,E, F,G,Q *(formerly IND)*

Subway-Lines J,L,M,N,R,Z *(formerly BMT)*

Subway-Line S 42nd St. Shuttle, Manhattan & Franklin Av. Shuttle, Brooklyn

Local ⊙ Express ◯ — Subway Stations

PATH Tubes and Stations *(Port Authority Trans-Hudson Railway)*

Tramway-Roosevelt Island

Passenger ┼─□┼─┼■─┼ Freight Only — Railroad Lines and Stations

– – – – — Ferries

State Boundaries

County Boundaries

1920 — Building Numbers

14 — Postal Zones

Finance ● ◯ Carrier — Post Office Stations

▲ or Plgd/PG — Playgrounds

Parks

Golf Courses

Cemeteries

Government Lands

Points of Interest

Airports

H — Hospitals

SCALE FOR THE BOROUGH OF QUEENS
Scales (Approximate) 1:24,000 • 1" = 2,000 Feet

0   4,000 Feet

0   1,000 Meters

SCALE FOR ALL OTHER BOROUGHS
Scales (Approximate) 1:21,000 • 1" = 1,750 Feet

0   3,000 Feet

0   1,000 Meters

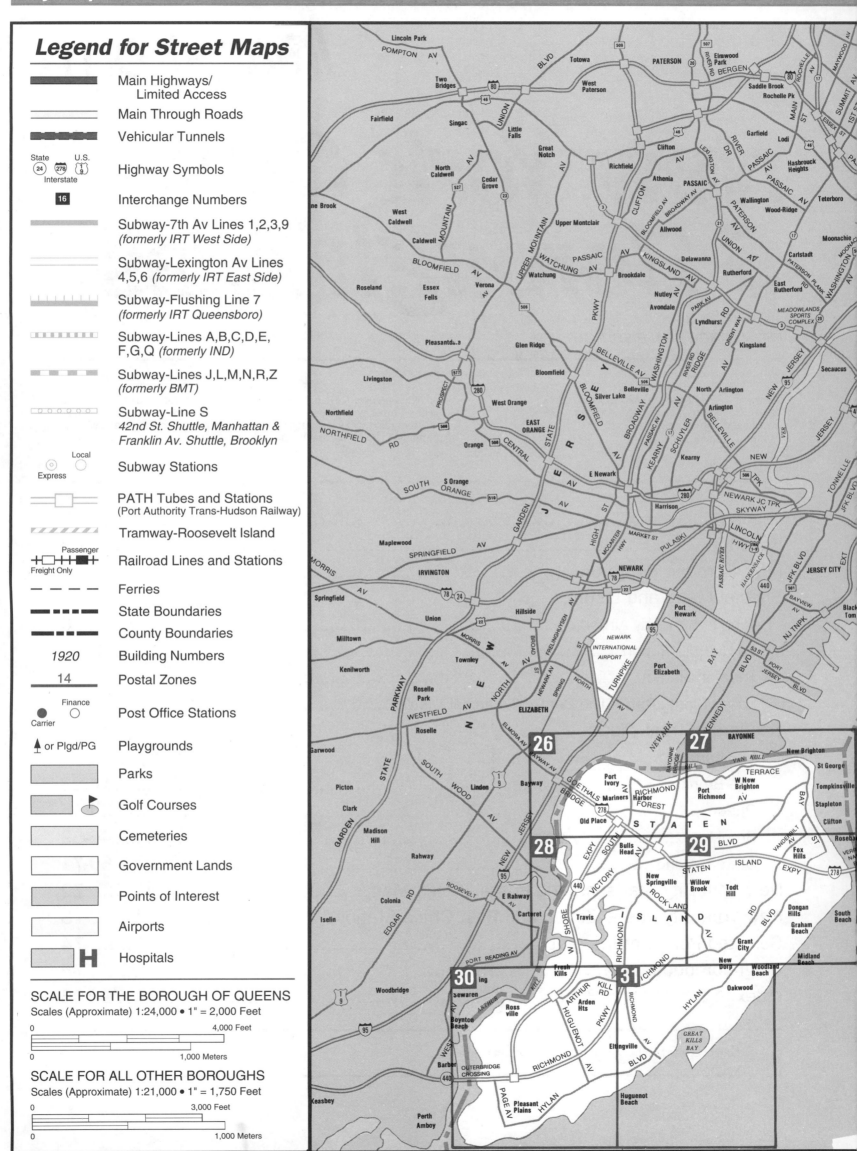

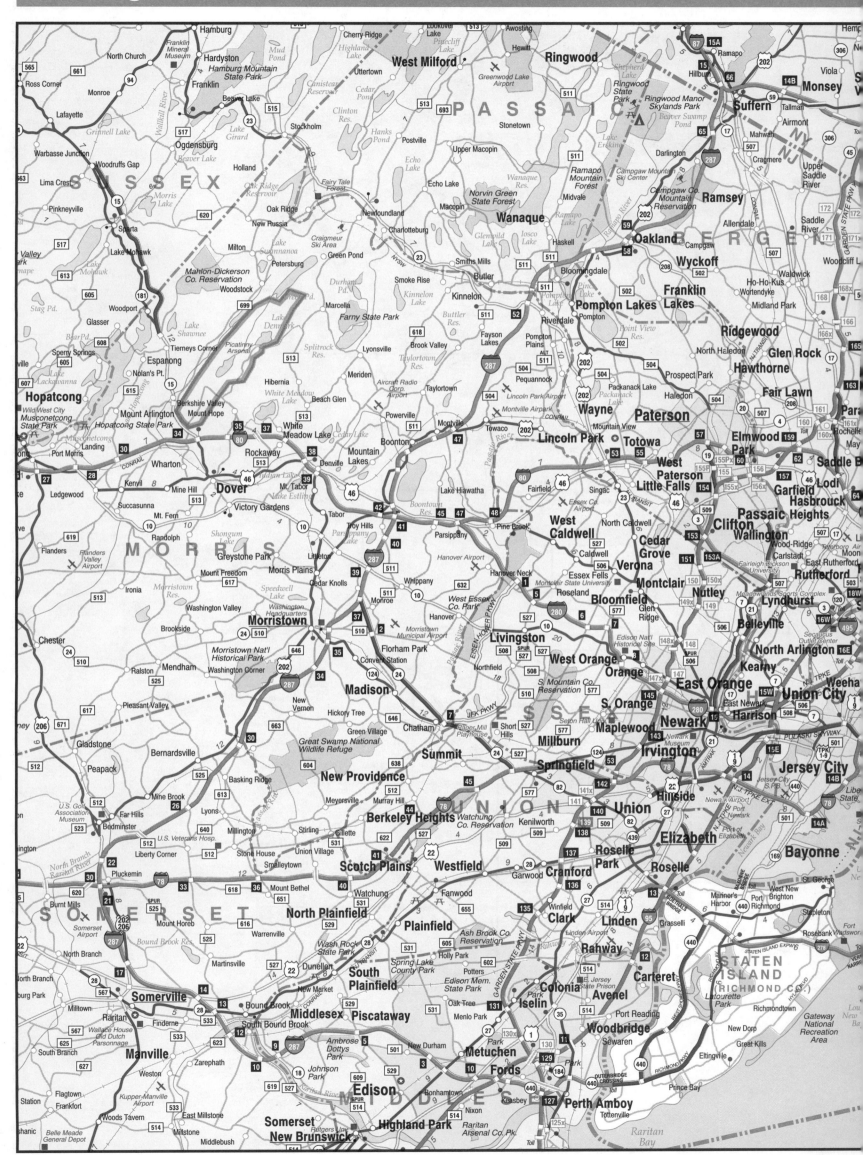

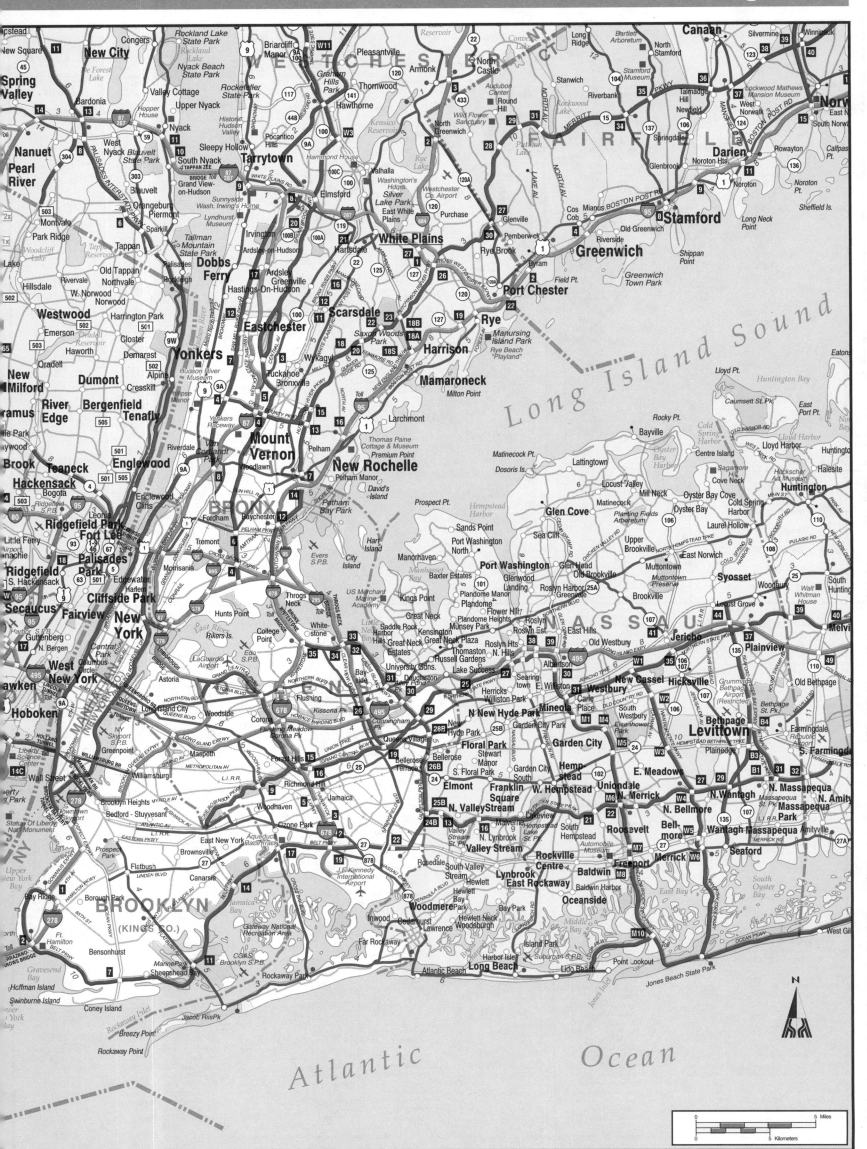

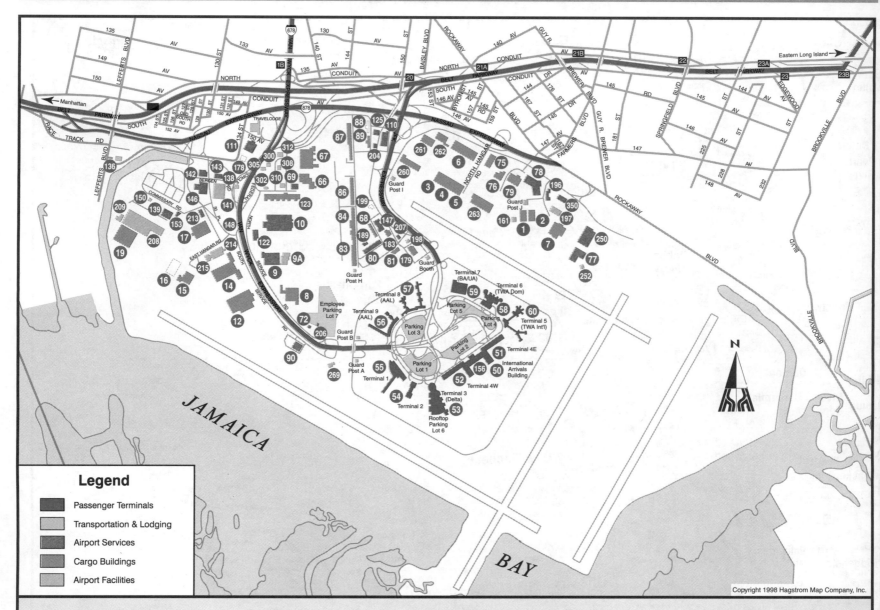

Copyright 1998 Hagstrom Map Company, Inc.

Legend

- Passenger Terminals
- Transportation & Lodging
- Airport Services
- Cargo Buildings
- Airport Facilities

AIRPORT FACILITIES

FAA Control Tower	156
Ground Equipment	214
Jet Testing Cell	215
Medical Office	198
Port Authority Administration	141
Port Authority Central Heating and Refrigeration Plant	49
Port Authority Fire Station	161
Port Authority Maintenance	9A
Port Authority Police Lost and Found (Motor Vehicle Inspection)	197
Port Authority Police and Aeronautical Services	269
Port Authority Satellite Garage	252
Utilities	209

AIRPORT SERVICES

AMR Services	78
Aeronautical Radio	10
Air Freight Inc. Warehouse	197
Air Navigation	263
Airmar	263
Allied Aviation Services	142
Allied New York Services (Fueling)	90
American Express	50
Amoco Gas Station	138
Avis Car Rental (Maintenance)	207
Baggage Storage	50
Barclays Bank	59
Brinks Security	263
Brooklyn Union Gas	153
CitiBank	50
Emery Worldwide	123
Federal Aviation Administration	111
Federal Building	111
Freight Forwarders and Custom Brokers	80
General Aviation Terminal	269
Hertz Corporation (Maintenance)	206
Hudson General	11,69
IDF Services	59
Interim Passenger Terminal	213
International Arrival Building	50,51,52
International Shoppes	50
JFKids Port	350
Lansdell Protective Agency	110
Loomis Armored	68
Mariott In-Flight Services	139
NYNEX	147
National Car Rental (Maintenance)	204
Ogden Foods Bldg.	196
Ogden In-Flight Kitchen	146
Ogden Security	110
Overseas Industries	263
Port Authority Public Services (US Customs, US Dept. of Agriculture, US Public Health Services US Dept. of Immigration)	155

Post Office	50,52,250
Servair Inc.	4
Sky Chefs	122
Sky Supply	263
Sky-Del	110
Teletrip Paging	50
Thamas Cook Foreign Exchange	50
Travellers Aid	50
Triangle Aviation	89
U.S. Air Mail Facility	250
U.S. Customs	77
U.S. Dept. of Plant Protection and Quarantines	50
U.S. Military Liason Office	53
U.S. National Weather Service	50
Vetport	189
Wells Fargo	263

CARGO AIRLINES

Aer Lingus	87
AeroMexico	67
Aerolineas Argentinas	76
Air Afrique	83
Air China	67
Air Europa	68
Air France	83
Air India	86
Air Jamaica	87
Airborne	78
Alitalia Airlines	7
American Airlines	123
Asiana	263
Avianca	84
BWIA International	84
British Airways	66
Cargo Lux.	263
China Air	76
Continental Airlines	75
DHL Worldwide	179, 263
Delta Airlines	67
EVA	79
El Al Israel Airlines	83
Federal Express Cargo Building	83
Finnair	151
Ghana Airways	87
Iberia Airlines	76
Japan Airlines	263
KLM Royal Dutch Airlines	87
Korean Airlines	260
Kuwait Airways	261
LOT Polish Airlines	87
Lufthansa	261
Nippon Cargo Airlines	79
Northwest Airlines	1,2
Pakistan Airlines	86
Quantas	66
Royal Jordanian	86
Swissair	15

TACA International	7
Trans World Airlines (TWA)	12
Transbrasil	83
US Airways	84
United Airlines	4, 8
United Parcel Service (UPS)	84
Varig Airlines	7

PASSENGER AIRLINES

APA (Dominicana)	51
Aer Lingus	51
Aero Peru	51
AeroMexico	54
Aeroflot	53
Aerolineas Argentinas	51
Air Afrique	52
Air China	53
Air Europa	57
Air France	52
Air India	52
Air Jamaica	52
Air Ukraine	53
Alitalia Airlines	52
All Nippon Airways	53
Allegro Airlines	52
America West	54
American Airlines	56
American Eagle	56
American TransAir	54
Asiana	51
Austrian Airlines	51
Aviacsa	52
Avianca	53
BWIA International	57
Balkan Bulgarian	51
Biman Bangladesh	52
British Airways	59
Canadian Airlines	56
Carnival	51
Cathay Pacific	53
China Air	53
Continental Express	54
Corsair	52
Delta Airlines	52
EVA Airways	51
Egypt Air	52
El Al Israel Airlines	52
Equatoriana	51
Finnair	54
Ghana Airways	52
Guyana Airways	51
Iberia Airlines	51
Icelandair	51
Japan Airlines	51
KLM Royal Dutch Airlines	51
Korean Airlines	51
Kras Air	52

Kuwait Airways	51
L.T.U.	51
Lacsa	54
Lan Chile	59
Lot Polish Airlines	57
Lufthansa	51
Malev Hungarian	53
Mexicana	52
Miami Air International	52
North American	60
Northwest Airlines	51
Oasis	52
Olympic Airlines	51
Pakistan Airlines	52
Pan Am	51
Quantas Air	56
Royal Air Maroc	51
Royal Jordanian	51
Sabena Airlines	53
Saeta	59
Saudia	54
Scandinavian Airlines System (SAS)	59
Servivensa	52
Singapore	53
South African Airways	57
Spanair	52
Sun Country	58
Swissair	53
TAP Air Portugal	53
TW Express	60
Taca	54
Taesa	52
Tarom-Romanian Airlines	53
Tower Air	213
Trans World Airlines (TWA-Domestic)	58
Trans World Airlines (TWA-International)	60
Transbrazil	52
Turkish Airlines	52
US Airways	59
US Airways Express	59
United Airlines	59
United Express	59
Uzbekistan Airways	52
VASP	52
Varig Airlines	54
Virgin Atlantic	54

TRANSPORTATION SERVICES

Airway Bus Service	Lot 5
Avis Car Rental	305
Budget Car Rental	310
Carey Transporation	199
Dollar Car Rental	312
Hertz Car Rental	302
Hertz Corporation	150
Salem Transportation	136
Taxi-Limousine Commission	197

Note: Location of tenants subject to change without notice.　　　　**Source:** The Port Authority of New York and New Jersey.

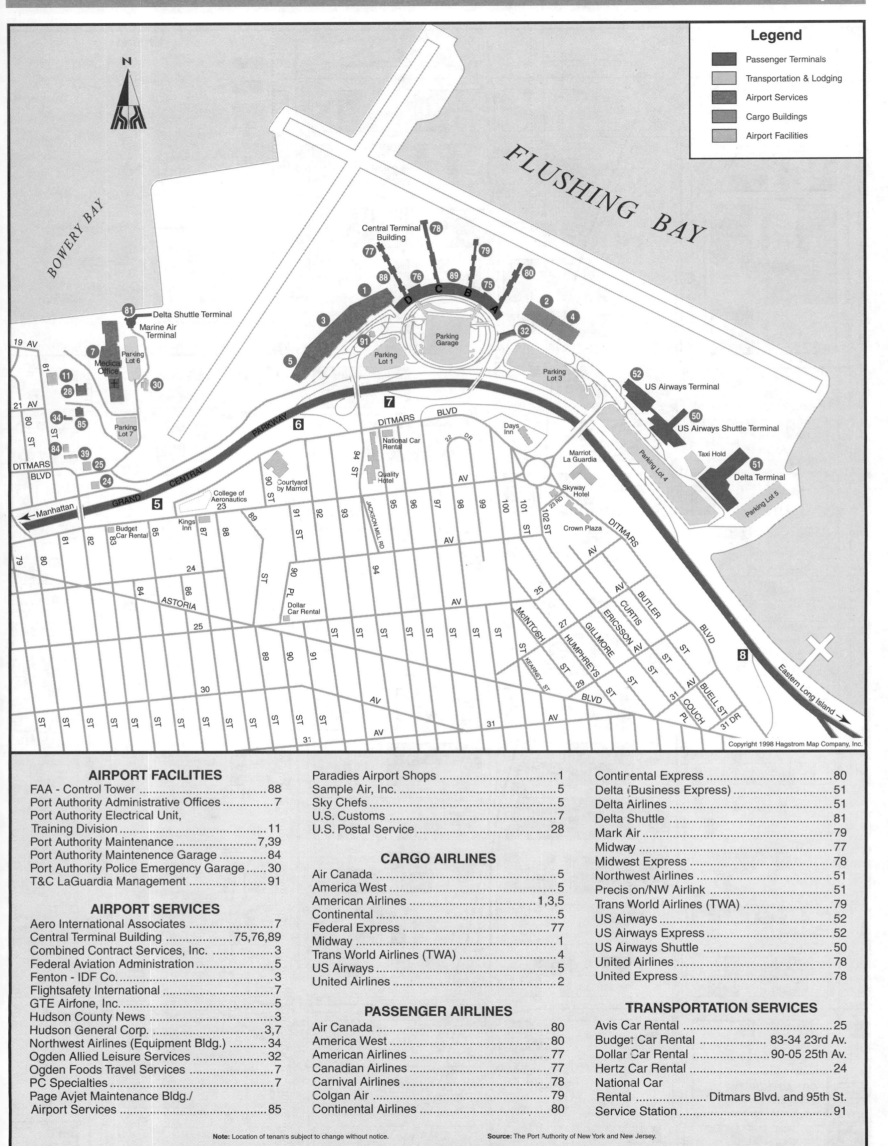

Copyright 1998 Hagstrom Map Company, Inc.

Legend
- Passenger Terminals
- Transportation & Lodging
- Airport Services
- Cargo Buildings
- Airport Facilities

AIRPORT FACILITIES

FAA - Control Tower	88
Port Authority Administrative Offices	7
Port Authority Electrical Unit, Training Division	11
Port Authority Maintenance	7,39
Port Authority Maintenence Garage	84
Port Authority Police Emergency Garage	30
T&C LaGuardia Management	91

AIRPORT SERVICES

Aero International Associates	7
Central Terminal Building	75,76,89
Combined Contract Services, Inc.	3
Federal Aviation Administration	5
Fenton - IDF Co.	3
Flightsafety International	7
GTE Airfone, Inc.	5
Hudson County News	3
Hudson General Corp.	3,7
Northwest Airlines (Equipment Bldg.)	34
Ogden Allied Leisure Services	32
Ogden Foods Travel Services	7
PC Specialties	7
Page Avjet Maintenance Bldg./ Airport Services	85

Paradies Airport Shops	1
Sample Air, Inc.	5
Sky Chefs	5
U.S. Customs	7
U.S. Postal Service	28

CARGO AIRLINES

Air Canada	5
America West	5
American Airlines	1,3,5
Continental	5
Federal Express	77
Midway	1
Trans World Airlines (TWA)	4
US Airways	5
United Airlines	2

PASSENGER AIRLINES

Air Canada	80
America West	80
American Airlines	77
Canadian Airlines	77
Carnival Airlines	78
Colgan Air	79
Continental Airlines	80

Continental Express	80
Delta (Business Express)	51
Delta Airlines	51
Delta Shuttle	81
Mark Air	79
Midway	77
Midwest Express	78
Northwest Airlines	51
Precis on/NW Airlink	51
Trans World Airlines (TWA)	79
US Airways	52
US Airways Express	52
US Airways Shuttle	50
United Airlines	78
United Express	78

TRANSPORTATION SERVICES

Avis Car Rental	25
Budget Car Rental	83-34 23rd Av.
Dollar Car Rental	90-05 25th Av.
Hertz Car Rental	24
National Car Rental	Ditmars Blvd. and 95th St.
Service Station	91

Note: Location of tenants subject to change without notice. **Source:** The Port Authority of New York and New Jersey.

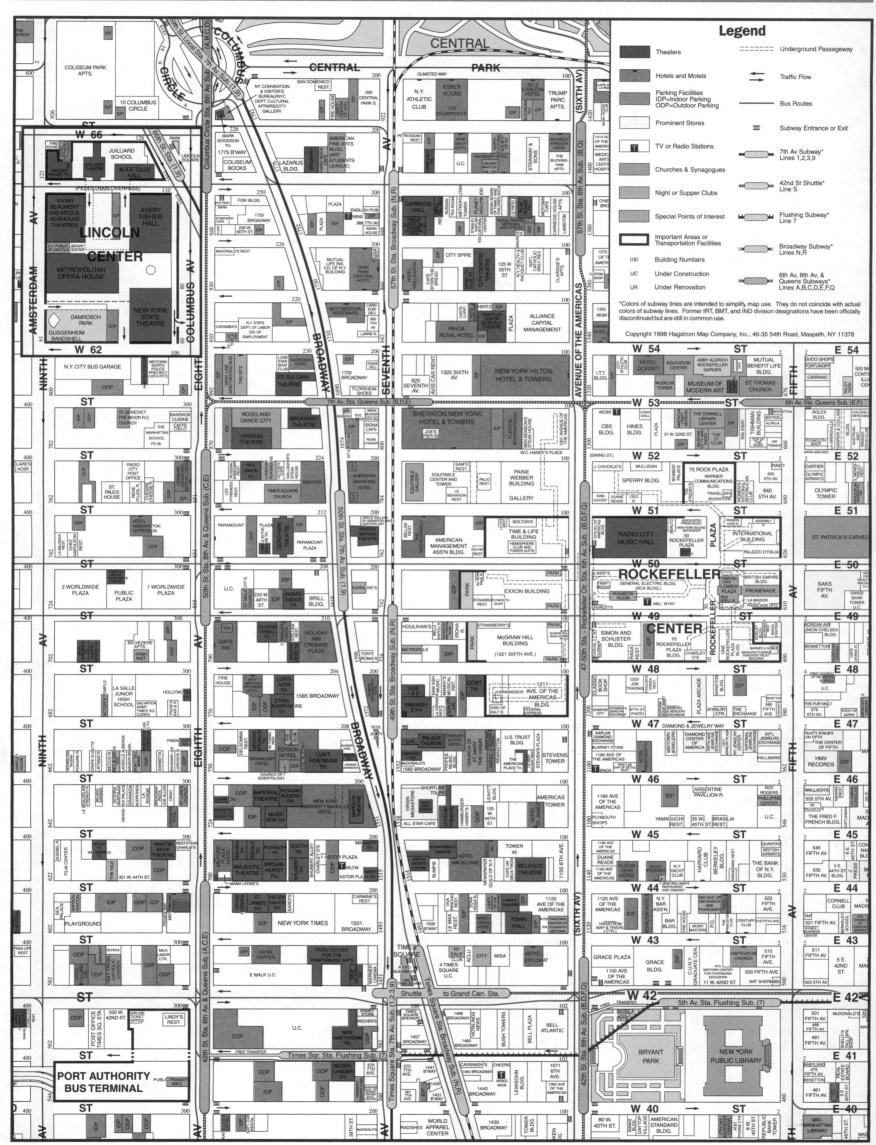

HUDSON RIVER

EAST RIVER

QUEENS BROOKLYN
MANHATTAN

LONG ISLAND CITY

QUEENSBORO BRIDGE (59th ST)

TURTLE BAY

MURRAY HILL

KIPS BAY

GRAMERCY PARK

FLATIRON

UNION SQUARE

MIDTOWN

THEATER DISTRICT

TIMES SQUARE

FASHION CENTER

MIDTOWN SOUTH

CLINTON

CHELSEA

GRAND CENTRAL TERMINAL

ROCKEFELLER CENTER

BRYANT PARK / PUBLIC LIBRARY

EMPIRE STATE BLDG

MADISON SQUARE PARK

PENN STATION

GENERAL POST OFFICE

JACOB K. JAVITS CONVENTION CENTER

LINCOLN TUNNEL (TOLL)

QUEENS-MIDTOWN TUNNEL (TOLL)

UNITED NATIONS HEADQUARTERS

BELLEVUE HOSPITAL CENTER

WATERSIDE PLAZA

STUYVESANT TOWN

AMTRAK

LONG ISLAND RAIL ROAD

"INTREPID" SEA, AIR, AND SPACE MUSEUM

NYC PASSENGER SHIP TERMINAL (PORT AUTHORITY)

CONRAIL PENN-CENTRAL TUNNELS

US POSTAL

CHELSEA PIERS AND SPORTS AND ENTERTAINMENT COMPLEX

AVENUE OF THE AMERICAS (SIXTH AV)

BROADWAY

PARK AVE

LEXINGTON AV

MADISON AV

FIFTH AV

SEVENTH AV

EIGHTH AV

NINTH AV

TENTH AV

ELEVENTH AV

FIRST AV

SECOND AV

THIRD AV

WILLIAMSBURG BRIDGE

EAST RIVER

EAST VILLAGE

GREENWICH VILLAGE

WEST SIDE

SOHO

LITTLE ITALY

BOWERY

CHINATOWN

MANHATTAN BRIDGE

BROOKLYN BRIDGE

CIVIC CENTER

BROOKLYN HEIGHTS

CITY HALL

FEDERAL PLAZA

WORLD TRADE CENTER

BATTERY PARK CITY

BATTERY PARK

Brooklyn Battery Tunnel

NORTH RIVER

HUDSON RIVER

HOLLAND TUNNEL (EASTBOUND)

NEW YORK
NEW JERSEY

NEW YORK CO.
HUDSON CO.

Ferry to Port Imperial N.J. (From White Hall Terminal)

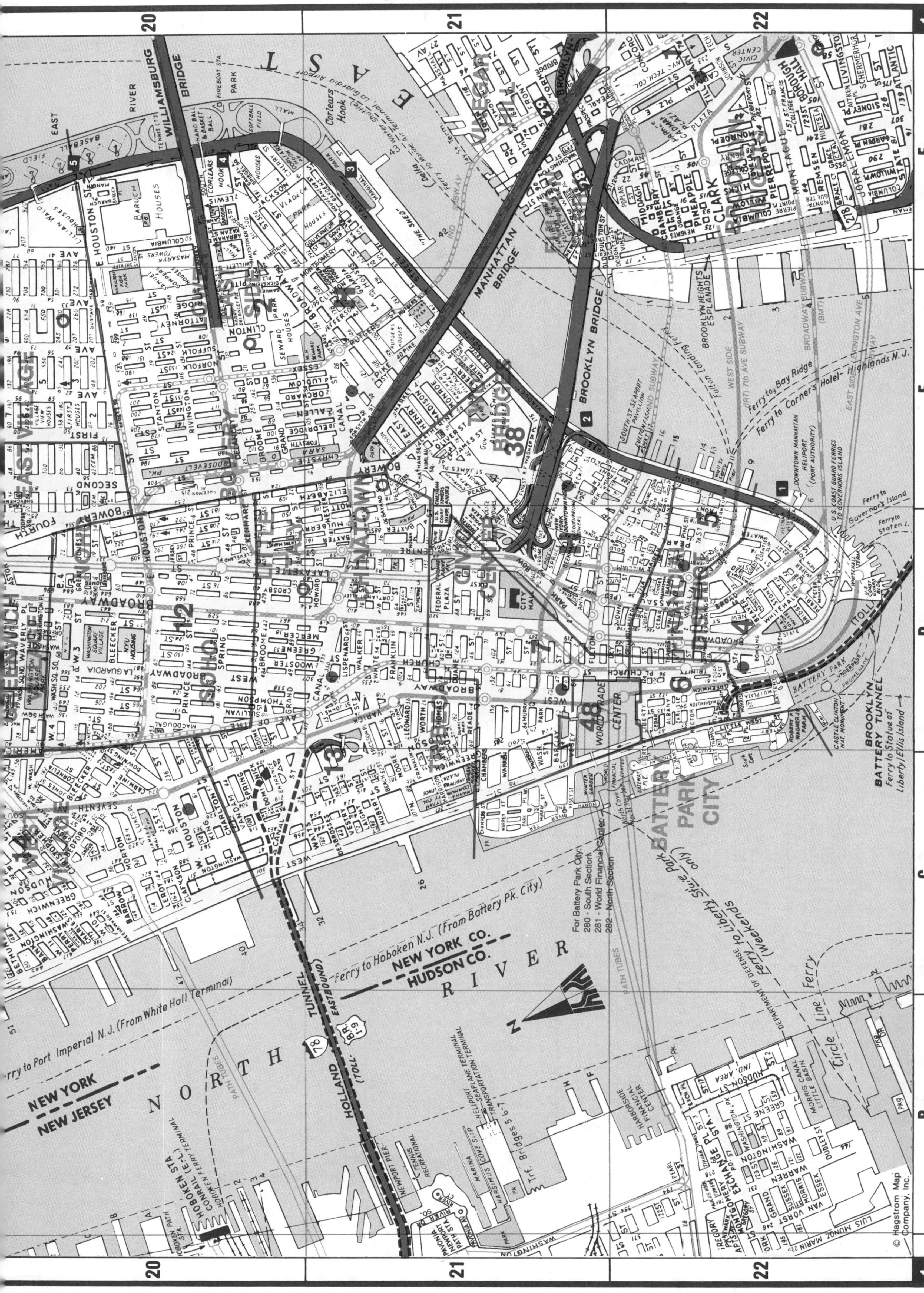

Ferry to Hoboken N.J. (From Battery Pk. City)

For Battery Park City:
280 - South Section
281 - World Financial Center
282 - North Section

Ferry to Statue of Liberty, Ellis Island

Ferry to Governor's Island

Ferry to Staten I.

Ferry to Bay Ridge

Ferry to Corner's Hotel - Highlands N.J.

HOBOKEN STA. - ELI.

NEWPORT PIER

HARBORSIDE FINANCIAL CENTER

COMMERCE EXCHANGE STA.

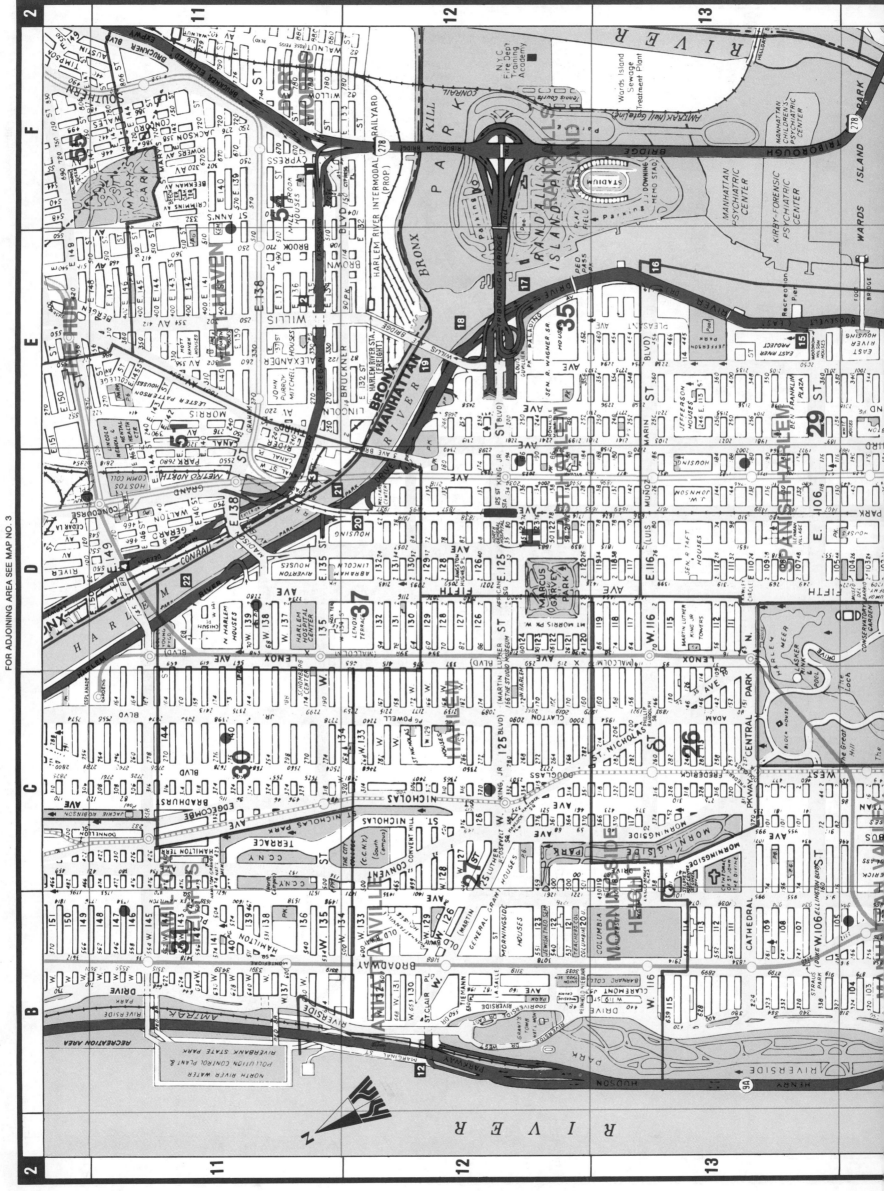

MANHATTAN
QUEENS

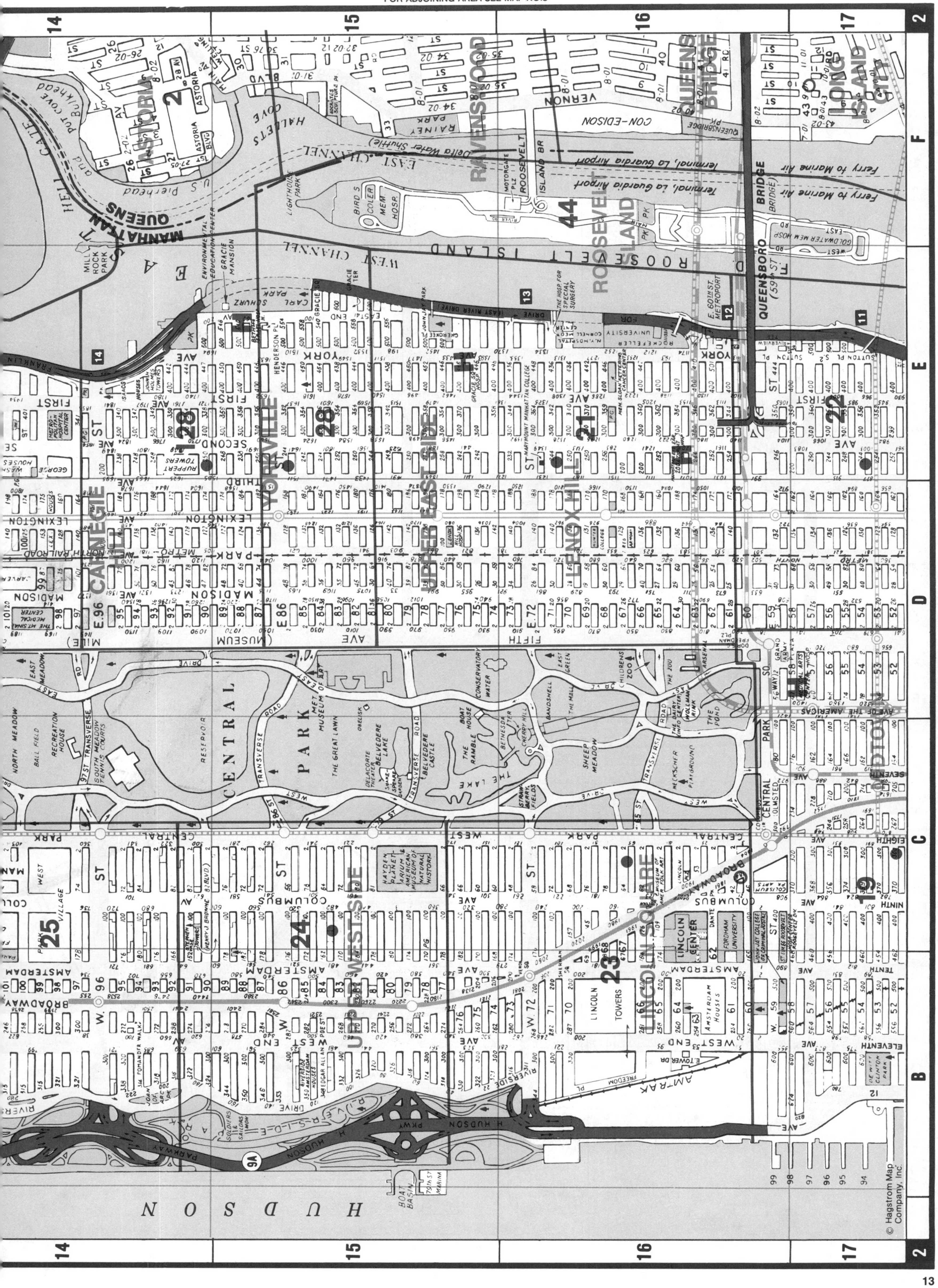

ASTORIA

RAVENSWOOD

QUEENS
BRIDGE

LONG ISLAND CITY

EAST CHANNEL

WEST CHANNEL

ROOSEVELT ISLAND

QUEENSBORO BRIDGE

HELL GATE and BRIDGE

HALLET'S COVE

HUDSON

CENTRAL PARK

RESERVOIR
NORTH MEADOW
EAST MEADOW
THE GREAT LAWN
METROPOLITAN MUSEUM OF ART
THE LAKE
THE RAMBLE
SHEEP MEADOW
THE POND
THE MALL
BETHESDA
BELVEDERE CASTLE
BELVEDERE LAKE
DELACORTE THEATER
CONSERVATORY WATER
CHILDREN'S ZOO
THE ZOO
WOLLMAN RINK
STRAWBERRY FIELDS
HECKSCHER PLAYGROUND
BALL FIELD
RECREATION HOUSE
97 ST TRANSVERSE
79 ST TRANSVERSE
TRANSVERSE ROAD
65 ST TRANSVERSE

YORKVILLE

UPPER EAST SIDE

LENOX HILL

UPPER WEST SIDE

LINCOLN SQUARE

CARNEGIE HILL

CENTRAL PARK WEST

COLUMBUS AVE

AMSTERDAM AVE

WEST END AVE

BROADWAY

RIVERSIDE DRIVE

FIFTH AVE

MADISON AVE

PARK AVE

LEXINGTON AVE

THIRD AVE

SECOND AVE

FIRST AVE

YORK AVE

FRANKLIN

GRACIE MANSION
CARL SCHURZ PARK
RUPPERT TOWERS
METROPOLITAN HOSPITAL CENTER
THE MT. SINAI MEDICAL CENTER
N.Y. HOSPITAL CORNELL MED CENTER
ROCKEFELLER UNIVERSITY
MEM SLOAN KETTERING CANCER CENTER
HOSP. FOR SPECIAL SURGERY
MARYMOUNT MANHATTAN COLLEGE
HUNTER COLLEGE
LENOX HILL HOSP.
GRAND ARMY PLAZA

LINCOLN CENTER
LINCOLN TOWERS
FORDHAM UNIVERSITY
AMERICAN MUSEUM OF NATURAL HISTORY
HAYDEN PLANETARIUM
DANTE PARK
JOHN JAY COLLEGE
COLISEUM
AMSTERDAM HOUSES
THEODORE ROOSEVELT PARK

LAGUARDIA AIRPORT
TERMINAL, LaGuardia Airport
Ferry to Marine Air
MOTORGATE PLZ
ROOSEVELT ISLAND BR
COLER MEM. HOSP.
BIRD'S EYE
GOLDWATER MEM HOSP WEST
GOLDWATER MEM HOSP EAST
LIGHTHOUSE PARK
JOHN JAY PARK
CHEROKEE PL
CARL SCHURZ

CON-EDISON

VERNON

RAINEY PARK

QUEENSBRIDGE PK

AVE OF THE AMERICAS

SEVENTH AVE

EIGHTH AVE

NINTH AVE

TENTH AVE

ELEVENTH AVE

HENRY HUDSON PKWY

HUDSON RIVER

BOAT BASIN

RIVERSIDE PARK

EAST RIVER DRIVE (F.D.R. DRIVE)

MUSEUM MILE

E. 96
E. 86
E. 72
E. 59

W. 96
W. 86
W. 72
W. 59

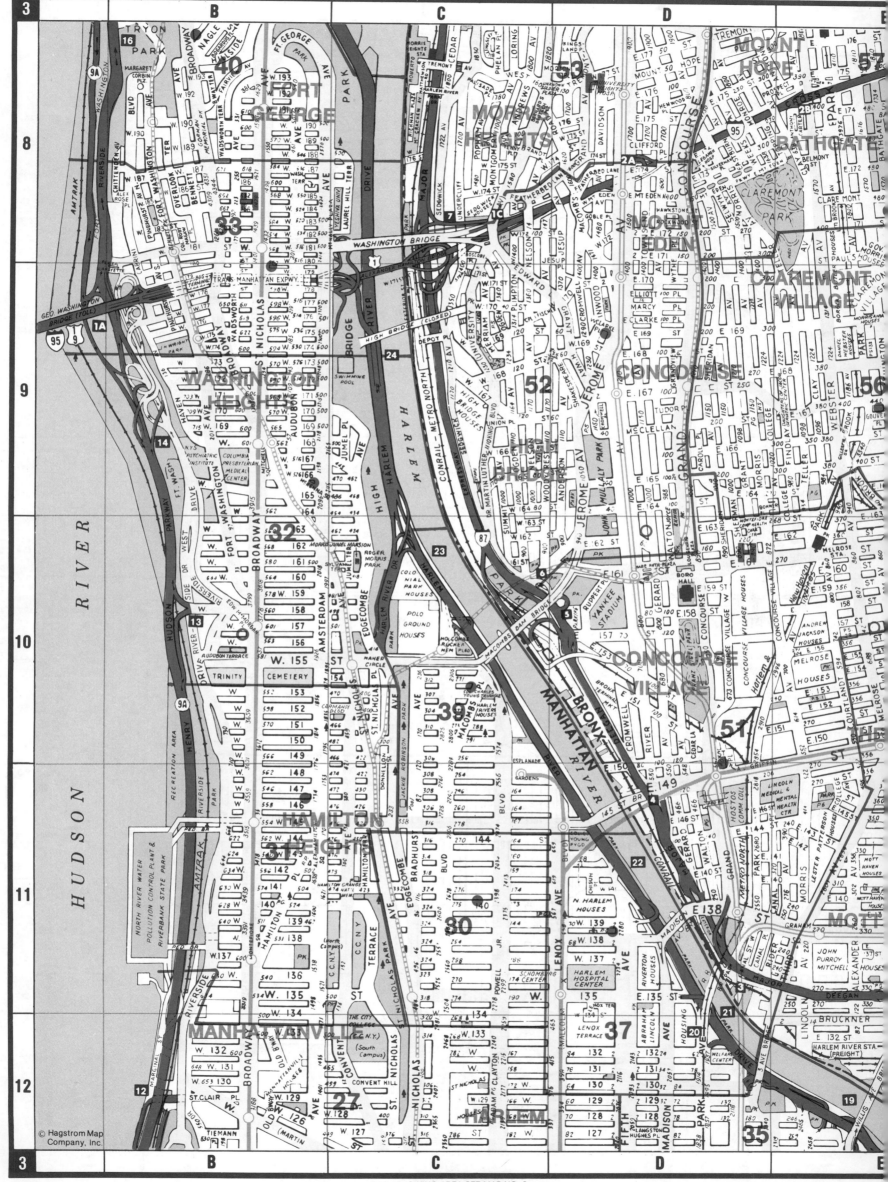

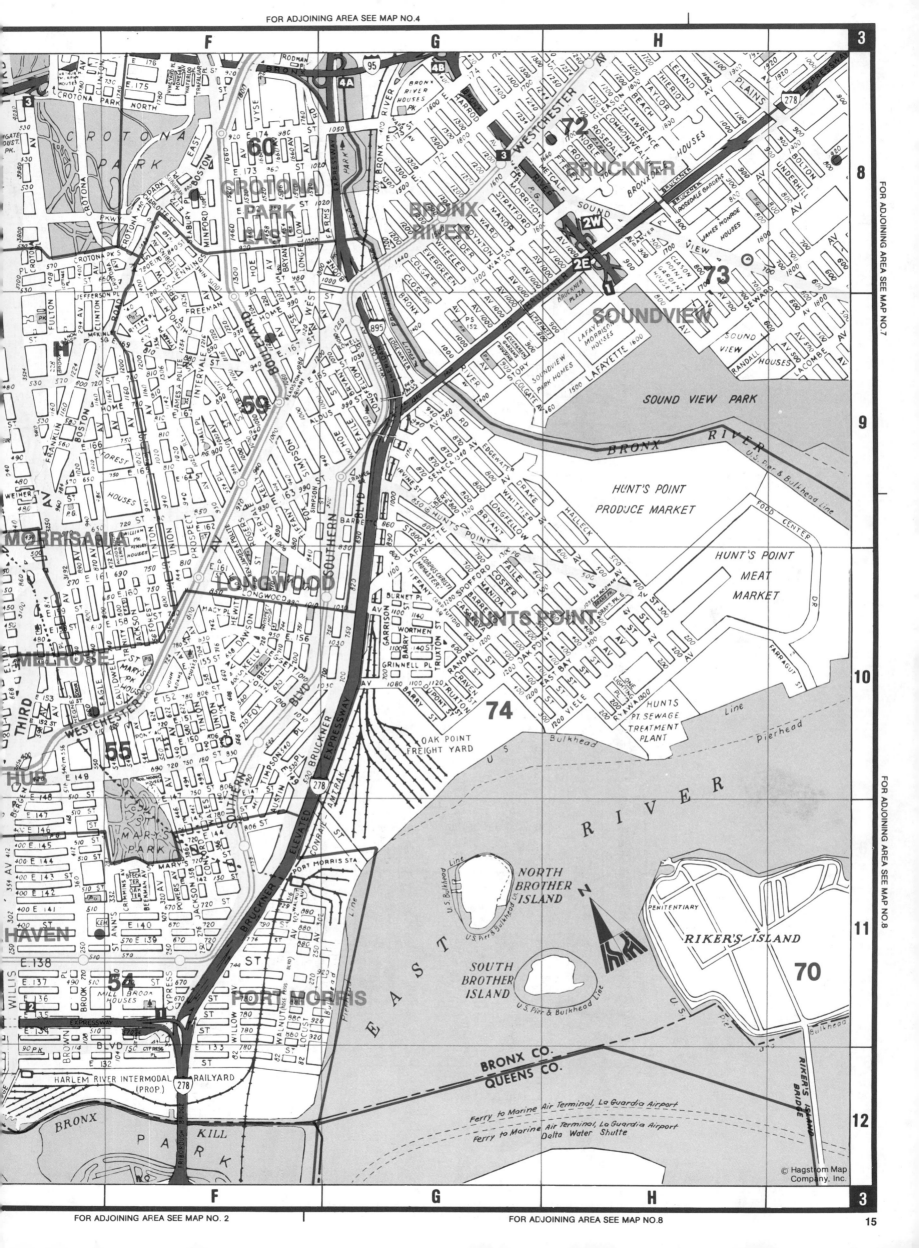

© Hagstrom Map Company, Inc.

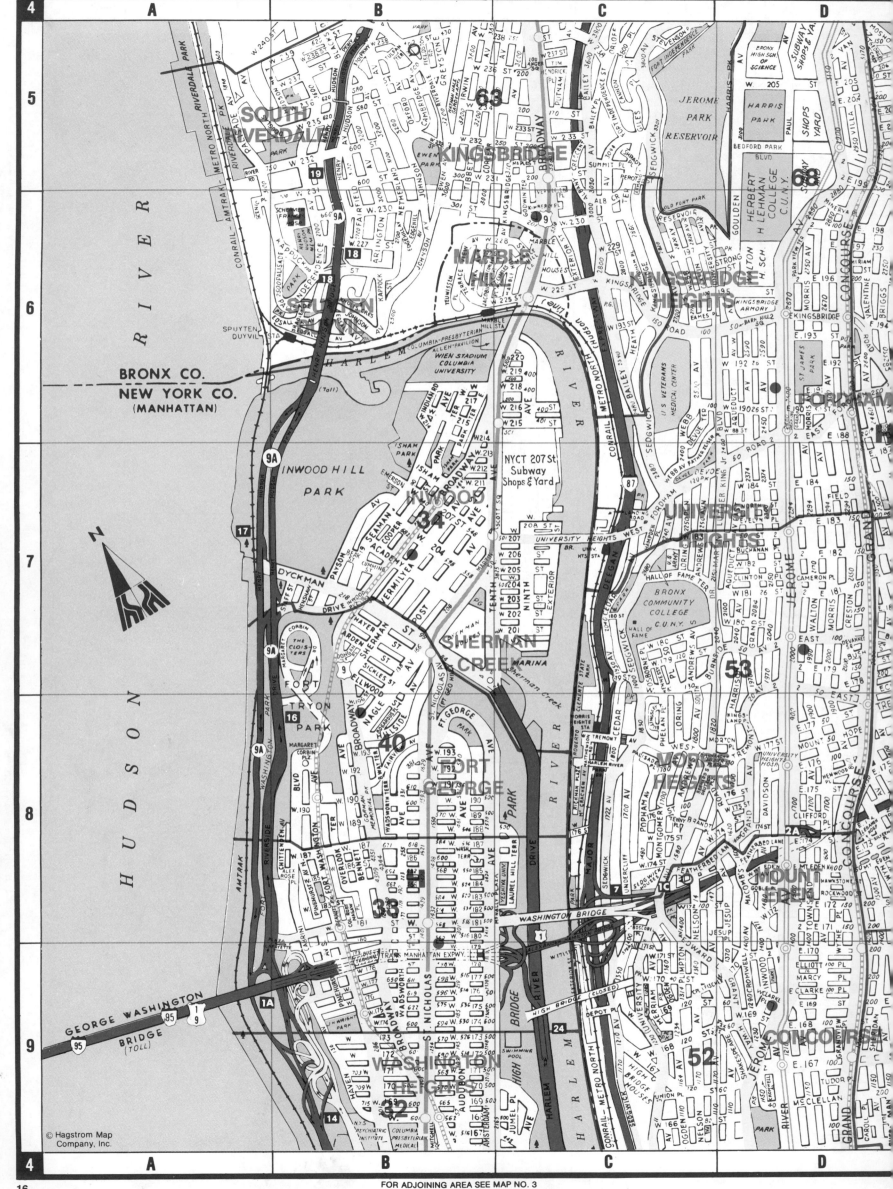

ALLERTON

BRONXDALE

PELHAM PARKWAY

MORRIS PARK

BEDFORD PARK

BRONX MUNICIPAL HOSP. CENTER

NEW YORK INSTITUTE FOR THE BLIND

FORDHAM UNIVERSITY

BOTANICAL GARDEN STA.

ROSE HILL PARK

BELMONT

BRONX PARK

BRONX ZOO

INT'L WILDLIFE CENTER

VAN NEST

PARKCHESTER

TREMONT

EAST TREMONT

ST. BARNABAS HOSP. FOR CHRONIC DISEASES

BRONX PARK SOUTH

WEST FARMS

MOUNT HOPE

CROTONA PARK

BATHGATE

CROTONA PARK EAST

BRONX RIVER

BRUCKNER

CLAREMONT PARK

CLAREMONT VILLAGE

SOUNDVIEW

SOUND VIEW PARK

© Hagstrom Map Company, Inc.

BRONX RIVER

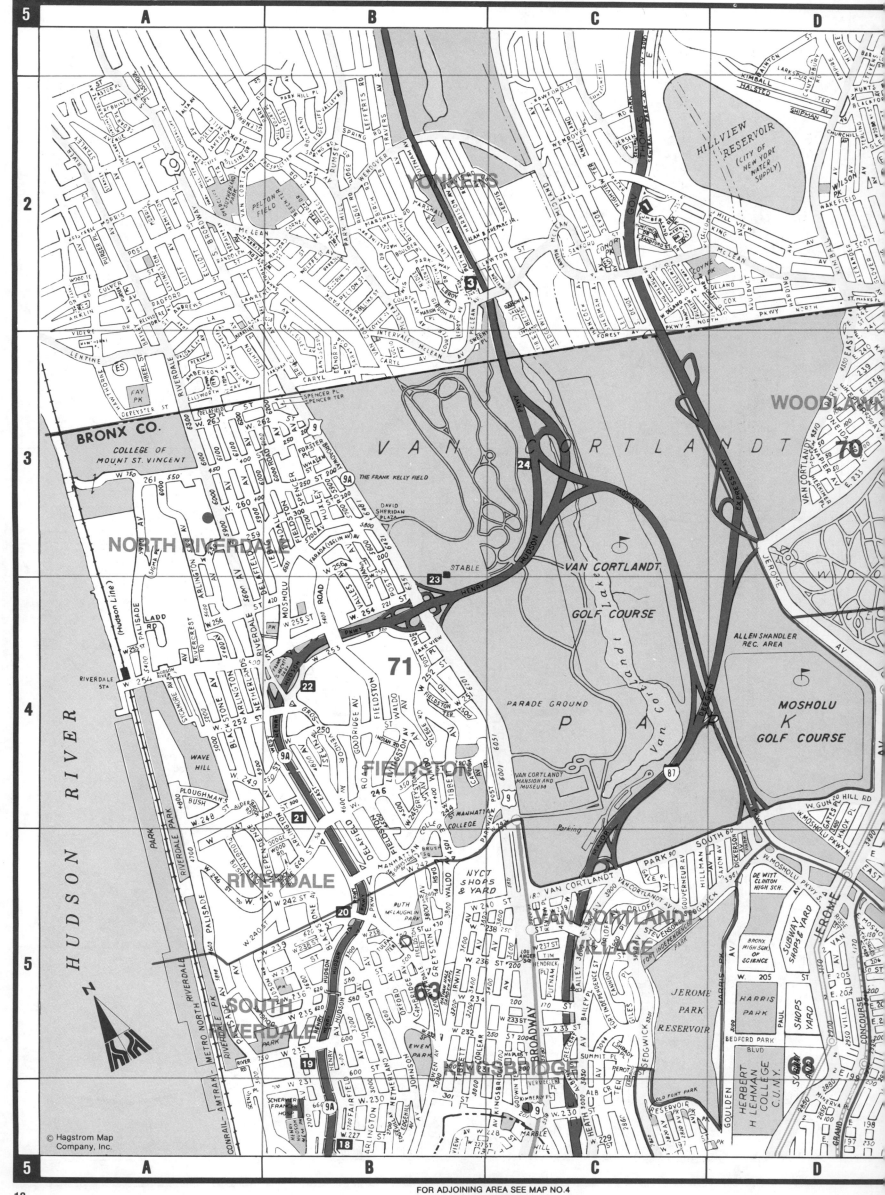

MOUNT VERNON

WAKEFIELD

EASTCHESTER

EDENWALD

WILLIAMSBRIDGE

OLINVILLE

NORWOOD

BRONXDALE

ALLERTON

BAYCHESTER

PELHAM GARDENS

BEDFORD PARK

SETON FALLS PARK

NYCT SUBWAY SHOPS & YARDS

MOUNT ST. MICHAEL SCHOOL

BRONX MUNICIPAL HOSP. CENTER

NEW YORK INSTITUTE FOR THE BLIND

HEBREW HOSP. FOR CHRONIC SICK

58   61   66   67   69   70   75

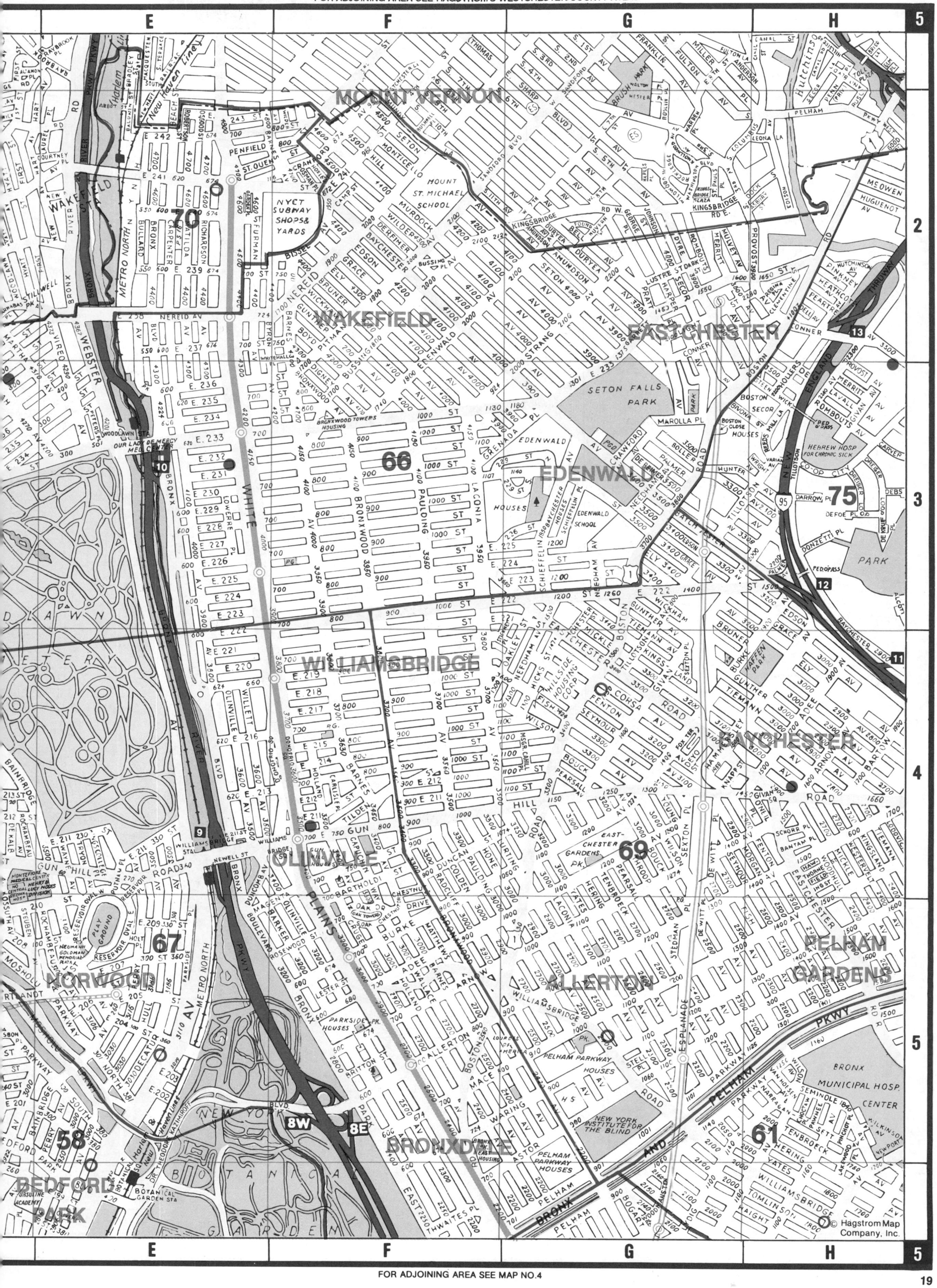

FOR ADJOINING AREA SEE MAP NO.6

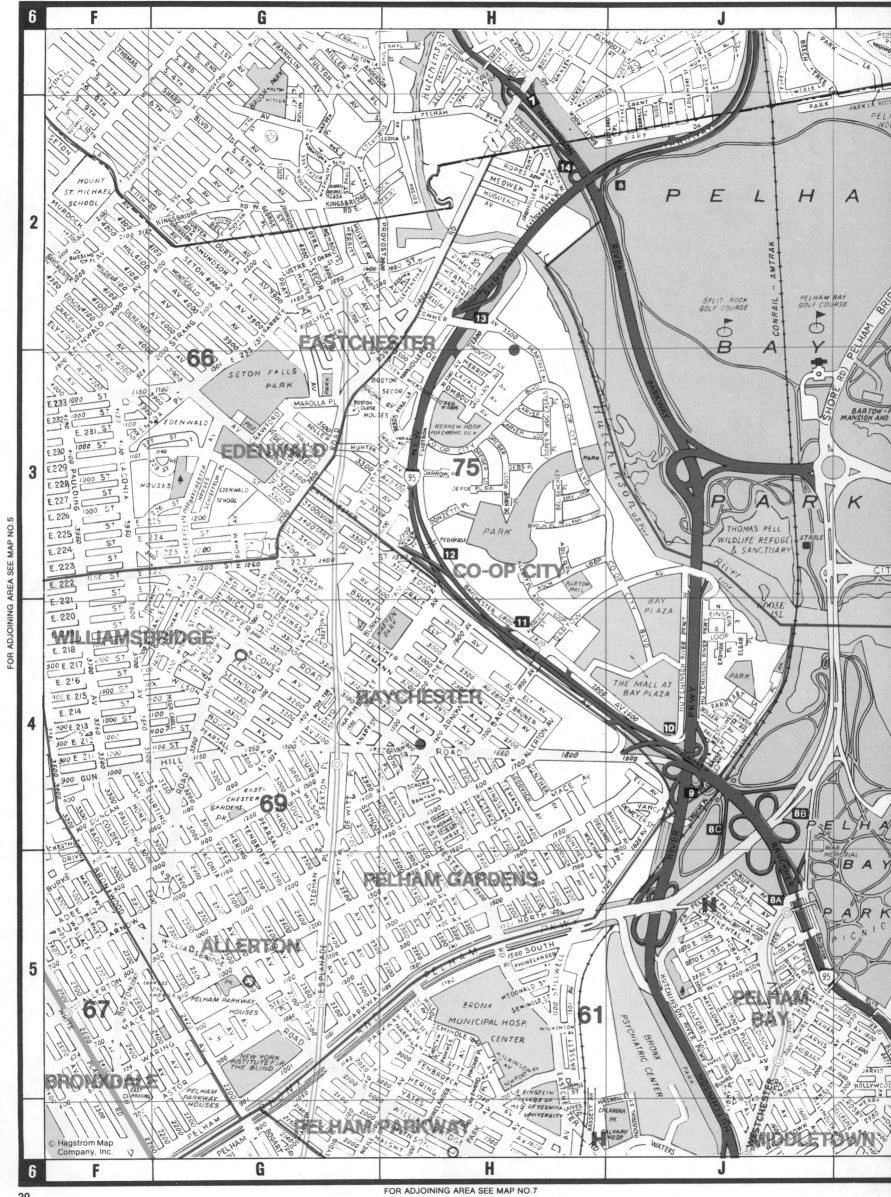

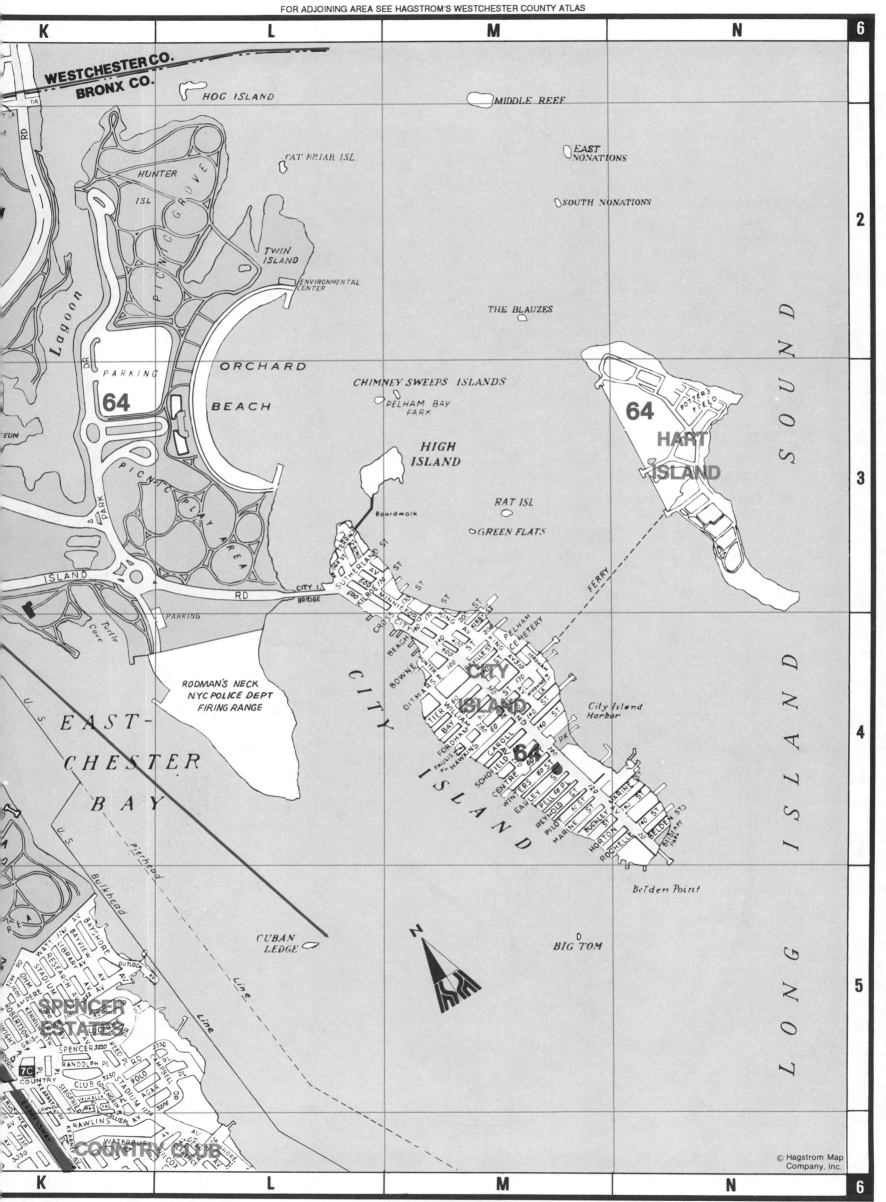

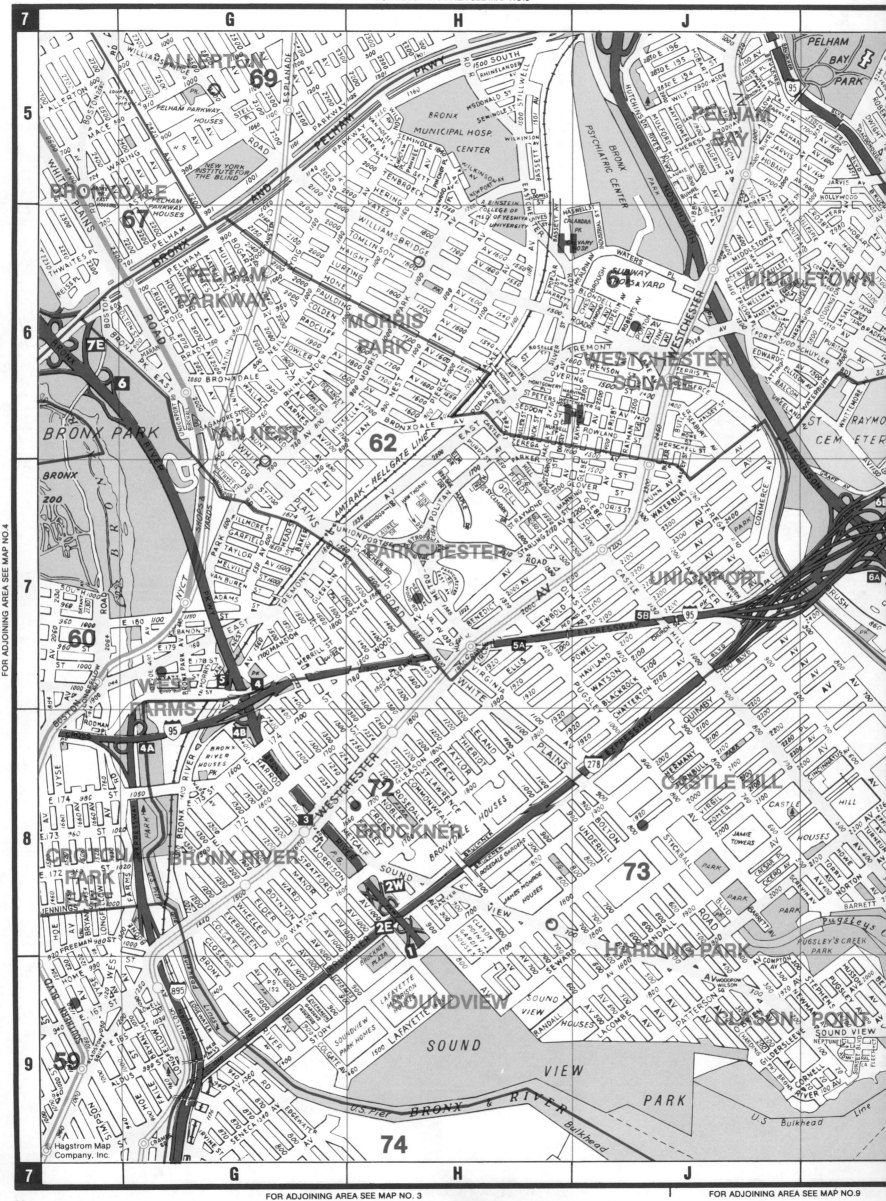

K L M N 7

CUBAN EDGE

N

SPENCER ESTATES

LONG ISLAND SOUND

COUNTRY CLUB

EASTCHESTER BAY

THROGS NECK

EDGEWATER PARK

Locust Point

THROGS NECK BRIDGE (TOLL)

THROGS NECK L.H.

SCHUYLERVILLE

TREMONT

THROG'S NECK HOUSES 65

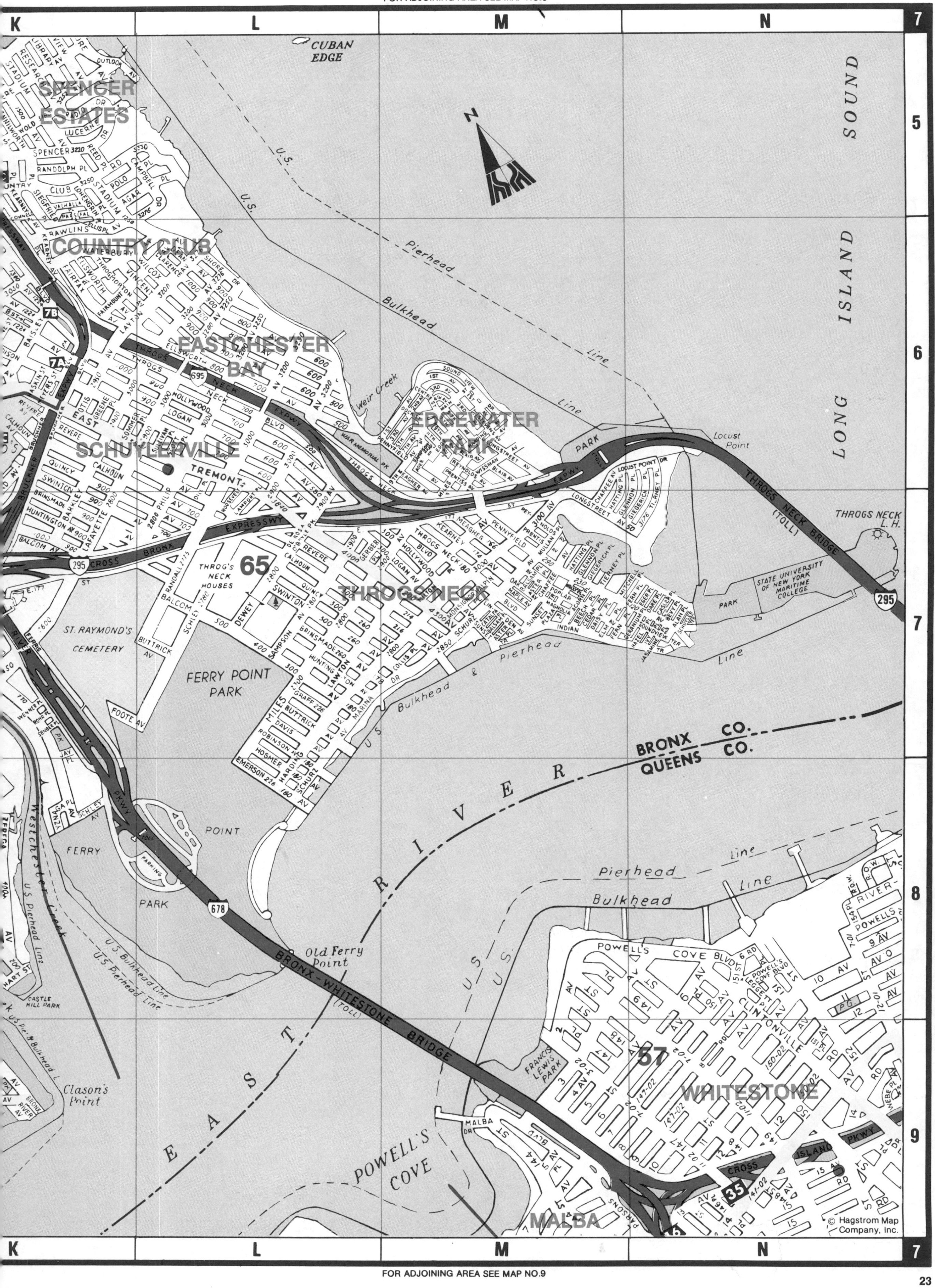

THROGS NECK

STATE UNIVERSITY OF NEW YORK MARITIME COLLEGE

ST. RAYMOND'S CEMETERY

FERRY POINT PARK

Pierhead Line
Bulkhead

BRONX CO.
QUEENS CO.

FERRY POINT PARK

EAST RIVER

CASTLE HILL PARK

BRONX-WHITESTONE BRIDGE (TOLL)

Old Ferry Point

Pierhead Line
Bulkhead

POWELL'S COVE BLVD

CLINTONVILLE

57

WHITESTONE

Clason's Point

Francis Lewis Park

MALBA

POWELL'S COVE

CROSS ISLAND PKWY

K L M N 7

© Hagstrom Map Company, Inc.

8 E F

7

HARLEM
26
EAST HARLEM
35
BRONX PARK
54 PORT MORRIS

CENTRAL PARK
SPANISH HARLEM
29
FRANKLIN PLAZA
RANDALLS ISLAND
RANDALLS ISLAND
35

8

CARNEGIE HILL
1 28
YORKVILLE
28
WARDS ISLAND
Manhattan Psychiatric Center
Kirby-Forensic Psychiatric Center
Manhattan Children's Psychiatric Center
HELL GATE
PUT COVE
DITMARS
DITMARS
5

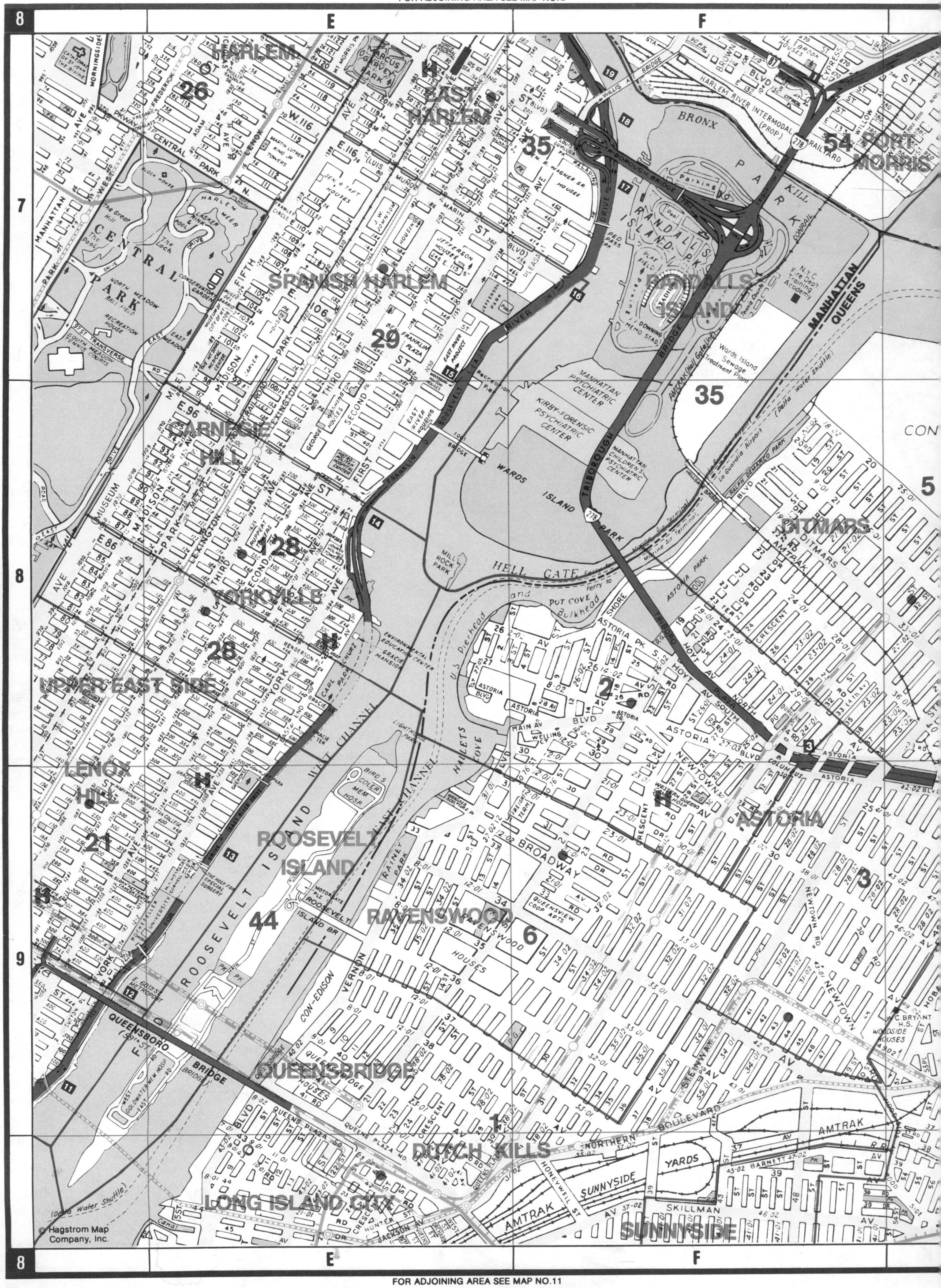

UPPER EAST SIDE
ASTORIA
2
ASTORIA BLVD

LENOX HILL
21
ROOSEVELT ISLAND
44
RAVENSWOOD
6
ASTORIA
3
BROADWAY

9

QUEENSBORO BRIDGE
QUEENSBRIDGE
QUEENSBRIDGE HOUSES
1
DUTCH KILLS
LONG ISLAND CITY
SUNNYSIDE YARDS
AMTRAK
SUNNYSIDE

© Hagstrom Map Company, Inc.

8 E F

G H J 8

EAST RIVER

7

N

NORTH BROTHER ISLAND

SOUTH BROTHER ISLAND

BRONX CO.
QUEENS CO.

RIKER'S ISLAND
70

PENITENTIARY

HUNTS POINT

Hunt's Point

U.S. Pierhead Line

COVE
KETCH CT

HERMAN A. MacNEIL PARK

POPPENHUSEN AV

BERRIAN'S ISL.

EDISON

Luyster Creek

U.S. Pierhead Line

BRIDGE

BOWERY BAY SEWAGE TREATMENT PLANT

BERRIAN BLVD

EDO SEAPLANE BASE
56
COLLEGE POINT

FLUSHING

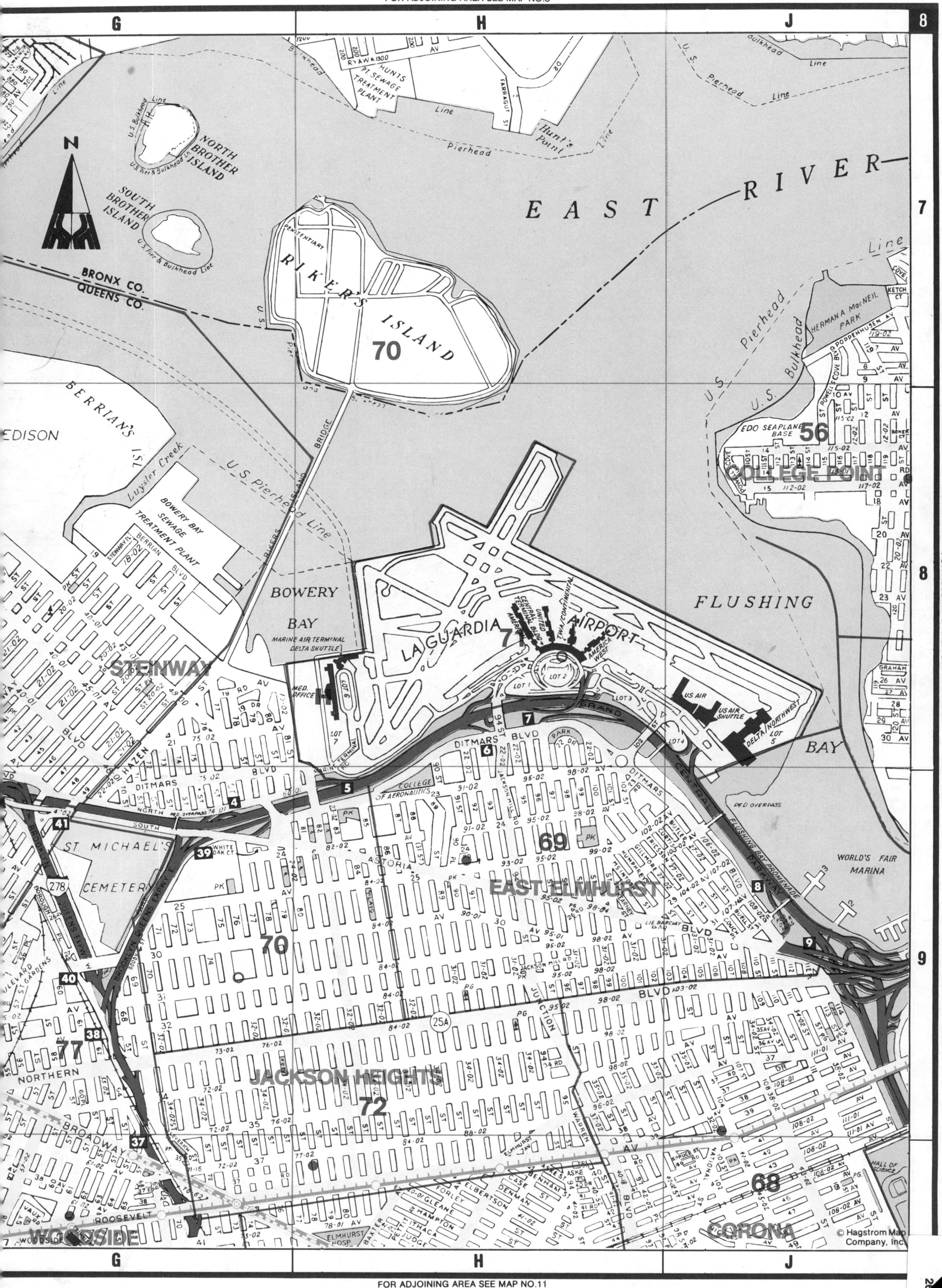

FOR ADJOINING AREA SEE MAP NO.9

8

BOWERY BAY

MARINE AIR TERMINAL
DELTA SHUTTLE

STEINWAY

LA GUARDIA **7** AIRPORT

CENTRAL BLDG
UNITED TERMINAL
TWA/CONTINENTAL
AMERICA WEST

DELTA/NORTHWEST LOT 5
US AIR
US AIR SHUTTLE

MED. OFFICE

LOT 9
LOT 7

GRAND
CENTRAL

BAY

HAZEN

DITMARS

COLLEGE OF AERONAUTICS

DITMARS BLVD

PARK

6

7

WORLD'S FAIR MARINA

NORTH

SOUTH

5
4
41

ST. MICHAEL'S CEMETERY

39
WHITE OAK CT

278

ASTORIA

69

EAST ELMHURST

FLUSHING BAY PROMENADE

PED OVERPASS

8

70

JACKSON HEIGHTS
72

NORTHERN

JUNCTION

BLVD

25A

9

HALL OF SCIENCE

40

38
77

68

BROADWAY

37

ROOSEVELT

VAUX

WOODSIDE

ELMHURST HOSP.

CORONA

© Hagstrom Map Company, Inc

G H J

9

H   J

7

E A S T — R I V E R

POWELL'S COVE

N

PENITENTIARY

R I K E R S   I S L A N D
70

HUNTS PT SEWAGE TREATMENT PLANT
Hunt's Point
Pierhead Line

TALLMAN ISLAND SEWAGE TREATMENT PLANT

HERMAN A. MacNEIL PARK

POWELL'S COVE PARK
FRANK GOLDEN PARK

COLLEGE POINT
56

EDO SEAPLANE BASE

8

BOWERY BAY

F L U S H I N G

LA GUARDIA AIRPORT
7
CENTRAL BLDG
UNITED BLDG
TWA/CONTINENTAL
AMERICA WEST
US AIR
US AIR SHUTTLE
DELTA/NORTHWEST LOT 5
LOT 1 LOT 2 LOT 3 LOT 4
Marine Air Terminal Delta Shuttle
MED. OFFICE
LOT 6 LOT 7

COLLEGE POINT INDUSTRIAL PARK

COLLEGE POINT

BAY

WORLD'S FAIR MARINA

5

College of Aeronautics

DITMARS BLVD

69

EAST ELMHURST

70

ASTORIA

GRAND CENTRAL PARKWAY

8

9

68
PARKING FIELD
Shea Stadium
N.Y.C.T.A.
SHEA STADIUM STA.

14

13

NORTHERN BLVD

9

NORTHERN

JACKSON HEIGHTS
72

Parking Pedestrian Ramp

U.S.T.A. NATIONAL TENNIS CENTER (ARTHUR ASHE AND LOUIS ARMSTRONG STADIUMS)

FLUSHING MEADOWS

678

ROOSEVELT

73

HALL OF SCIENCE

CORONA PARK
QUEENS ZOO
QUEENS MUSEUM
UNISPHERE

12A

68

C O R O N A

12B

© Hagstrom Map Company, Inc.

9

H   J

K   L   M   9

BRONX CO.
QUEENS CO.

1 WILLETS ST.
2 LITTLE BAY RD
3 CIRCLE DRIVE
4 BAYSIDE ST.
5 CHAPEL RD.
6 ABBOT RD.
7 NORTH LOOP
8 LEE RD.
9 ORDNANCE RD.
10 SHORE RD.
11 WHISTLER AV.
12 WALTER REED RD
13 JARMAN RD.
14 SYLVESTER LA.
15 MURRAY AV.

16 WEAVER AV.
17 OFFICER'S DR.
18 UNDERHILL RD.
19 STORY AV.
20 SPILLER RD.
21 WESTAWAY RD
22 PRATT AV.
23 EAST LOOP
24 RED CROSS LA.
25 THEATER RD.
26 DUANE RD.
27 BOUNDARY RD
28 SGT. BEERS AV.
29 SGT. BEERS LA.

1. BRIAN CRESCENT
2. EMILY RD
3. ROBIN LA.
4. LORI DR
5. ESTATES LA.
6. MELISSA CT
7. DARREN DR
8. DIANE PL
9. ROBERT RD
10. MICHAEL CT
11. MICHAEL PL
12. ESTATES DR
13. BONNIE LA.
14. JORDAN DR
15. JORDAN CT

US U.S.

Pierhead Line
Bulkhead Line

FRANCIS LEWIS PARK

WHITESTONE

MALBA

BEECHHURST

LITTLE BAY

59

Willets Point

57

CLEAR-VIEW

BAY TERRACE

32

34

33   32

6B   60

BAY TERRACE SHOPPING CENTER

CLEARVIEW PARK
CLEARVIEW GOLF COURSE

LINDEN HILL

BAYSIDE

BOWNE PARK

MURRAY HILL

54

FLUSHING HOSP. MED. CENTER

58

6A

61

NORTHERN

FLUSHING

AUBURNDALE

55

QUEENS BOTANICAL GARDENS

FLUSHING CEMETERY

KISSENA L.

65

QUEENSBORO HILL

KISSENA PARK

KISSENA PARK

BICYCLE TRACK

28

K   L   M

7   8   9

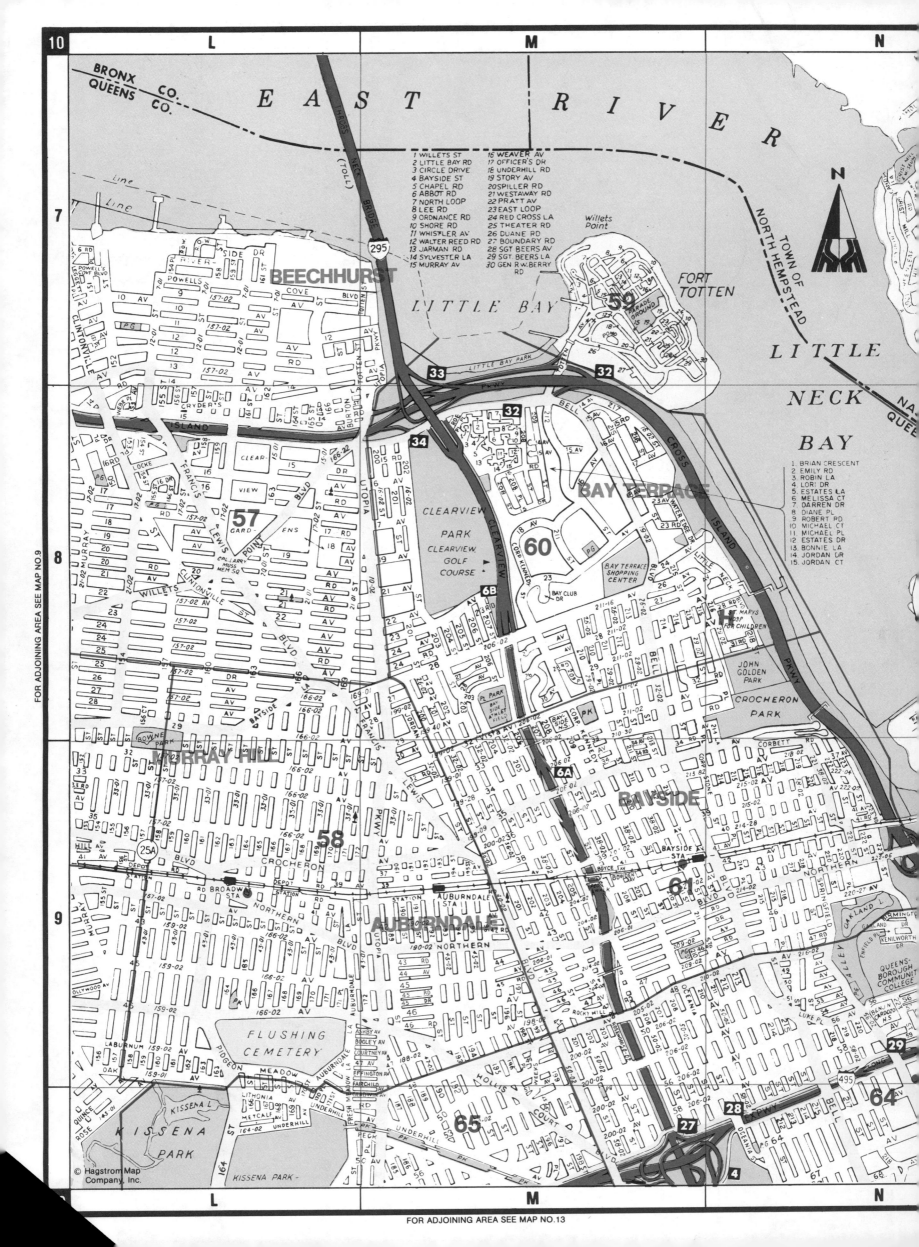

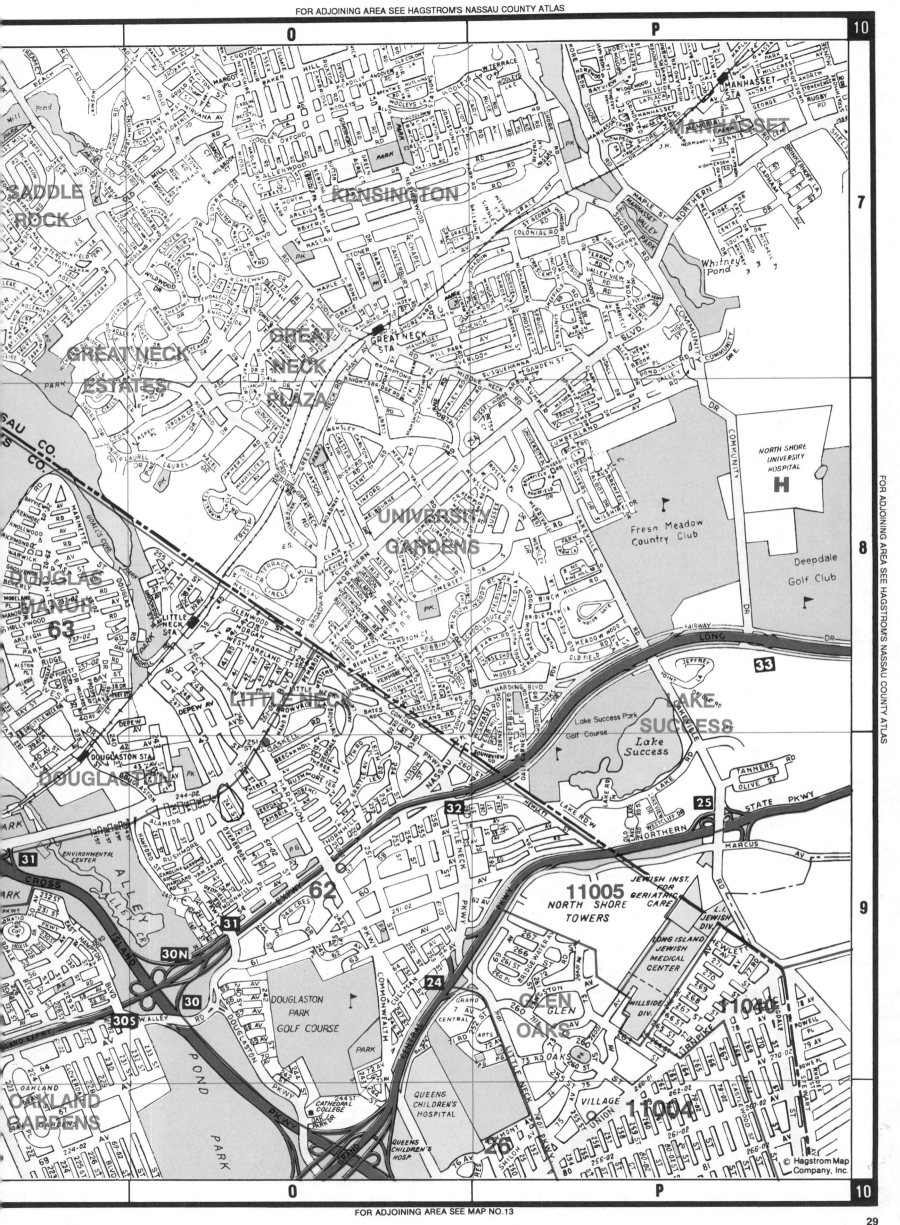

DUTCH KILLS

LONG ISLAND CITY

SUNNYSIDE

HUNTERS POINT

BLISSVILLE

NEW CALVARY CEMETERY

CALVARY CEMETERY

WEST MASPETH

GREENPOINT

NORTHSIDE

SOUTHSIDE

WILLIAMSBURG

EAST WILLIAMSBURG

MASPETH

BUSHWICK

Brooklyn Union Gas Co.

Woodhull Medical & Mental Center

© Hagstrom Map Company, Inc.

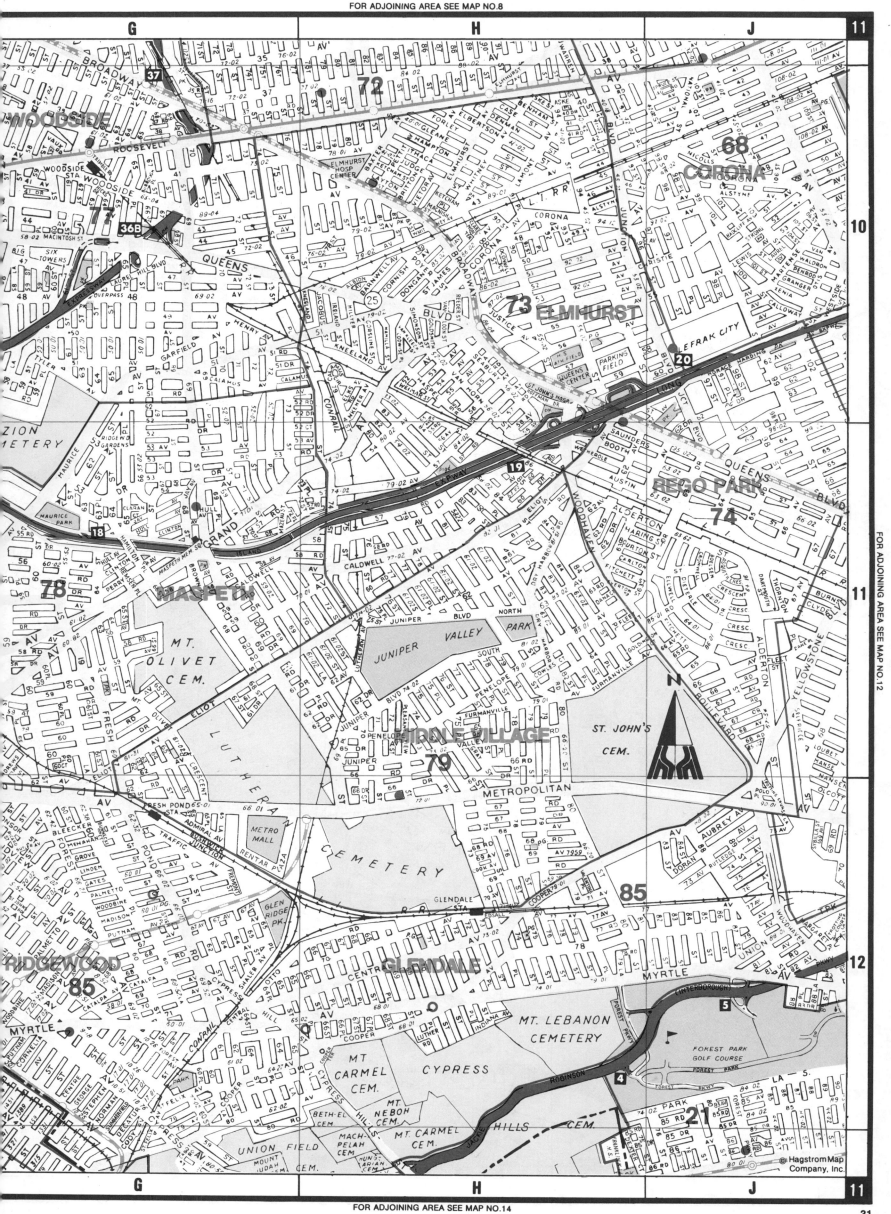

72

ELMHURST

CORONA

68

FLUSHING MEADOWS

CORONA

U.S.T.A. NATIONAL TENNIS CENTER
ARTHUR ASHE AND LOUIS
ARMSTRONG STADIUMS

HALL OF SCIENCE
Queens Museum
Unisphere
Queens Zoo
Terrace on The Park
Queens Theater

73

ROOSEVELT AV

ELMHURST HOSP CENTER

L.I.R.R.

JUSTICE

LEFRAK CITY

ST. JOHN'S HOSP.

20

19

21

22

10

QUEENS BLVD

REGO PARK

74

75

N.S.U. HOSP. FOREST HILLS

CONRAIL

CALDWELL

JUNIPER VALLEY PARK

NORTH PARK

MIDDLE VILLAGE

79

JUNIPER

METROPOLITAN

ST. JOHN'S CEMETERY

FOREST HILLS STADIUM

FOREST HILLS

CONTINENTAL (7 AV)

TURNPIKE

85

LUTHERAN CEM.

GLENDALE STA.

MYRTLE

JACKIE ROBINSON

5

6

GLENDALE

MT. LEBANON CEMETERY

FOREST PARK GOLF COURSE

TWIN FIELD

VICTORY FIELD

4

MT CARMEL CEM.

CYPRESS

MT NEBOH CEM.

MT. CARMEL CEM.

HILLS CEM.

BETH-EL CEM.

MACH-PELAH CEM.

21

JAMAICA

18

FOREST PARK

© Hagstrom Map Company, Inc.

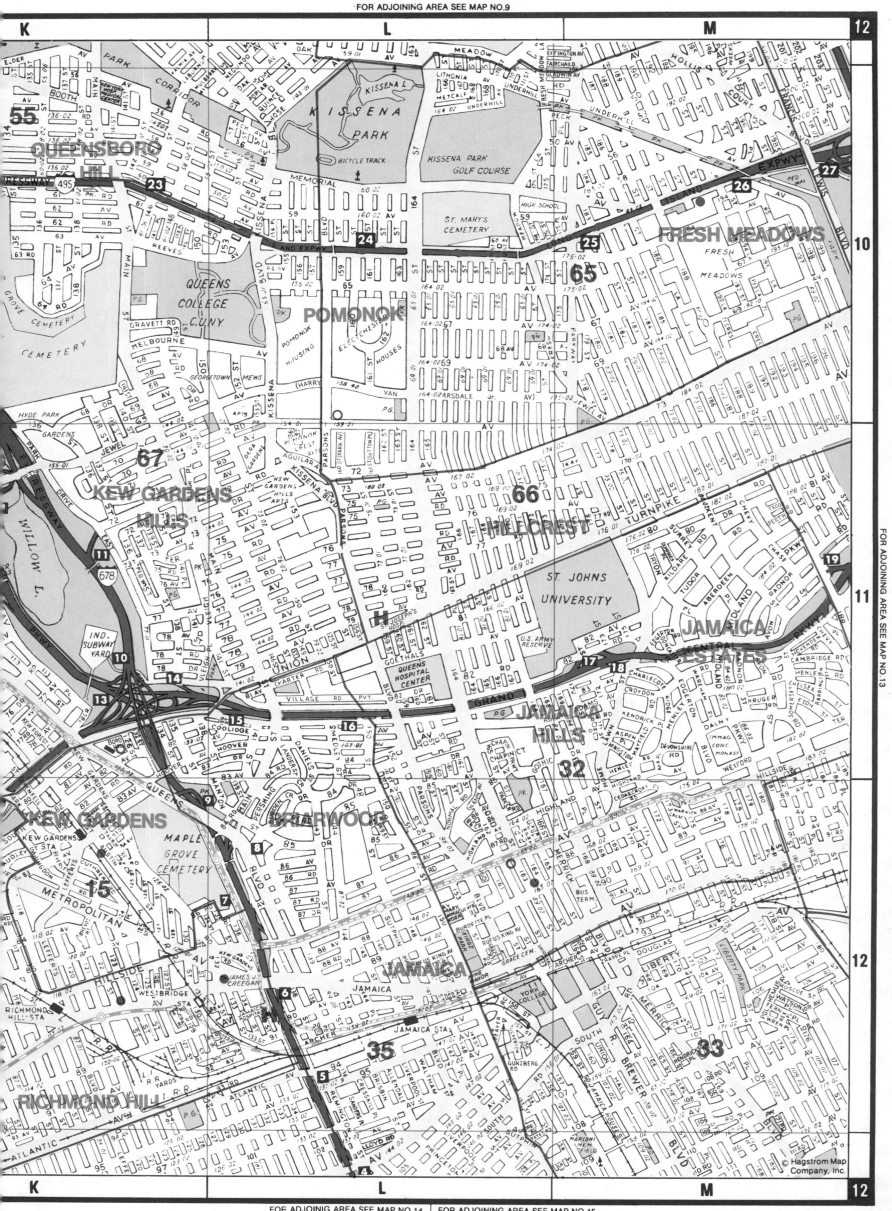

13   L   M   N

FOR ADJOINING AREA SEE MAP NO.12

KISSENA PARK

KISSENA L

BICYCLE TRACK

KISSENA PARK - GOLF COURSE

ST. MARY'S CEMETERY

HIGH SCHOOL

POMONOK

POMONOK HOUSING

ELECTCHESTER HOUSES

FRESH MEADOWS

65

FRESH MEADOWS

CUNNINGHAM PARK

WINDSOR PARK APTS

HOLLIS COURT GARDENS

CUNNINGHAM PARK

66

HILLCREST

ST. JOHNS UNIVERSITY

U.S. ARMY RESERVE

ST. JOSEPH'S HOSP.

GOETHALS

QUEENS HOSPITAL CENTER

HOLLISWOOD

HOLLISWOOD HOSPITAL

JAMAICA ESTATES

23

JAMAICA

JAMAICA HILLS

ABIGAIL ADAMS

IMMAC. CONC. MONAST.

BRIARWOOD

32

PK.

RUFUS KING AV

GRACE CEM.

JAMAICA

YORK COLLEGE

JAMAICA STA.

35

33

HOLLIS

HOLLIS STA.

LIBERTY PARK

ST. ALBANS

© Hagstrom Map Company, Inc.

13   L   M   N

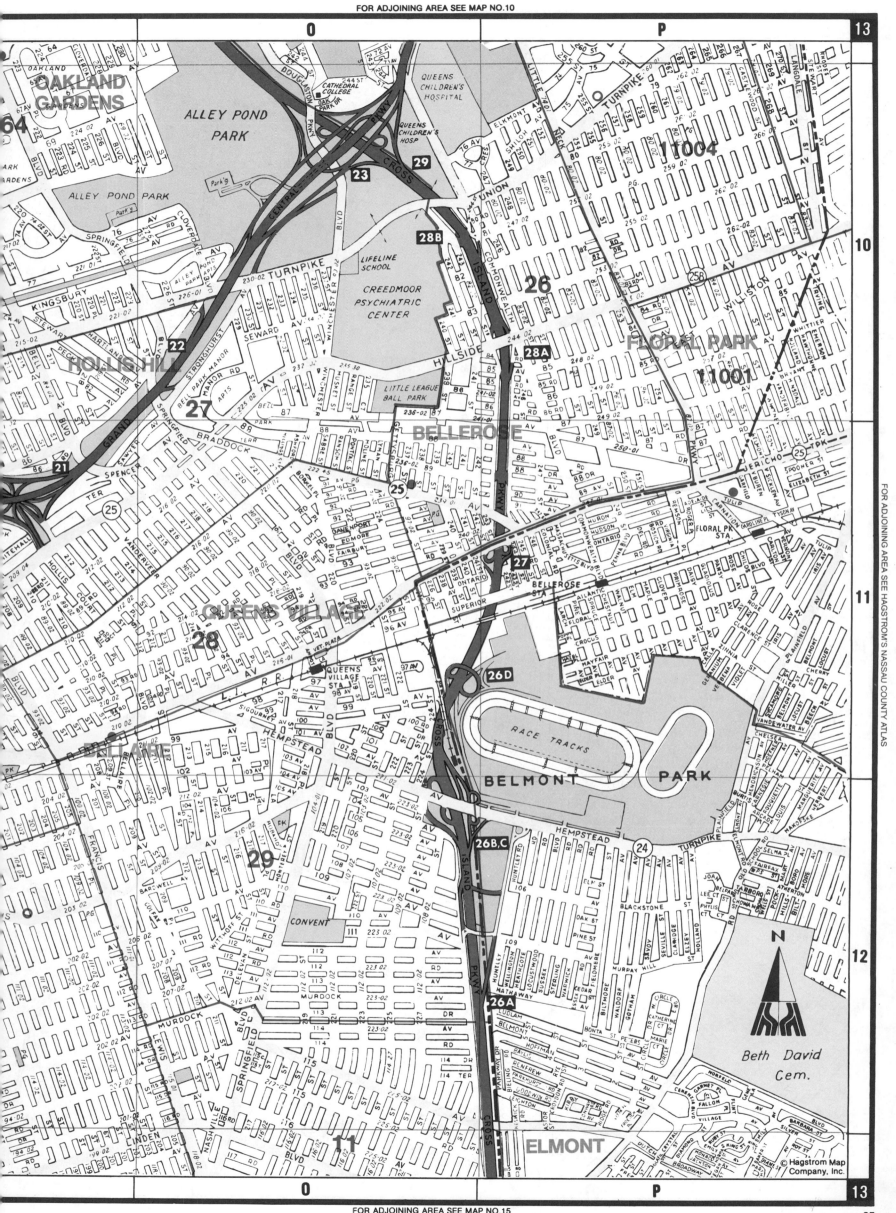

14

G   H   J

13

14

15

14

G   H   J

FOR ADJOINING AREA SEE MAP NO.21

MT CARMEL CEM.
CYPRESS
MT. NEBOH CEM.
MT. CARMEL CEM.
BETH-EL CEM.
MACH-PELAH CEM.
UNION FIELD CEM.
MOUNT JUDAH CEM.
KNOLLWOOD PK. CEM.
TRINITY CEM.
JUDAH CEM.
CEMETERY OF THE EVERGREENS
CEM OF THE B'NAI JESHURUM AND SHERETH ISRAEL
SALEM FIELD CEMETERY
NATIONAL CEMETERY
MT. HOPE CEM.
CYPRESS HILLS CEMETERY
RIDGEWOOD RESERVOIR
HIGHLAND PARK
GOLF COURSE FOREST PARK
FOREST PARKWAY
JAMAICA
CYPRESS HILLS
CITY LINE
HIGHLAND PARK
BROADWAY JUNCTION
PITKIN
EAST NEW YORK
BROWNSVILLE
NEW LOTS
SPRING CREEK
STARRETT CITY
SPRING CREEK PARK (NO ACCESS)
CANARSIE
U.S. P.O.
CYPRESS HILLS P.G. HOUSING
LOUIS H. PINK HOUSING
26TH WARD SEWAGE TREATMENT PLANT
NYS OFFICE OF MENTAL RETARDATION AND DEVELOPMENTAL DISABILITIES
FRESH CREEK PARK

BROADWAY
FULTON
PITKIN AV
GLENMORE AV
LIBERTY AV
ATLANTIC AV
SUTTER AV
BELMONT AV
DUMONT AV
LINDEN BLVD
FLATLANDS AV
LINDEN BLVD
WORTMAN AV
HEGEMAN AV
ROCKAWAY AVENUE
ROCKAWAY PARKWAY
SEAVIEW AV
FLATLANDS AV

© Hagstrom Map Company, Inc.

85
7
8
6
21
12
7
8
36
39
1 2 3 4
27
14

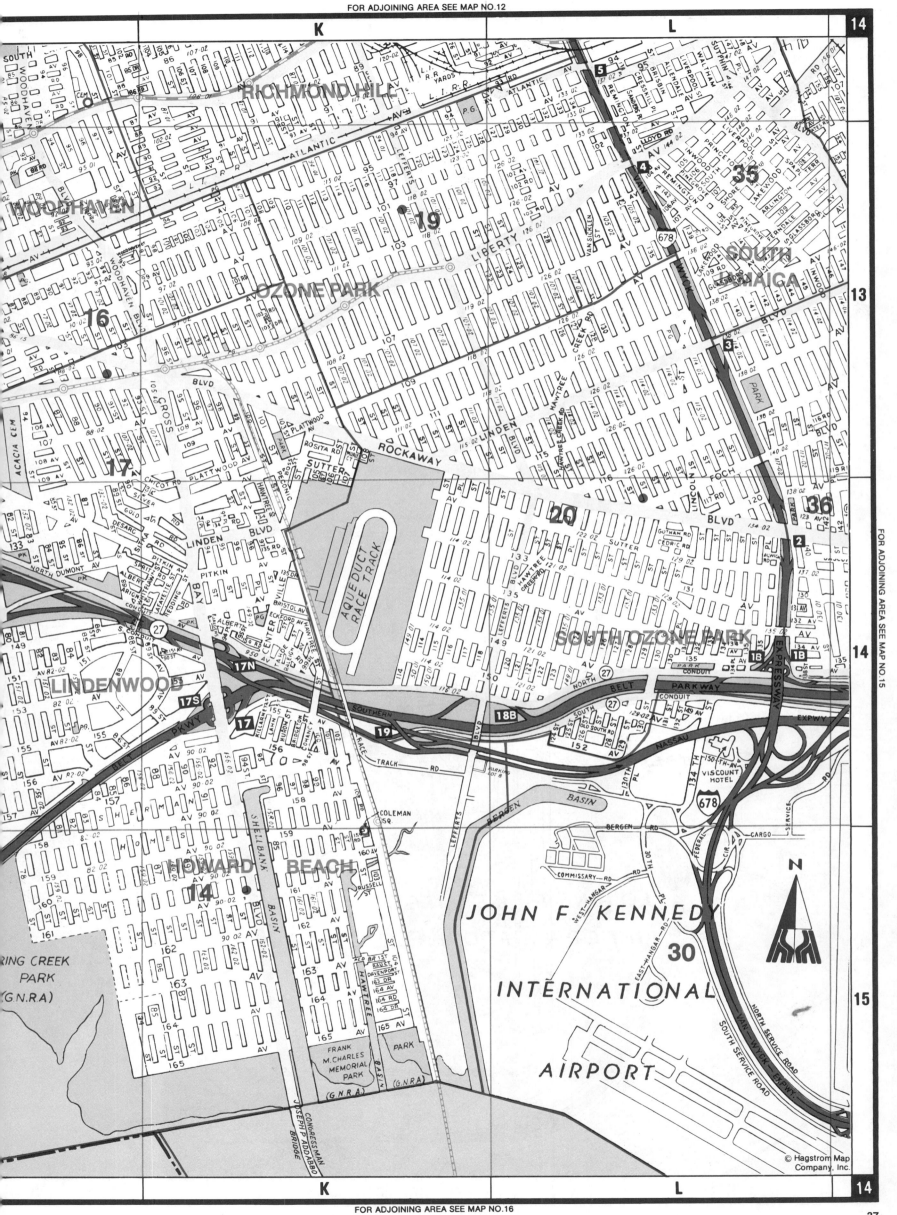

15   L   M   N

ATLANTIC AV

LIBERTY

19

35

33

ST. ALBANS

25 ST. ALBANS VETERANS ADM. EXT. CARE CENTER

ROY WILKINS SOUTHERN QUEENS PARK

13

SOUTH JAMAICA

CEDAR MANOR HOUSES

BAISLEY PARK HOUSES

BAISLEY'S POND

34 ROCHDALE VILLAGE

LOCUST MANOR STA.

SPRINGFIELD

ROCKAWAY

20

36

BAISLEY POND

PARK

21A

21B

SOUTH OZONE PARK

18   **18**

CONDUIT

20

BELT PARKWAY

CONDUIT

EXPRESSWAY

20

BASIN

VISCOUNT HOTEL

678

COMMISSARY RD

BERGEN RD

FEDERAL CIR

CARGO

**JOHN F. KENNEDY
INTERNATIONAL AIRPORT**

No

NORTH SERVICE ROAD

SOUTH SERVICE ROAD

VAN WYCK EXPWY

CENTER CARGO RD

COMPASS

PILOT RD

N. SERVICE CT

S. SERVICE RD

GUARD BOOTH

30

GEN. AVIATION TERMINAL

GUARD POST B

GUARD POST A

TERMINAL 1

TERMINAL 9 (AAL)

TERMINAL 8 (AAL)

TERMINAL 7 (BA/UA)

TERMINAL 6 (TWA DOM)

TERMINAL 5 (TWA INT'L)

TERMINAL 4E

PARKING LOT 2

PARKING LOT 3

PARKING LOT 4

PARKING LOT 5

INTERNATIONAL ARRIVALS BLDG

PARKING

© Hagstrom Map Company, Inc.

15   L   M   N

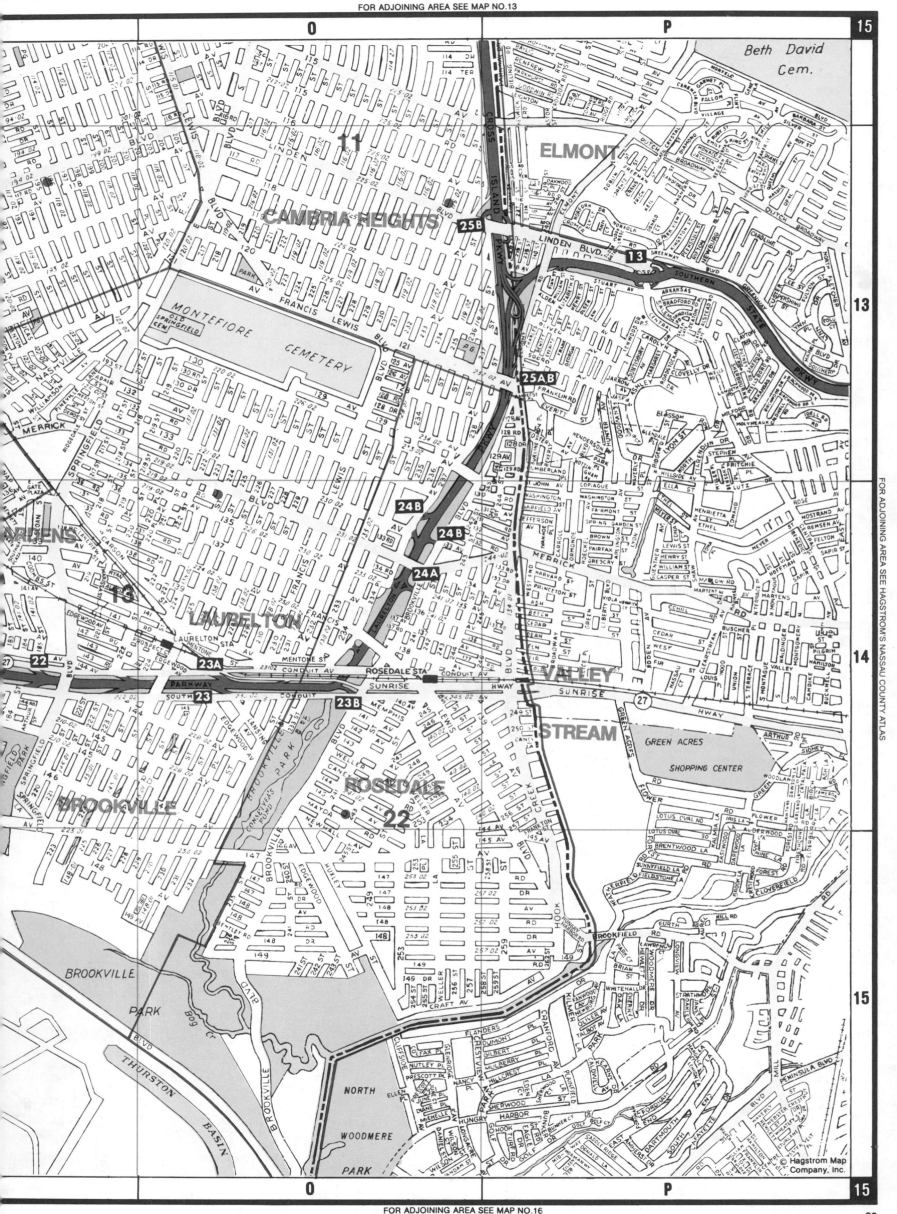

16   K   L   M

165 AV

14

FRANK M. CHARLES MEMORIAL PARK (GNRA)

PARK (GNRA)

N. SERVICE RD
S. SERVICE RD
VAN WYCK EXPWY

TERMINAL 9 (AAL)

PARKING LOT 3

GUARD POST B

GEN. AVIATION TERMINAL

GUARD POST A

TERMINAL 1

TERMINAL 2

ROOF PARKING LO

G R A S S Y

B A Y

JOSEPH P. ADDABBO BRIDGE
CONGRESSMAN

CROSS BAY BLVD

HASSOCK

East Pond

BROAD CREEK MARSH

16

PUMPKIN PATCH MARSH

BLACK BANK MARSH

RULERS BAR

West Pond

WILDLIFE REFUGE

PATCH CHANNEL

J A M A I C A

B A Y

COS

CHANNEL

EAST HIGH MEADOW

HASSOCK CREEK

JO

VISITOR CENTER

CHAMPLAIN RD
ACME RD
NOEL RD

BROAD CHANNEL MEM. PARK
E.5 RD

93

17

BLACK WALL CHANNEL

RULERS BAR

JAMAICA BAY UNIT

BIG MUCK CREEK

WINHOLE HASSOCK

SILVER HOLE MARSH

BROAD CHANNEL

SHAD CREEK RD
POWER RD

CROSS BAY CHANNEL BLVD

CHURCH RD
WALL RD
WEST RD
NOEL RD

9 RD
10 RD
11 RD
12 RD
13 RD
14 RD
15 RD
16 RD
17 RD
18 RD
19 RD
20 RD

E.12 RD
E.14 RD
E.16 RD
E.18 RD
E.20 RD

P.G.

GRASS

HASS

U.S. BULKH
JUDOS WILDLIFE

BLACK WALL MARSH

SPENCER

SHAD CREEK RD

BIG EGG MARSH

TOLL

GRASS

BROAD

CROSS BAY VETERANS MEM. BRIDGE

SOMERVILLE

92

BARBADOES DR
BAYFIELD AV
DE COSTA AV
HILLMEYER AV

ALMA
BURCHELL
ELIZABETH
THURSBY AV
HESSLER AV
GOUVERNEUR AV

VERNAM BASIN

ROCKAWAY INDUSTRIAL PARK

LITTLE EGG

MARSH

GIANT BAR MARSH

BARBADOES ST
BEACH ST
FINNARD AV

SCHEER ST
AMSTEL BLVD

FREEWAY

ARVERNE

16   K   L

N   0   16

22

NORTH WOODMERE PARK

30

JOHN F. KENNEDY INTERNATIONAL AIRPORT

Terminal 5 (TWA INT'L)
Terminal 4E
International Arrivals Bldg
Terminal 4W
Terminal 3 (Delta)
Parking Lot 5
Parking Lot 4
Parking Lot 2

N

16

HEAD OF BAY

TOWN OF HEMPSTEAD

THURSTON BASIN

BROOKVILLE BLVD

248 ST

INWOOD COUNTRY CLUB

96

PARK

MOTT BASIN

CHANNEL

BAYSWATER

FAR ROCKAWAY

REDFERN HOUSES

LAWRENCE STA.

INWOOD STA.

REDFERN STA.

CENTRAL

17

EDGEMERE PARK

NORTON BASIN

CONCH BASIN

SOMMERVILLE BASIN

91

BAYSWATER PARK

FAR ROCKAWAY

ST. JOHN'S EPISCOPAL HOSP.

PLAINVIEW AV

SEAGIRT BLVD

O'DONOHUE PARK

18

EDGEMERE HOUSES

PENINSULA HOSP.

ROCKAWAY

EDGEMERE

BOARDWALK

ROCKAWAY BEACH

(PUBLIC)

QUEENS CO.
NASSAU CO.

U.S. Coast Guard Station

ATLANTIC BEACH BRIDGE (Toll)

© Hagstrom Map Company, Inc.

N   0   16

FOR ADJOINING AREA SEE HAGSTROM'S NASSAU COUNTY ATLAS

17 F G

FOR ADJOINING AREA SEE MAP NO.25

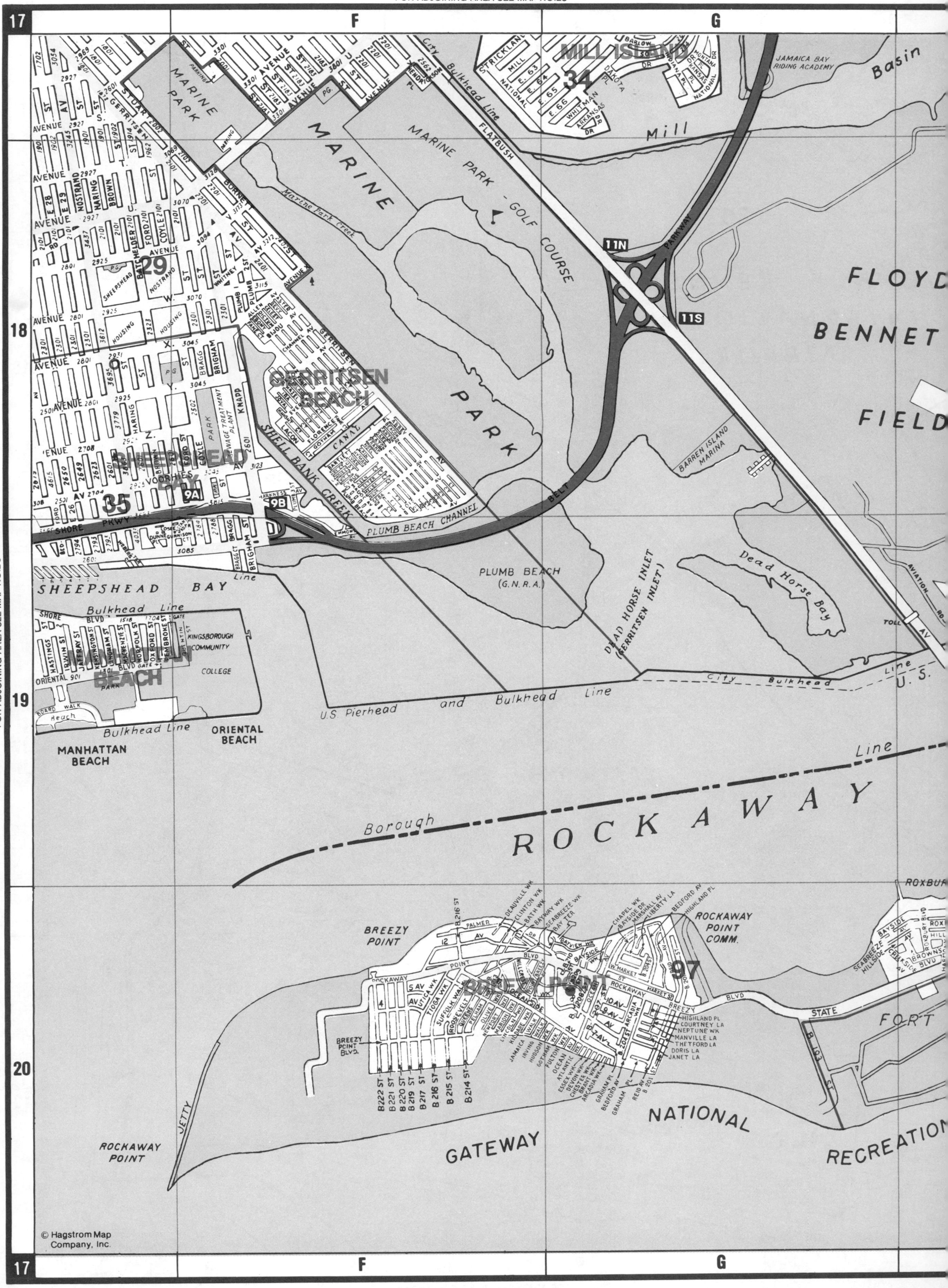

MILL ISLAND
34

JAMAICA BAY RIDING ACADEMY

Basin

Mill

MARINE PARK

MARINE PARK - GOLF COURSE

FLOYD
BENNET
FIELD

GERRITSEN BEACH
29

SHEEPSHEAD BAY
35
9A
9B

SHELL BANK CREEK

CANAL

PLUMB BEACH CHANNEL

PARK

BARREN ISLAND MARINA

DEAD HORSE INLET (GERRITSEN INLET)

Dead Horse Bay

TOLL

18

PLUMB BEACH (G.N.R.A.)

19

MANHATTAN BEACH

KINGSBOROUGH COMMUNITY COLLEGE

Bulkhead Line

ORIENTAL BEACH

SHEEPSHEAD BAY

U.S Pierhead and Bulkhead Line

City Bulkhead Line U.S.

Borough Line

R O C K A W A Y

ROXBUR

20

BREEZY POINT

ROCKAWAY POINT COMM.

BREEZY POINT
97

BAYSIDE

FORT

ROCKAWAY POINT

JETTY

GATEWAY

NATIONAL

RECREATION

STATE

© Hagstrom Map Company, Inc.

17 F G

H | J | K | **17**

18

ISLAND CHANNEL

SAILS PT. HASSOCK

HASSOCK

HORSE CHANNEL

OLD SWALE MARSH

RUFFLE BAR

THE RAUNT

LITTLE EGG

MARSH

U.S. COAST GUARD

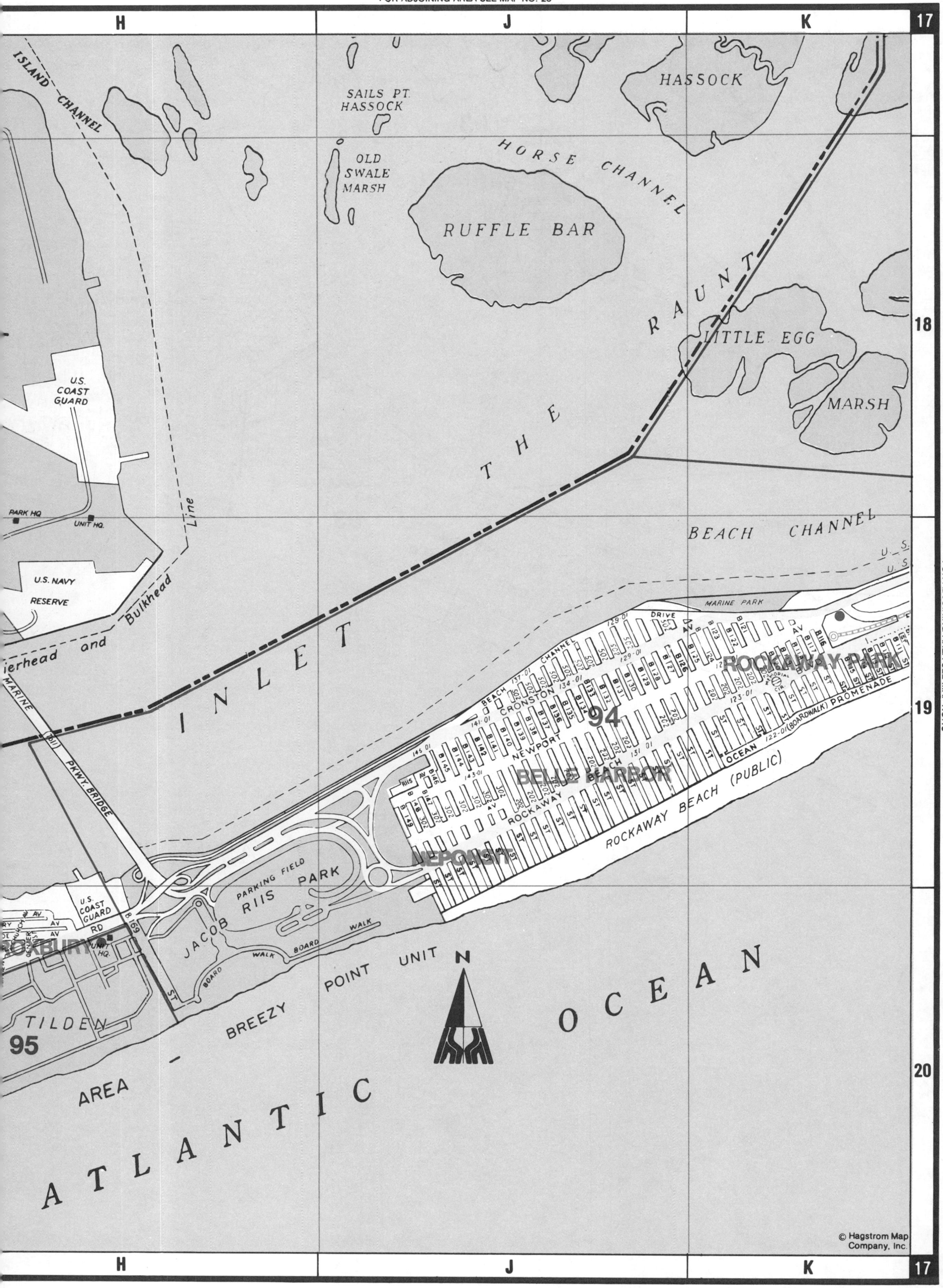

FOR ADJOINING AREA SEE MAP NO. 18

PARK HQ

UNIT HQ.

Bulkhead Line

U.S. NAVY RESERVE

BEACH CHANNEL

MARINE PARK

U.S.

19

ierhead and

INLET

ROCKAWAY PARK

MARINE

94

BELLE HARBOR

PKWY. BRIDGE

Newport

Rockaway

ROCKAWAY BEACH (PUBLIC)

(BOARDWALK) PROMENADE

U.S. COAST GUARD

RIIS AV

NEPONSIT

RD

B. 69

PARKING FIELD RIIS PARK

JACOB

BOARD WALK

BOARD WALK

ROXBURY

UNIT HQ.

ST

TILDEN

95

BREEZY

POINT UNIT

N

20

AREA

ATLANTIC OCEAN

H | J | K | **17**

18   K   L   M

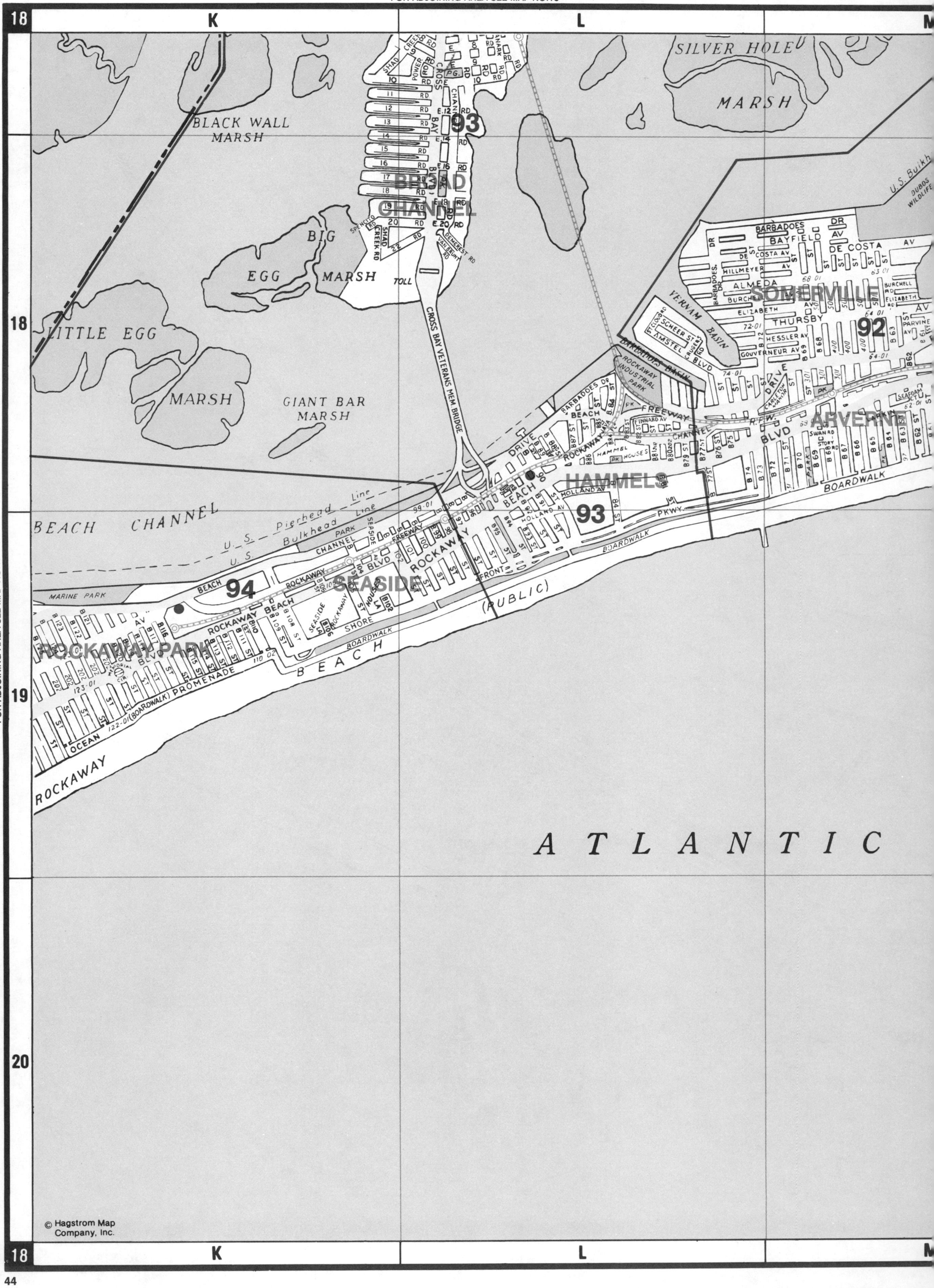

FOR ADJOINING AREA SEE MAP NO.17

SILVER HOLE
MARSH

BLACK WALL
MARSH

BROAD CHANNEL

93

CROSS BAY

BARBADOES
BAYFIELD
DR
AV
DE COSTA AV
HILLMEYER AV
ALMEDA
BURCHELL
SOMERVILLE
ELIZABETH
92
THURSBY
HESSLER AV
GOUVERNEUR AV

BIG
EGG MARSH

LITTLE EGG

18

VERNAM BASIN
SCHEER ST
AMSTEL
ST

MARSH

GIANT BAR
MARSH

CROSS BAY VETERANS MEM BRIDGE

TOLL

ROCKAWAY INDUSTRIAL PARK
FREEWAY
ARVERNE
BOARDWALK

DRIVE
BARBADOES DR
BEACH ST
ROCKAWAY
HAMMELS
HOLLAND AV
93
PKWY
BOARDWALK

BEACH CHANNEL

U.S. Pierhead Line
U.S. Bulkhead Line

MARINE PARK

94
SEASIDE
ROCKAWAY PARK

ROCKAWAY
SHORE FRONT
BOARDWALK
(PUBLIC)
BEACH

OCEAN
PROMENADE
(BOARDWALK)

ROCKAWAY

19

ATLANTIC

20

18   K   L   M

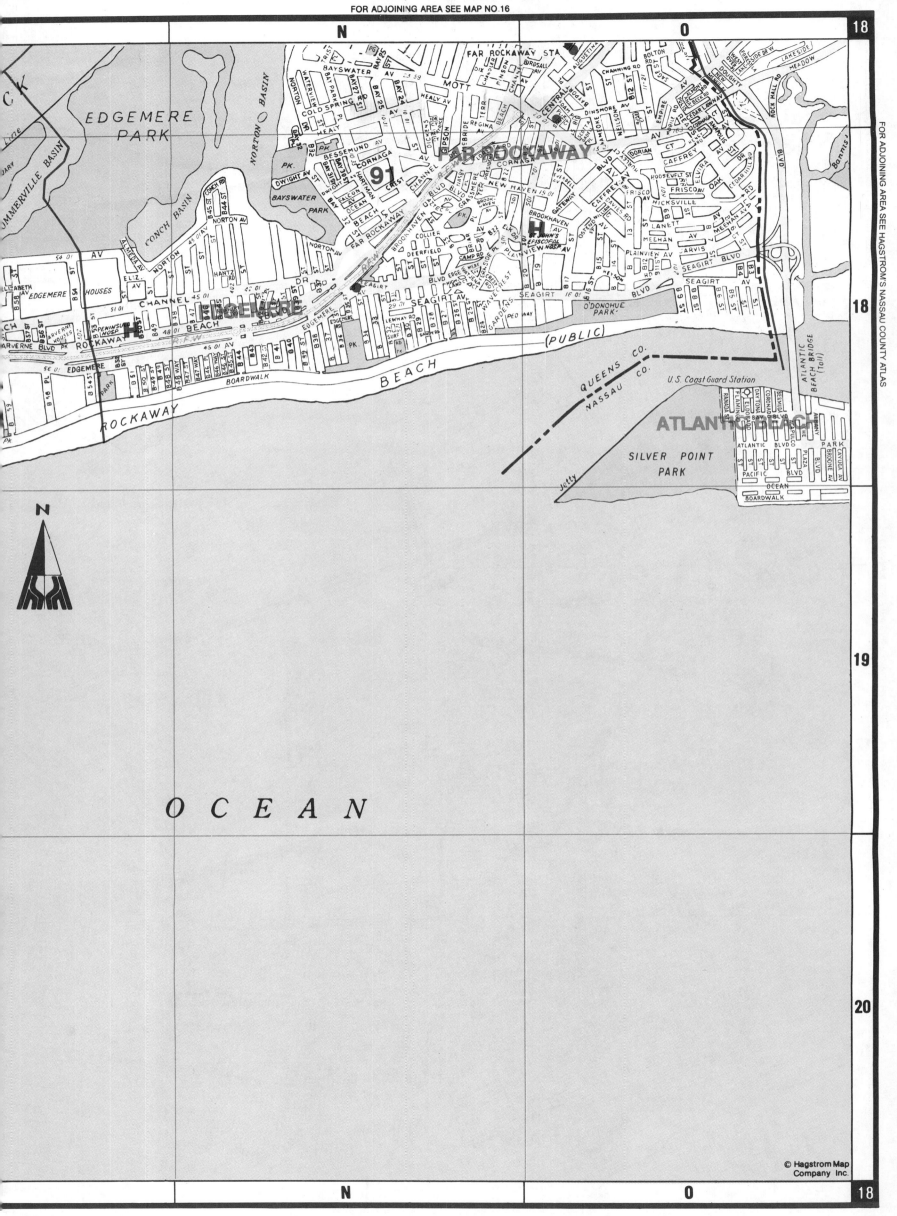

Neighborhoods and labels visible:

FLATIRON 10
GRAMERCY PARK
WEST VILLAGE 14
UNION SQUARE 3
GREENWICH VILLAGE
NOHO 12
SOHO
EAST VILLAGE 9
LITTLE ITALY
CHINATOWN
LOWER EAST SIDE 2
CIVIC CENTER
TWO BRIDGES 38
HUNTERS POINT
LONG ISLAND CITY STA
GREENPOINT
NORTHSIDE
SOUTHSIDE 41
WILLIAMSBURG
WILLIAMSBURG BRIDGE
MANHATTAN BRIDGE
BROOKLYN BRIDGE
DUMBO 28
VINEGAR HILL 29
FULTON FERRY
BROOKLYN HEIGHTS
BROOKLYN NAVY YARD INDUSTRIAL PARK
U.S. NAVAL STATION
DOWNTOWN BROOKLYN 1
BOROUGH HALL
FORT GREENE PARK
FORT GREENE
CLINTON HILL 5
MYRTLE
COBBLE HILL
BOERUM HILL 7
38

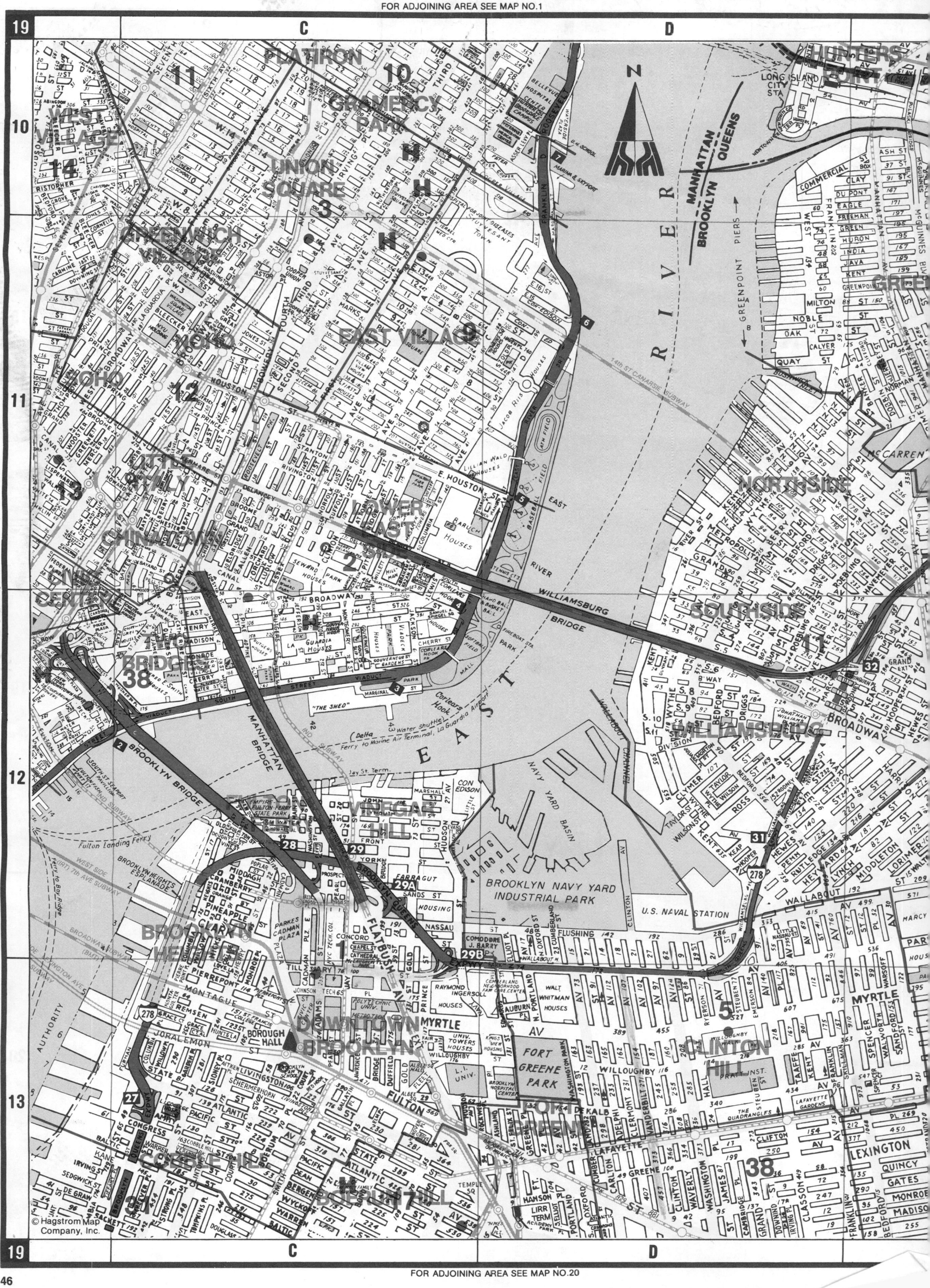

Water features:

EAST RIVER
WALLABOUT CHANNEL
NAVY YARD BASIN

© Hagstrom Map Company, Inc.

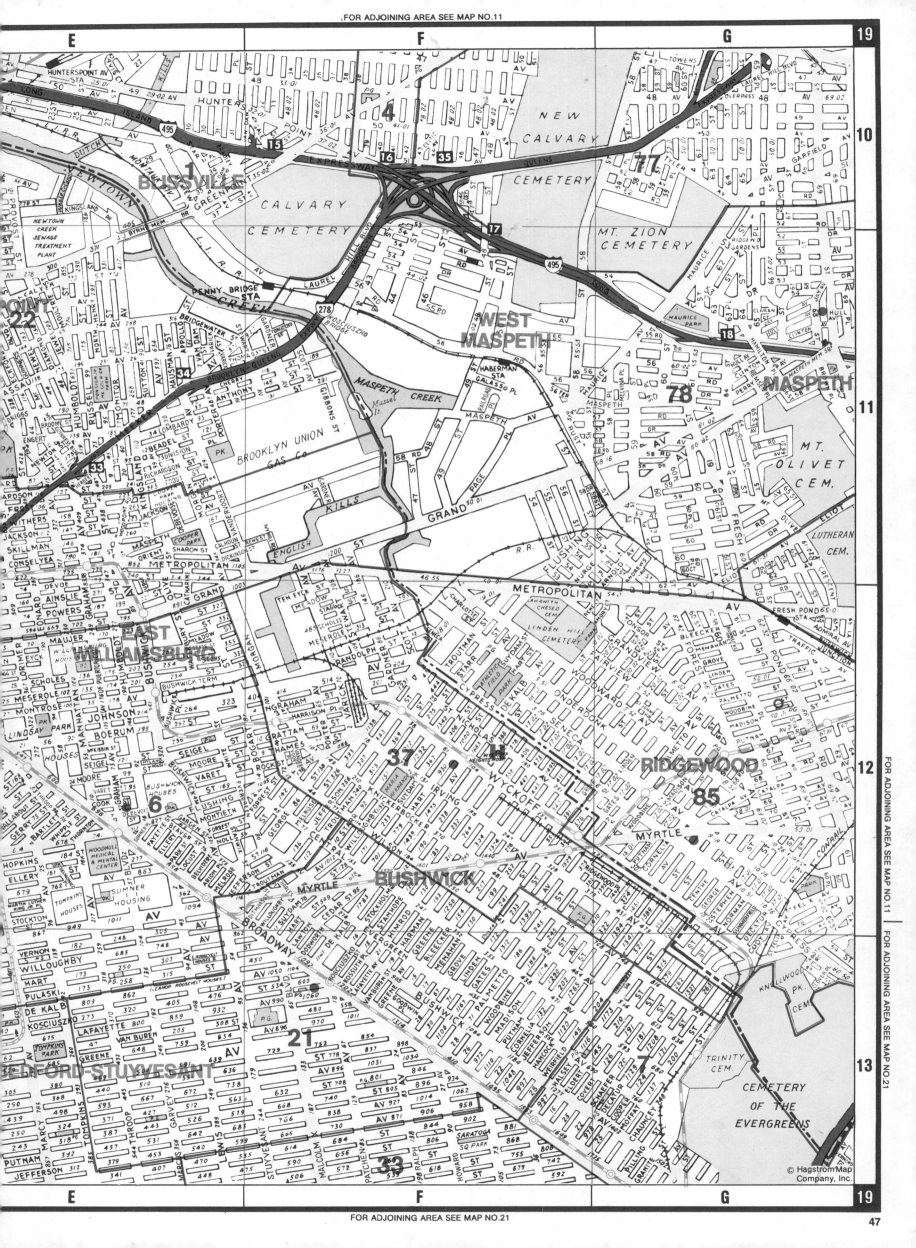

20   A   B   C

13

14

15

20   A   B   C

GOVERNORS ISLAND

U.S. COAST GUARD

BUTTERMILK CHANNEL

Ferry to Statue of Liberty / Ellis Island

Ferry to Staten Island

Ferry to Corner's Hotel - Highlands N.J.

Ferry to Bay Ridge

Ferry to Governor's Island

BKLYN.-BATTERY TUNNEL

EAST SIDE
Lexington Ave. (BMT)

Broadway Subway (BMT)

BROOKLYN HEIGHTS

CLARK ST

BOROUGH HALL

COBBLE HILL

BOERUM HILL

CARROLL GARDENS

GOWANUS

RED HOOK

ATLANTIC BASIN

Port of New York Co.
New York Co.
Kings Co.

PIER 11

ERIE BASIN

WAREHOUSE PIER

BREAKWATER

PORT OF NEW YORK
AUTHORITY PIERS

PORT AUTH GRAIN TERMINAL

PARK

GOWANUS BAY

31

32

GREENWOOD HEIGHTS

GREENWOOD CEMETERY

SUNSET PARK

BUSH TERMINAL DOCKS

Bush Terminal Warehouses

DRY Docks

LUTHERAN MEDICAL CENTER

BAY RIDGE R.R. STA.

20

19

278

N

© Hagstrom Map Company, Inc.

20

MYRTLE

FORT GREENE

FORT GREENE PARK

L.I. UNIV.

PRATT INST.

CLINTON HILL

BEDFORD-STUYVESANT

STUYVESANT HEIGHTS

BROADWAY

PROSPECT HEIGHTS

ATLANTIC AV

FULTON ST

CROWN HEIGHTS

GRAND ARMY PLAZA

BROOKLYN MUSEUM

BROOKLYN BOTANIC GARDEN

LITCHFIELD VILLA

PROSPECT PARK

EASTERN PARKWAY

BROWER PARK

ALBANY HOUSING

5TH

PARK SLOPE

WINDSOR TERRACE

PROSPECT LAKE

BOATHOUSE

PROSPECT LEFFERTS GARDEN

EMPIRE BOULEVARD

WINGATE

KINGS COUNTY HOSPITAL

KINGS CO. HOSPITAL

KINGSBORO PSYCHIATRIC CENTER

KINGSBROOK JEWISH MEDICAL CENTER

RUGBY

PARKSIDE PARADE GROUNDS

PROSPECT PARK SOUTH

CHURCH AV

ALBEMARLE ROAD

BEVERLY

HOLY CROSS CEMETERY

FARRAGUT

OCEAN AV

NOSTRAND AV

FLATBUSH AV

© Hagstrom Map Company Inc

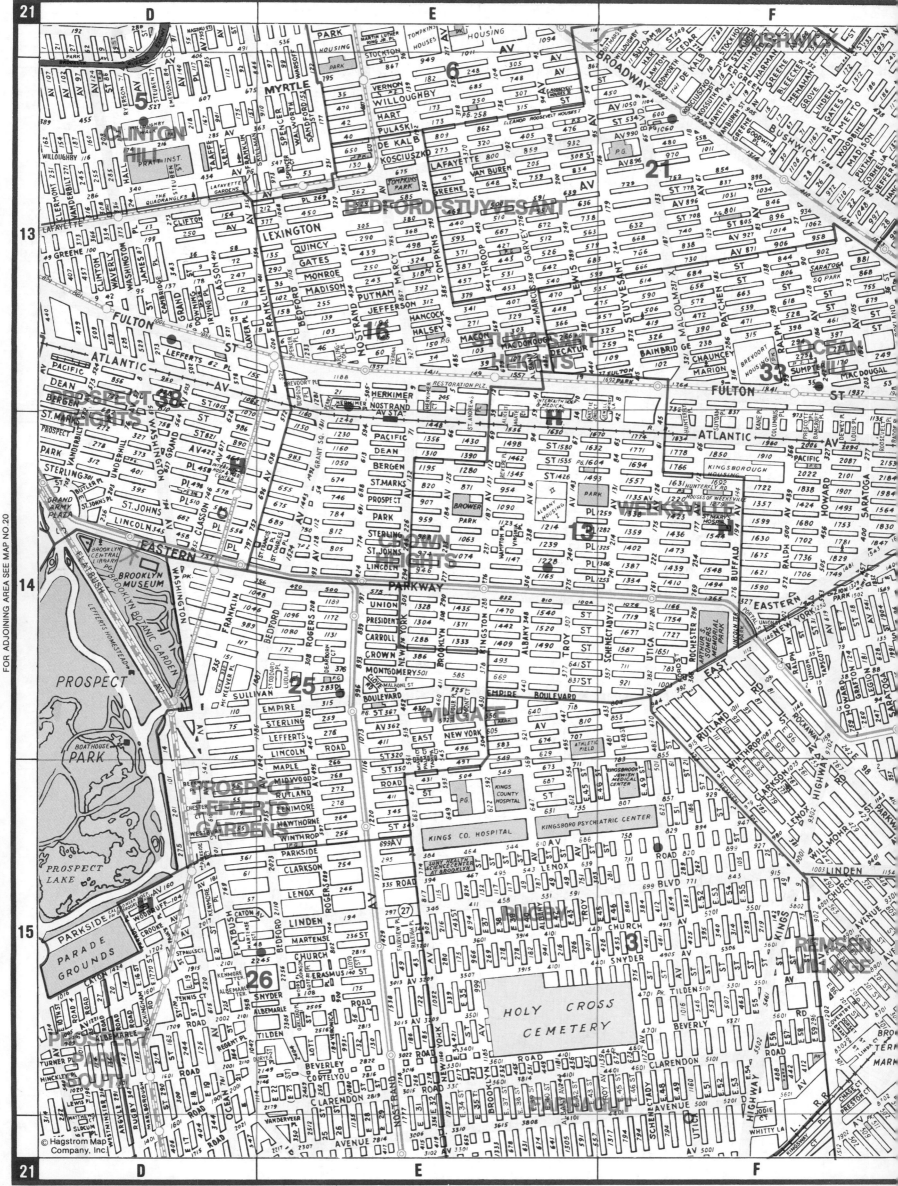

© Hagstrom Map Company, Inc

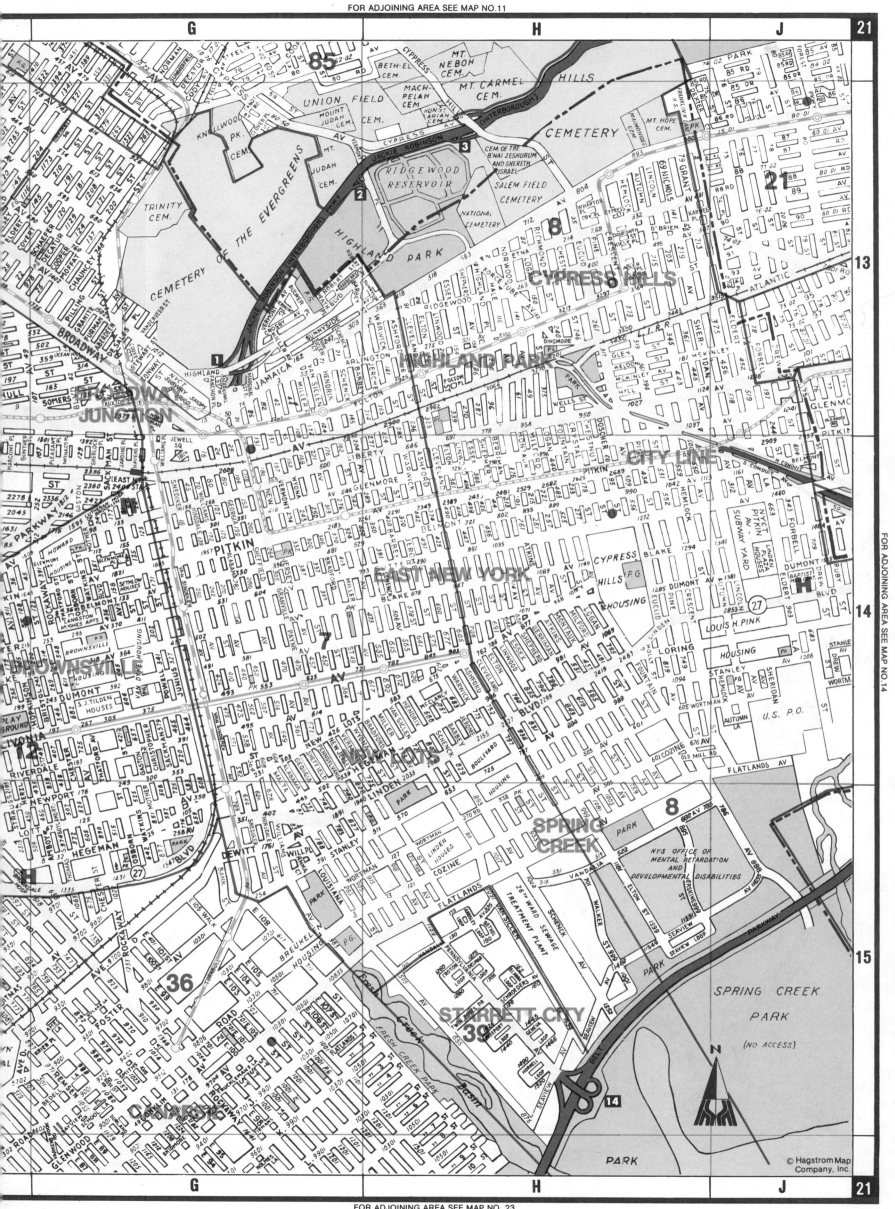

22

A B C

15

16

17

N

GREENWOOD HEIGHTS

GREENWOOD CEMETERY

SUNSET PARK

SUNSET PARK

BUSH TERMINAL DOCKS

Dry Docks

LUTHERAN MEDICAL CENTER

BAY RIDGE STA.

OWLS HEAD PK.

BMT YARD

MAIMONIDES MEDICAL CENTER

32

20

19

BOROUGH PARK

BAY RIDGE

Ft. Hamilton Field

GLD GLORY LOOK OUT

MONASTERY SQUARE

9

28

DYKER HEIGHTS

NEW UTRECHT

DYKER BEACH GOLF COURSE

BENSONHURST

FORT HAMILTON

U.S. GOVERNMENT RESERVATION

Fort Hamilton

Brooklyn Veterans ADM MED CENTER

DYKER BEACH PARK

14

VERRAZANO-NARROWS BRIDGE (TOLL)

278

SHORE PKWY

BATH BEACH

© Hagstrom Map Company, Inc

PROSPECT PARK

PROSPECT LAKE

WINDSOR TERRACE

PROSPECT LEFFERTS GARDENS

PARKSIDE PARADE GROUNDS

KINGS COUNTY HOSPITAL

KINGS CO. HOSPITAL

KINGSBORO PSYCHIATRIC CENTER

SUNY HEALTH SCIENCE CENTER AT BROOKLYN

KINGSBROOK JEWISH MEDICAL CENTER

HOLY CROSS CEMETERY

PROSPECT PARK SOUTH

KENSINGTON

DITMAS PARK

FARRAGUT

PARKVILLE

FLATBUSH

EAST FLATBUSH

BROOKLYN COLLEGE

WASHINGTON CEMETERY

ATHLETIC FIELD

MIDWOOD

MARLETON

OCEAN PARKWAY

MARINE PARK

MARINE PARK

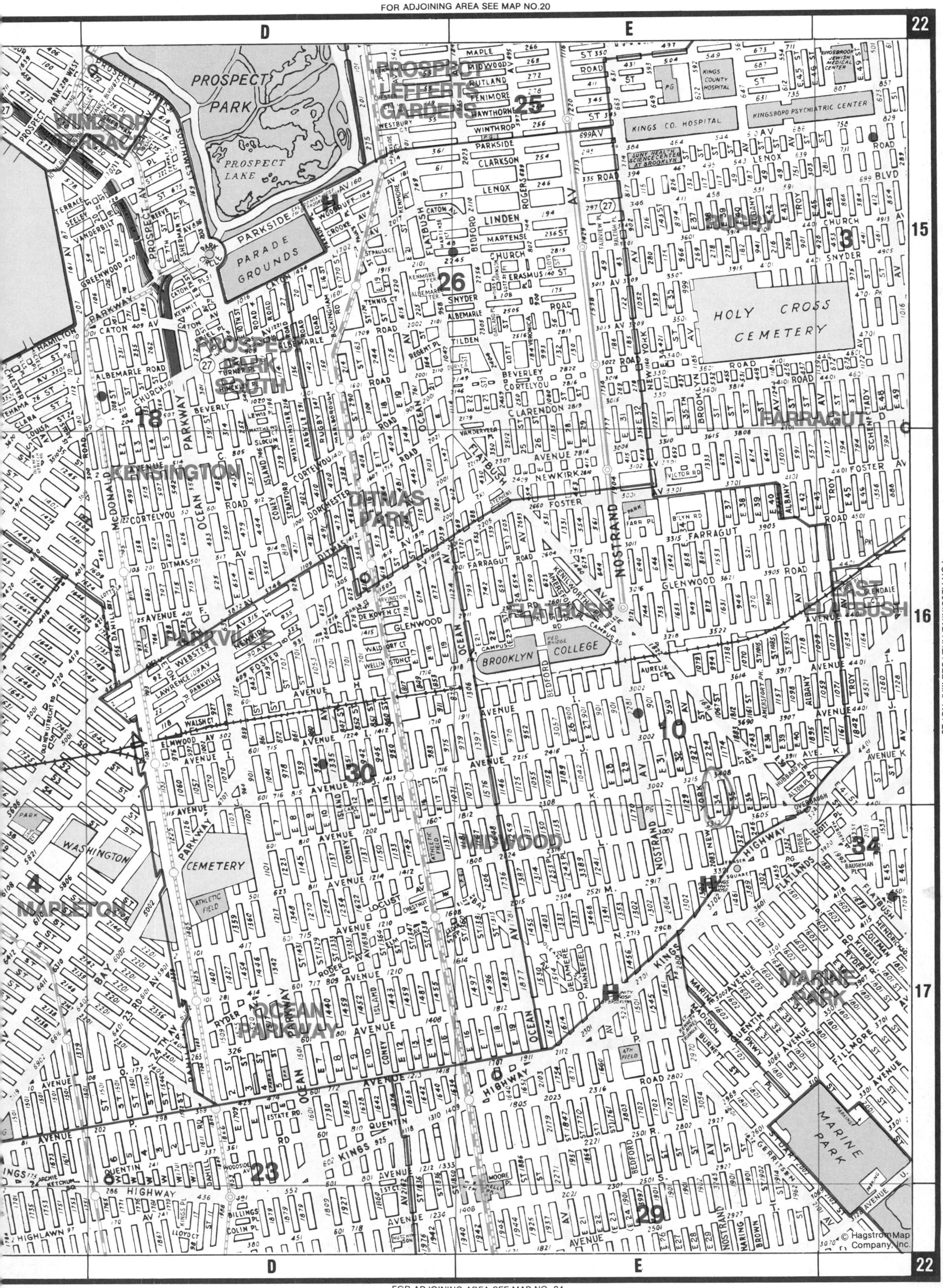

FOR ADJOINING AREA SEE MAP NO. 23

PROSPECT PARK

PROSPECT LEFFERTS GARDENS

PARKSIDE PARADE GROUNDS

PROSPECT PARK SOUTH

DITMAS PARK

FLATBUSH

BROOKLYN COLLEGE

MIDWOOD

OCEAN PARKWAY

KINGS CO. HOSPITAL

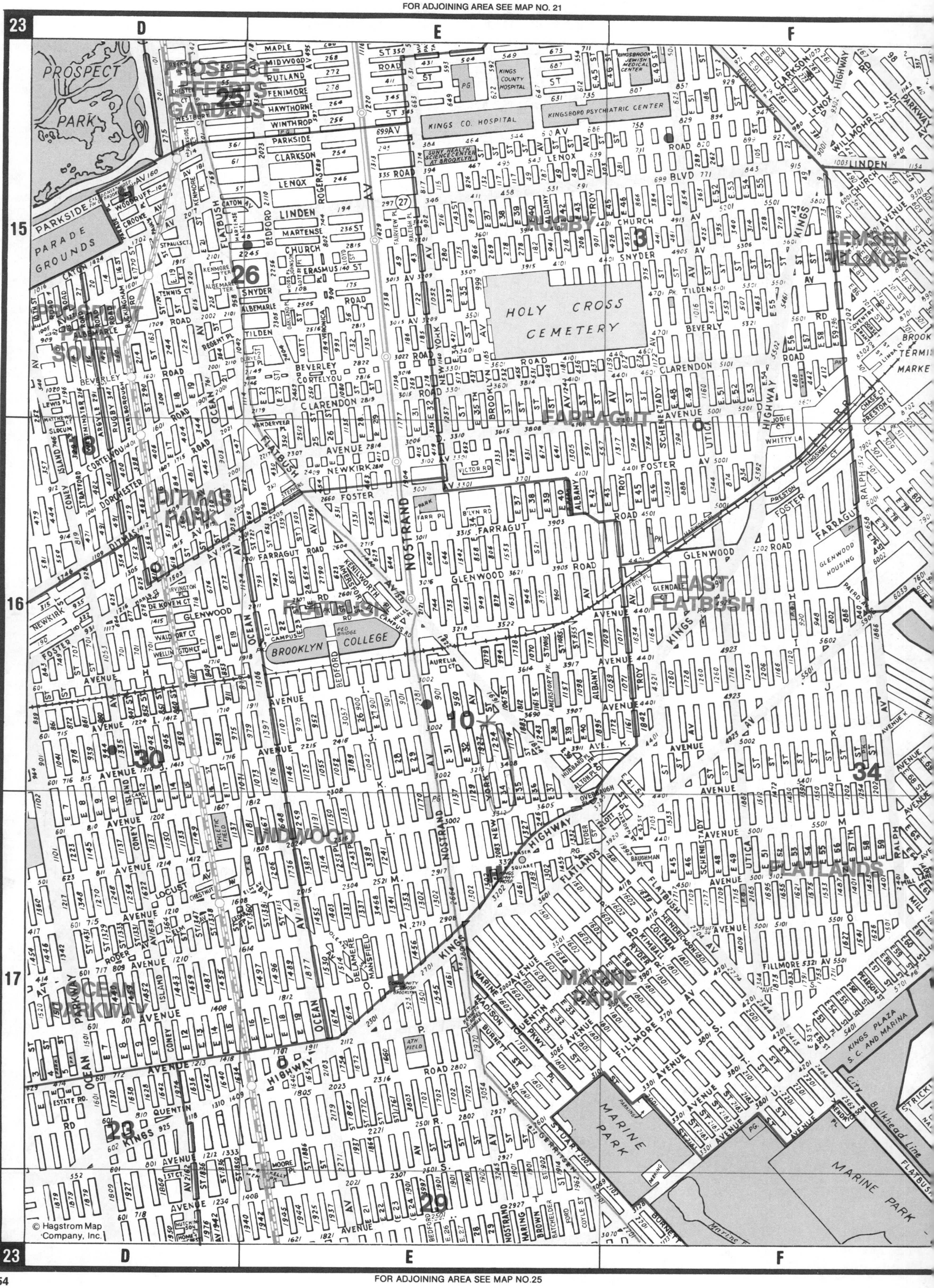

Kings County Hospital

Kingsbrook Jewish Medical Center

Kingsboro Psychiatric Center

SUNY HEALTH SCIENCE CENTER AT BROOKLYN

HOLY CROSS CEMETERY

FARRAGUT

EAST FLATBUSH

FLATLANDS

MARINE PARK

REMSEN VILLAGE

Glenwood Housing

KINGS PLAZA S.C. AND MARINA

MARINE PARK

© Hagstrom Map Company, Inc.

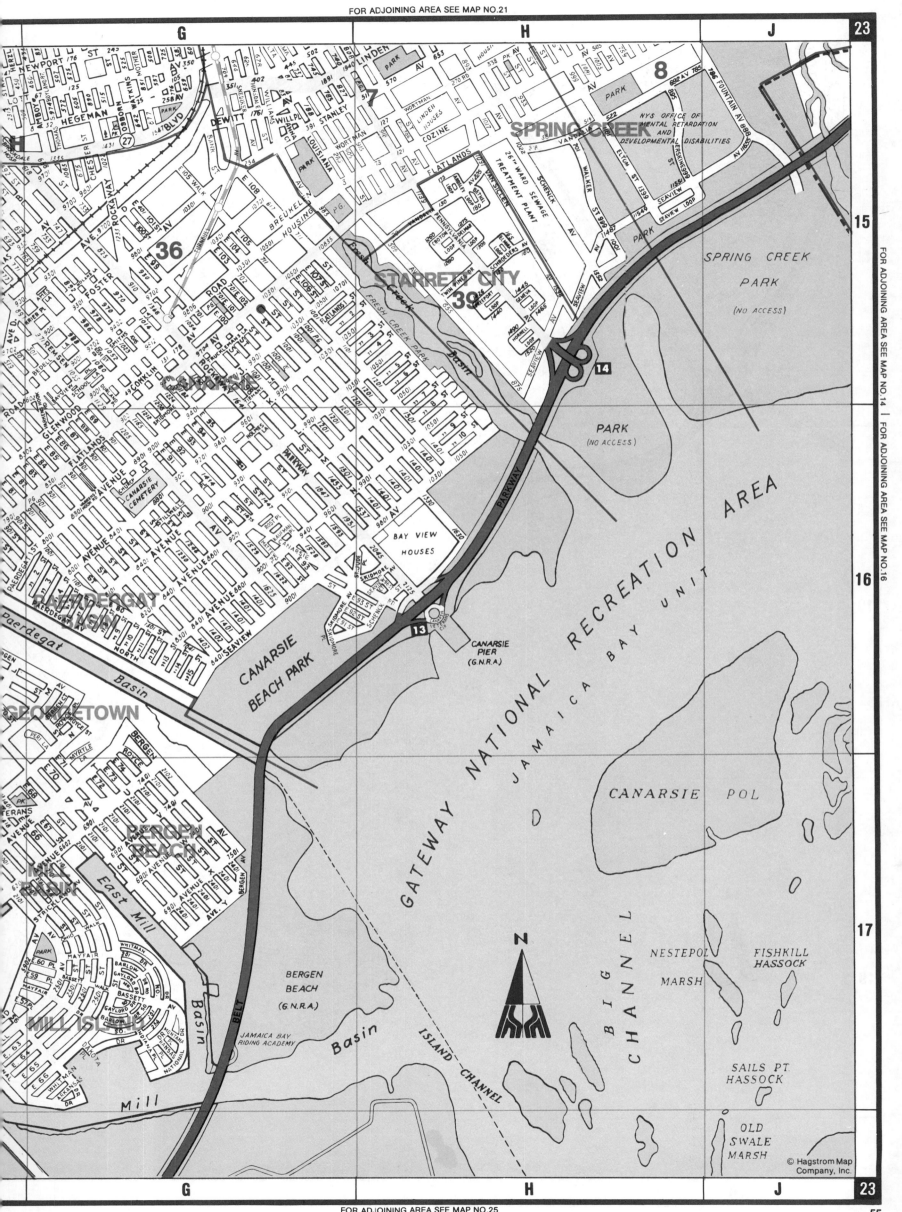

© Hagstrom Map Company, Inc.

FOR ADJOINING AREA SEE MAP NO 27
FOR ADJOINING AREA SEE MAP NO 29

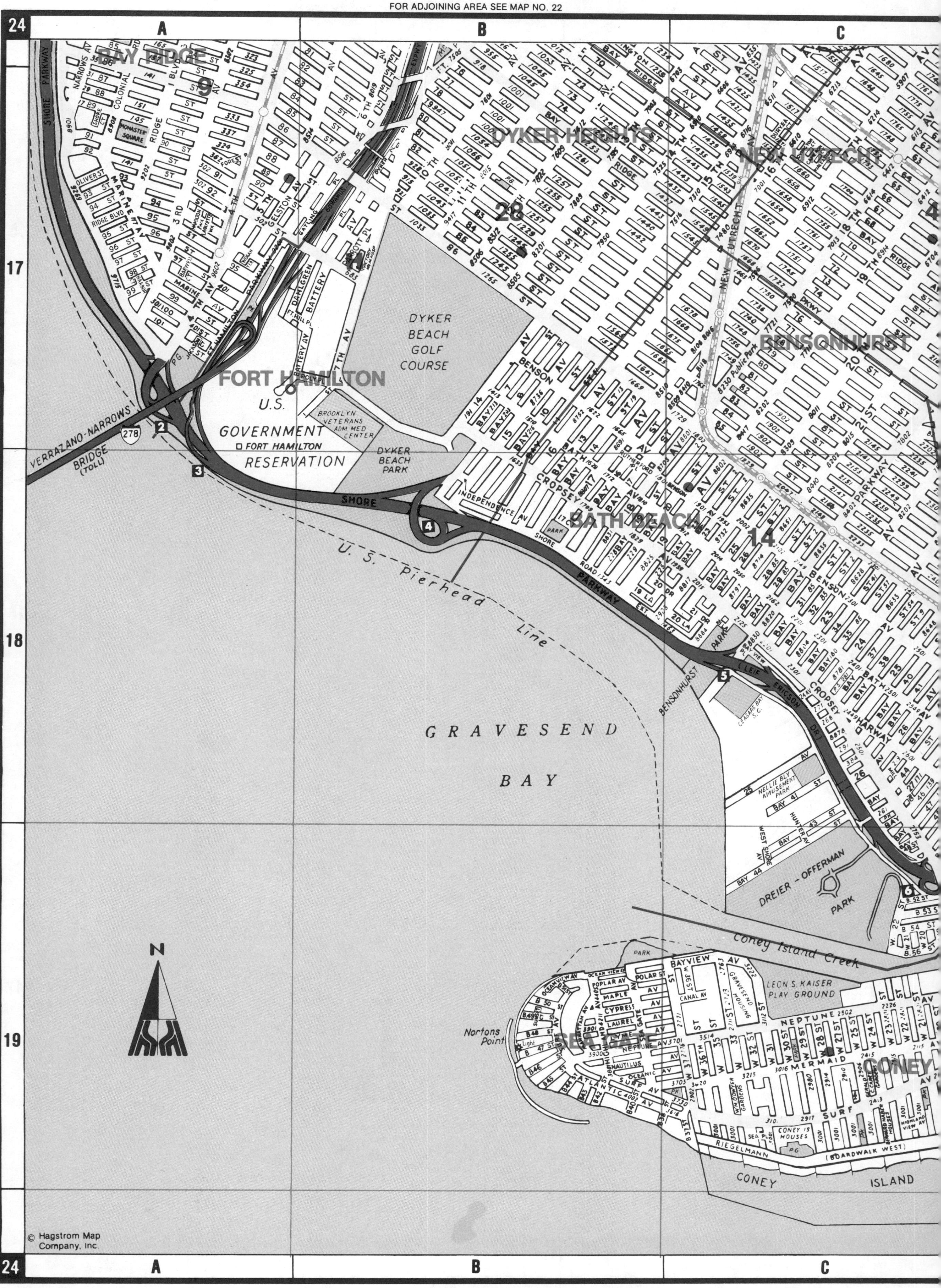

BAY RIDGE

9

DYKER HEIGHTS

NEW UTRECHT

28

BENSONHURST

DYKER
BEACH
GOLF
COURSE

FORT HAMILTON

U.S.
GOVERNMENT

FORT HAMILTON
RESERVATION

Brooklyn
Veterans
Adm Med
Center

DYKER
BEACH
PARK

BATH BEACH

14

SHORE

PARKWAY

U. S. Pierhead Line

GRAVESEND

BAY

Nellie Bly
Amusement
Park

DREIER - OFFERMAN
PARK

Coney Island Creek

N

LEON S. KAISER
PLAY GROUND

BAYVIEW

Nortons
Point

SEAGATE

CONEY

NEPTUNE

MERMAID

SURF

Coney Is
Houses

RIEGELMANN

CONEY   ISLAND

BOARDWALK WEST

Verrazano-Narrows
BRIDGE (Toll)

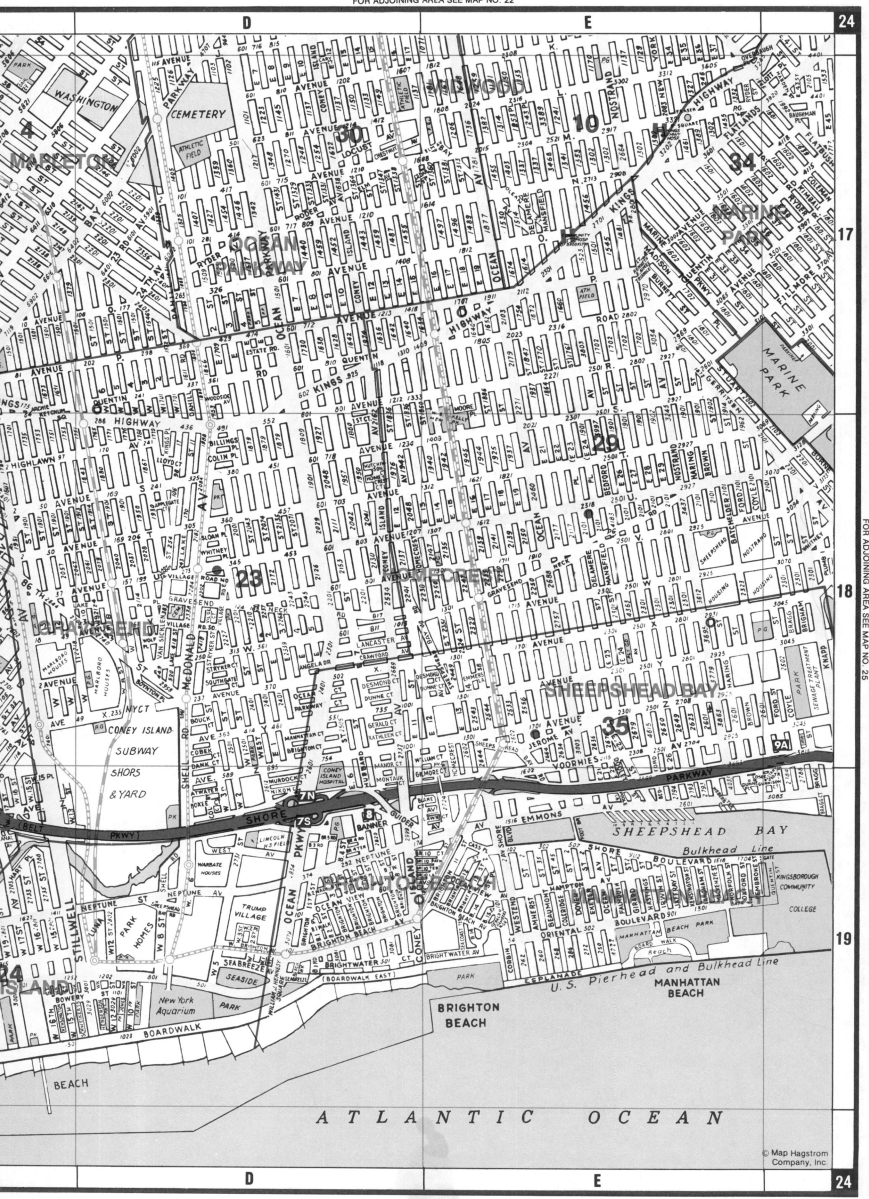

FOR ADJOINING AREA SEE MAP NO. 24

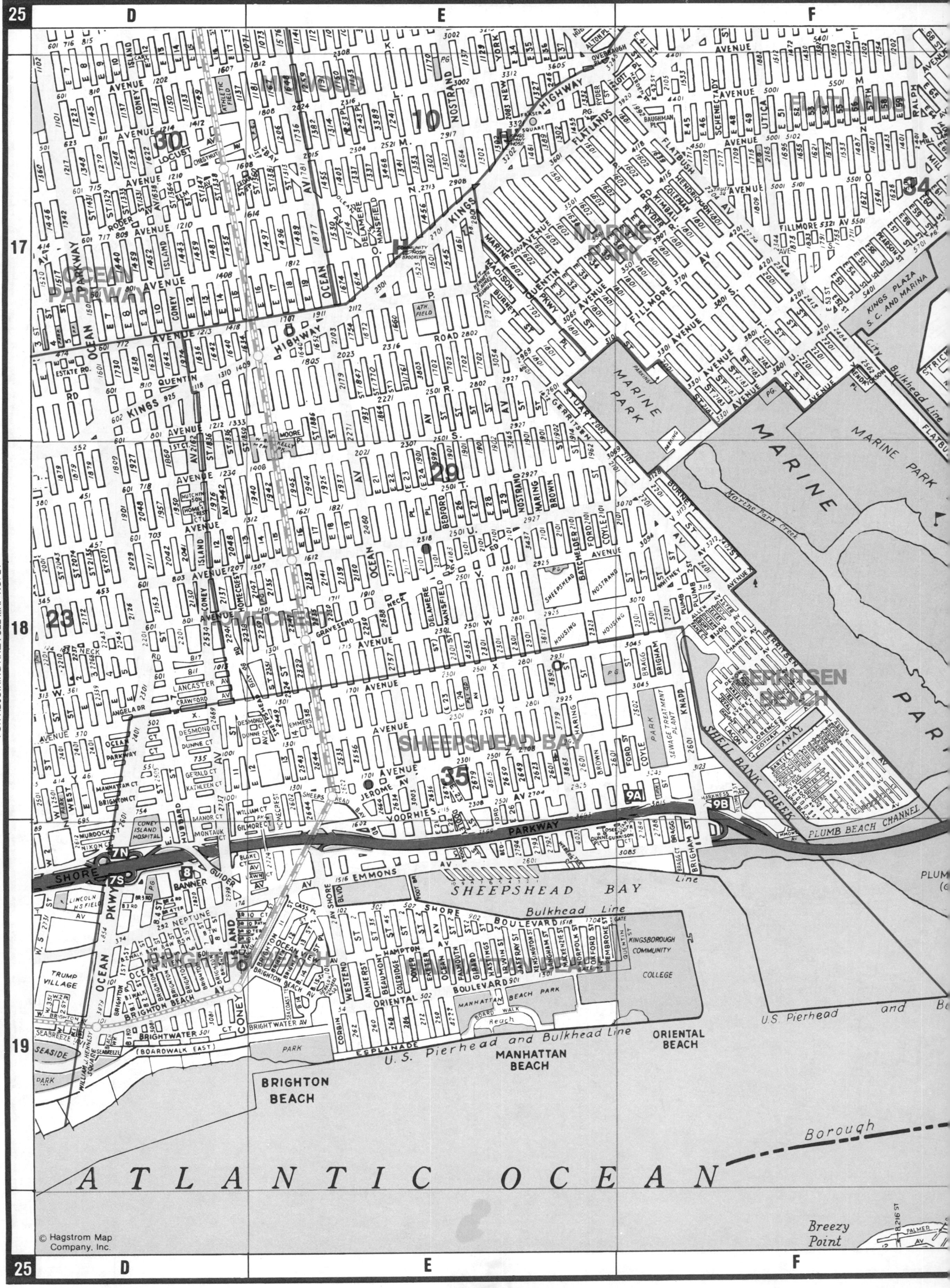

MIDWOOD

FLATLANDS

OCEAN PARKWAY

MARINE PARK

MARINE PARK

GERRITSEN BEACH

SHEEPSHEAD BAY

SHELL BANK CREEK

PLUMB BEACH CHANNEL

KINGS PLAZA S.C. AND MARINA

SHEEPSHEAD BAY

Bulkhead Line

SHORE BOULEVARD

Kingsborough Community College

TRUMP VILLAGE

BRIGHTON BEACH

Manhattan Beach Park

MANHATTAN BEACH

ORIENTAL BEACH

U.S. Pierhead and Bulkhead Line

Coney Island Hospital

Lincoln H.S. Field

SEASIDE PARK

BRIGHTWATER

U.S. Pierhead and Bulkhead Line

Borough Line

A T L A N T I C   O C E A N

Breezy Point

© Hagstrom Map Company, Inc.

FOR ADJOINING AREA SEE MAP NO. 23

G
H
J
25
17
18
19
GEORGETOWN
BERGEN BEACH
MILL BASIN
MILL ISLAND
East Mill
Basin
Mill
BELT PARKWAY
11N
11S
COURSE
GATEWAY NATIONAL RECREATION AREA
JAMAICA BAY UNIT
BERGEN BEACH (G.N.R.A.)
JAMAICA BAY RIDING ACADEMY
Basin
ISLAND CHANNEL
JAMAICA
FLOYD BENNETT FIELD
U.S. COAST GUARD
PARK HQ
UNIT HQ.
U.S. NAVY RESERVE
AVIATION RD
TOLL
AV
BARREN ISLAND MARINA
Dead Horse Bay
DEAD HORSE INLET (GERRITSEN INLET)
City Bulkhead Line
U.S. Pierhead and Bulkhead Line
MARINE PKWY. BRIDGE
ROCKAWAY INLET
CANARSIE POL
NESTEPOL MARSH
FISHKILL HASSOCK
SAILS PT. HASSOCK
OLD SWALE MARSH
BIG CHANNEL
BIG FISHKILL CHANNEL
N
ROXBURY
U.S. COAST GUARD
RD
BAYSIDE
HILLSIDE
ROCKAWAY POINT COMM
JACOB RIIS PARK
PARKING FIELD
WALK
94
NEPONSIT
© Hagstrom Map Company, Inc.

FOR ADJOINING AREA SEE MAP NO.17

FOR ADJOINING AREA SEE MAP NO.17

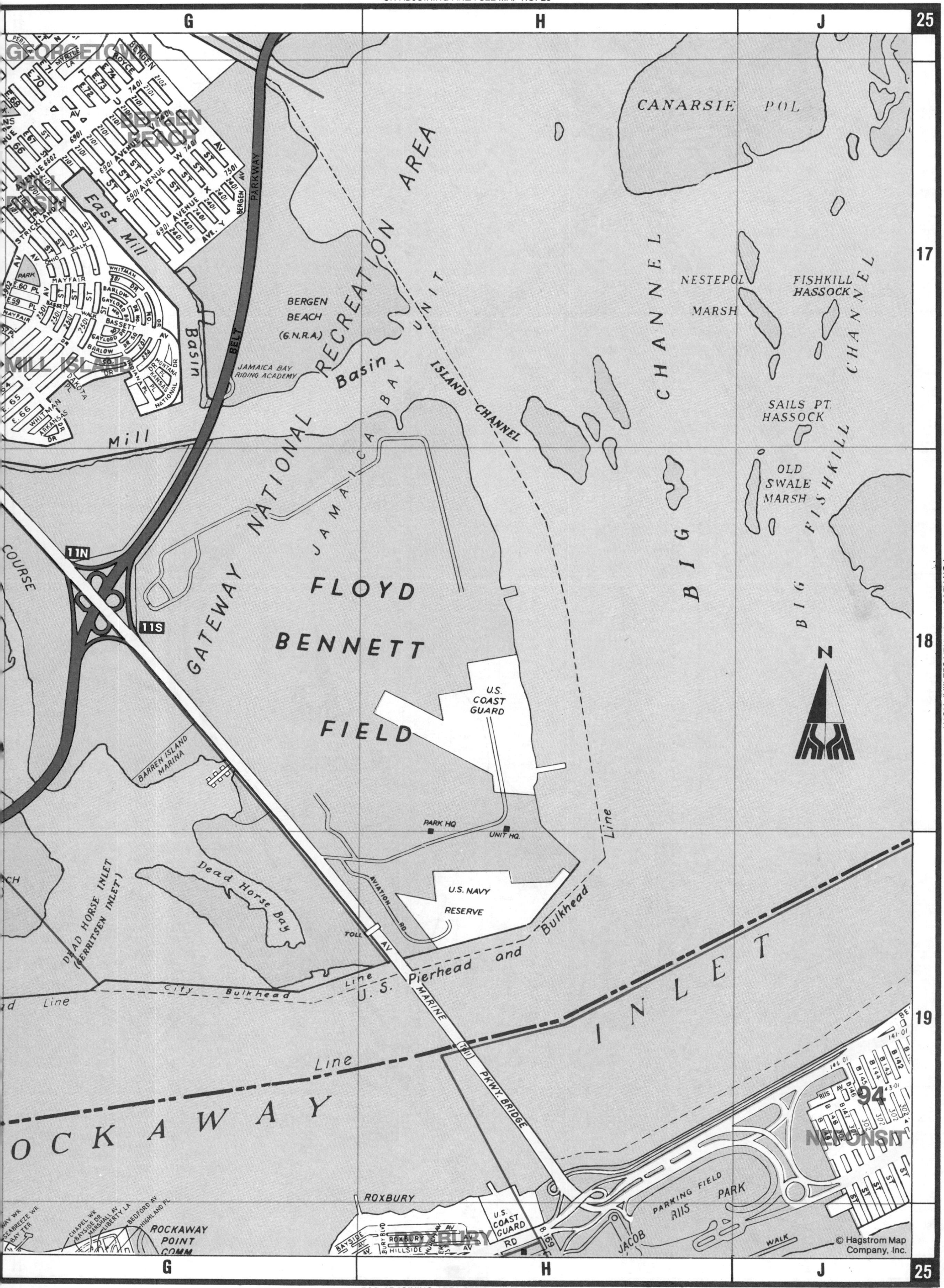

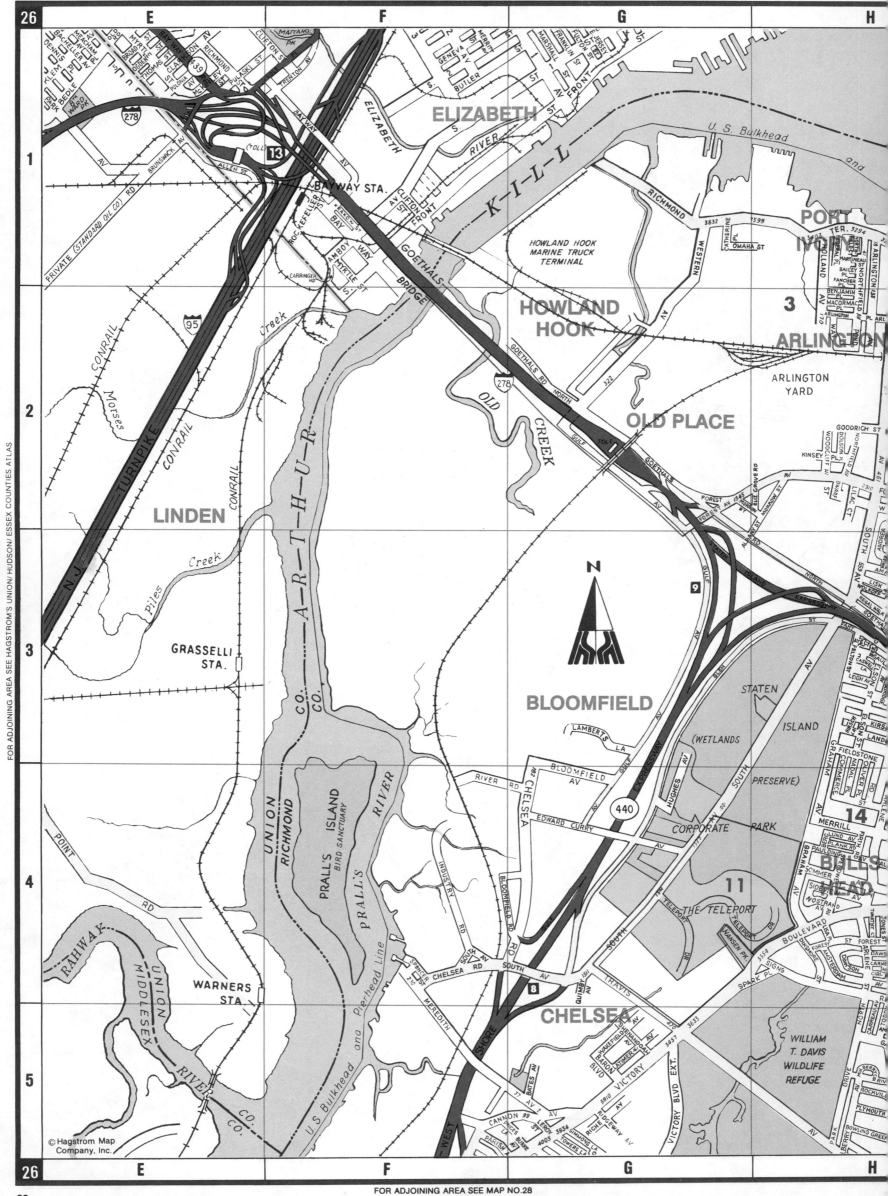

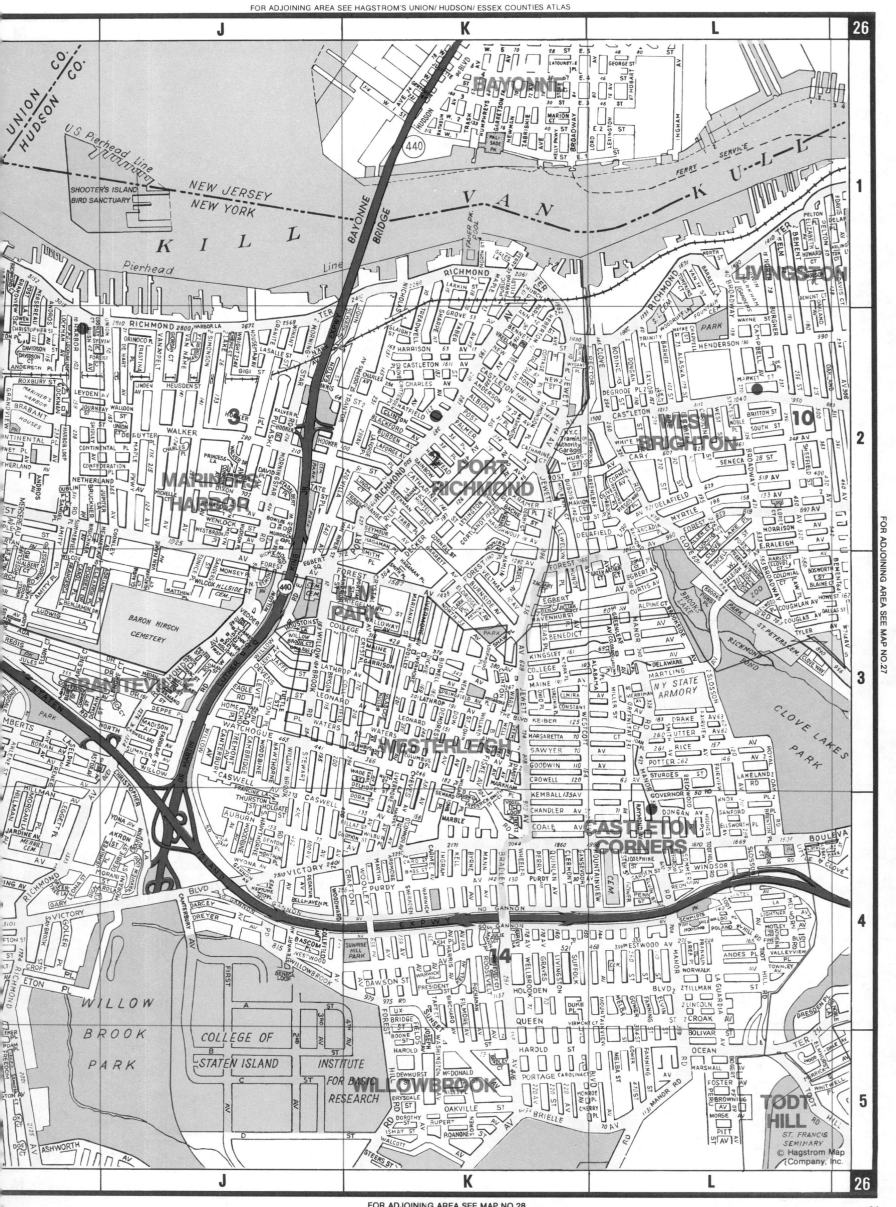

27

J   K   L   M

BAYONNE

440

FERRY

NEW JERSEY
NEW YORK

K I L L   V A N

Pierhead

Line

BAYONNE BRIDGE

LIVINGSTON

S.I. BOTANICAL GDNS.

SNUG HARBOR CULTURAL CENTER

RICHMOND

PORT RICHMOND

MARINERS HARBOR

10

WEST BRIGHTON

BARON HIRSCH CEM.

GRANITEVILLE

FOREST PARK

WESTERLEIGH

N.Y. STATE ARMORY

CLOVE LAKES PARK

CLOVE LAKES

SILVER LAKE

CASTLETON CORNERS

14

WILLOWBROOK

COLLEGE OF STATEN ISLAND INSTITUTE FOR BASIC RESEARCH

WILLOW BROOK PARK

COLLEGE OF S.I. SUNNYSIDE CAMPUS

DEER PARK

15

TODT HILL

ST. FRANCIS SEMINARY

BASKET WILLOW

© Hagstrom Map Company Inc.

27

J   K   L   M

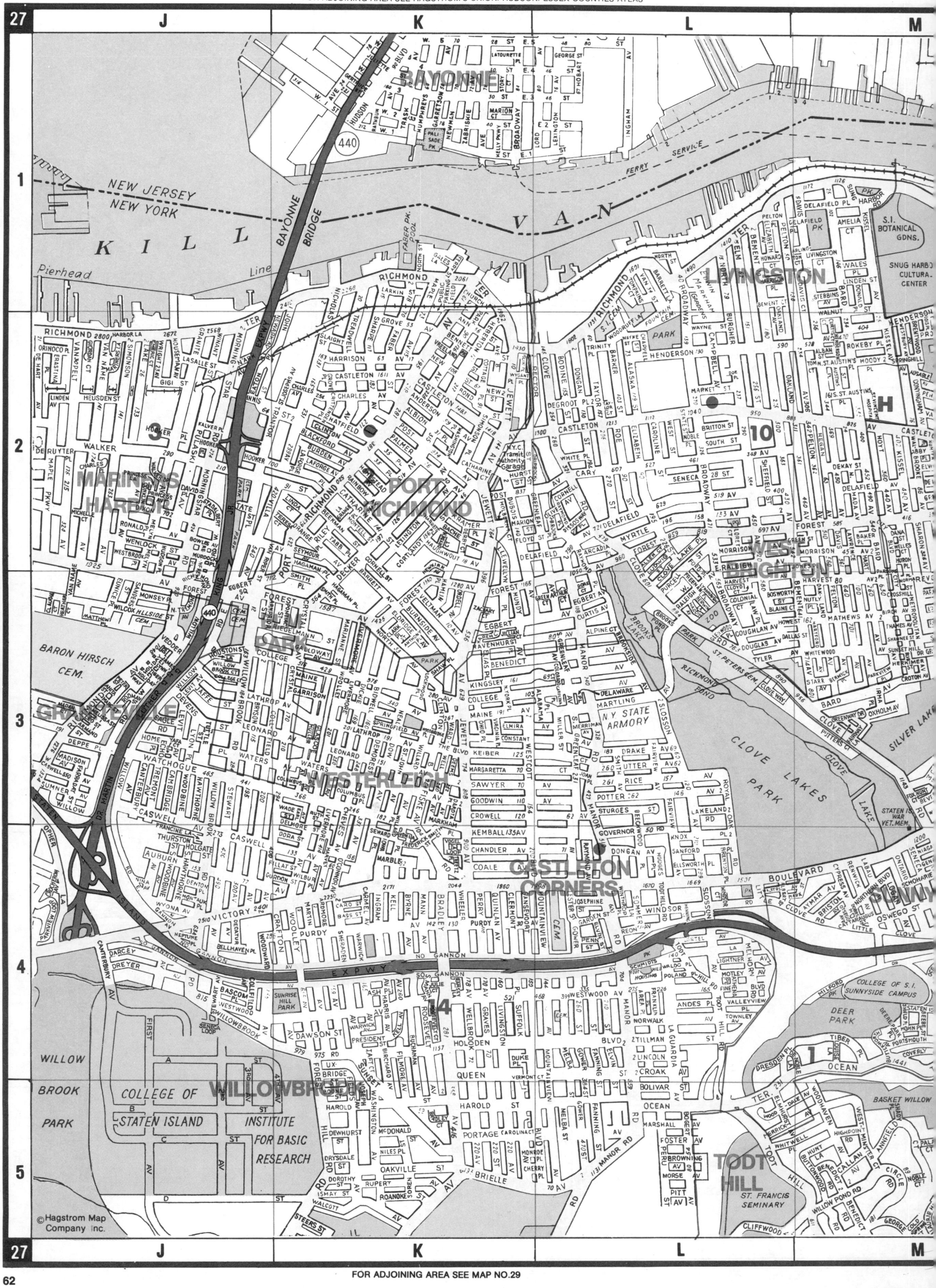

FOR ADJOINING AREA SEE MAP NO.26

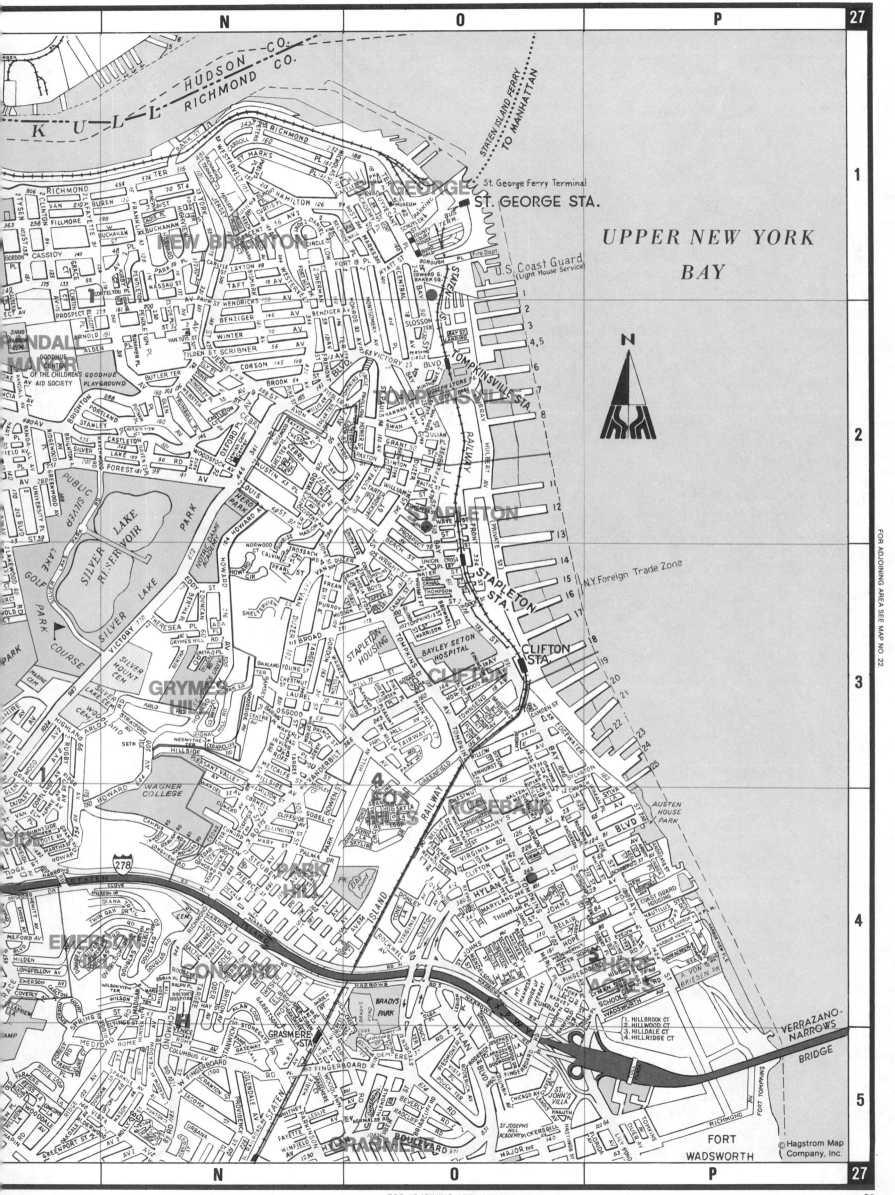

UPPER NEW YORK BAY

FOR ADJOINING AREA SEE MAP NO. 22

© Hagstrom Map Company, Inc.

E   F   G   H

THE TELEPORT

WARNERS STA.

CHELSEA

WILLIAM T. DAVIS WILDLIFE REFUGE

CARTERET

NEW SPRINGVILLE

FRESH KILLS PARK

Consolidated Edison Co.

VICTORY

FRESH KILLS LANDFILL

TRAVIS

CARTERET

CREEK

State Island Ma

LITTLE FRESH KILL

ISLAND OF MEADOW
BIRD SANCTUARY

FRESH KILLS

FRESH

Sewage Disposal Plant

KILLS

440

GREAT FRESH

14

RICHMOND

FRESH KILLS PARK

N

CREEK

LA

EXPRESSWAY

WEST SERVICE RD

GREENRIDGE

2326 ARTHUR

ARDEN

4

CHARLESTON

CITY PARK

12

SOUTH SHORE GOLF COURSE

© Hagstrom Map Company, Inc.

E   F   G   H

J K L

WILLOW BROOK PARK

COLLEGE OF STATEN ISLAND

INSTITUTE FOR BASIC RESEARCH

WILLOWBROOK

STATEN ISLAND DEVELOPMENTAL CENTER

N.Y.C. FARM COLONY

SEA VIEW HOSPITAL and HOME

BOY SCOUT CAMP

OHRBACH LAKE

TODT HILL

ST. FRANCIS SEMINARY

PARK

RICHMOND COUNTY COUNTRY CLUB

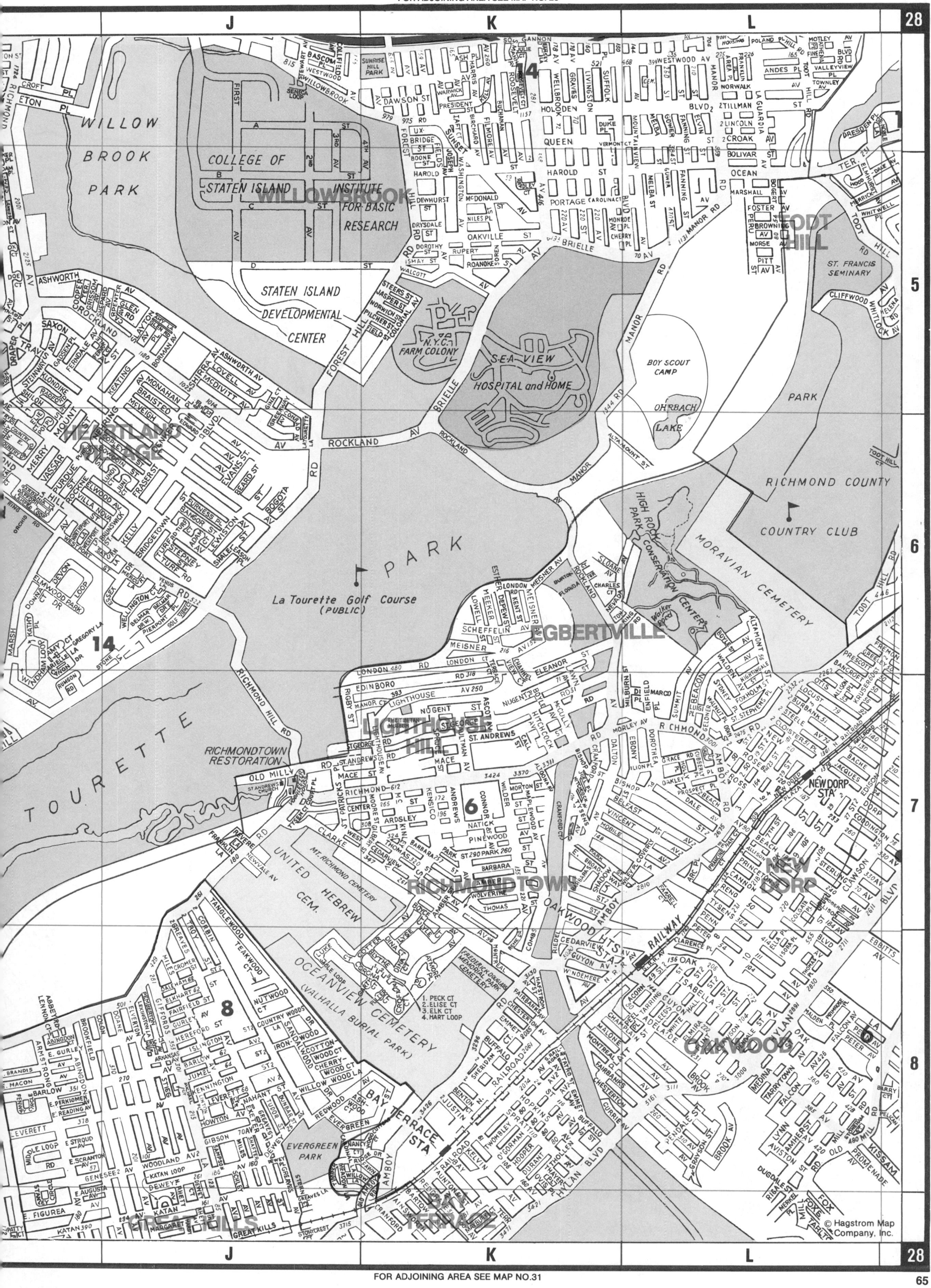

MORAVIAN CEMETERY

HEARTLAND VILLAGE

LA TOURETTE GOLF COURSE (PUBLIC)

PARK

HIGH ROCK PARK CONSERVATION CENTER

EGBERTVILLE

LIGHTHOUSE HILL

RICHMONDTOWN RESTORATION

RICHMONDTOWN

MT. RICHMOND CEMETERY

UNITED HEBREW CEM.

OCEANVIEW CEMETERY (VALHALLA BURIAL PARK)

FREDERICK DOUGLASS MEMORIAL PARK CEMETERY

NEW DORP STA.

NEW DORP

OAKWOOD

GREAT KILLS

EVERGREEN PARK

BAY TERRACE STA.

BAY TERRACE

1. PECK CT
2. ELISE CT
3. ELK CT
4. HART LOOP

TOURETTE

© Hagstrom Map Company, Inc.

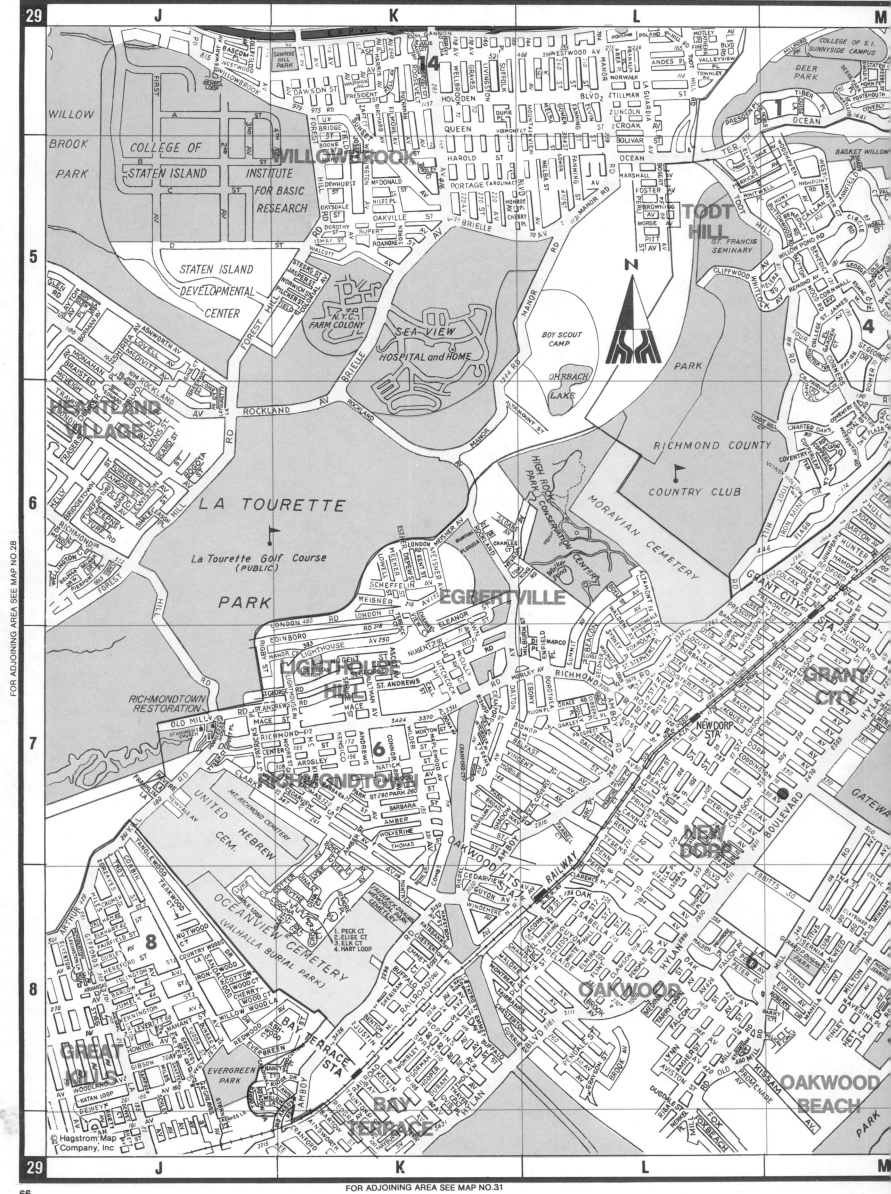

30

8

9

10

11

12

30

A   B   C

GENASCO

SEWAREN

Woodbridge Creek

NJ TRANSIT (NORTH JERSEY) CONRAIL (WEST JERSEY)

STATE H'WAY 35

ROAD TO MAURERS

BARBER

TYRELL'S (COAST LINE)

PERTH AMBOY

NEW JERSEY / NEW YORK

A-R-T-H-U-R   K-I-L-L

U.S Bulkhead and Pier

PORT MOBIL
MOBIL OIL CORP

CHARLESTON

STATE PARK PRESE

CLAY PIT STATE PAR

440

OUTERBRIDGE CROSSING

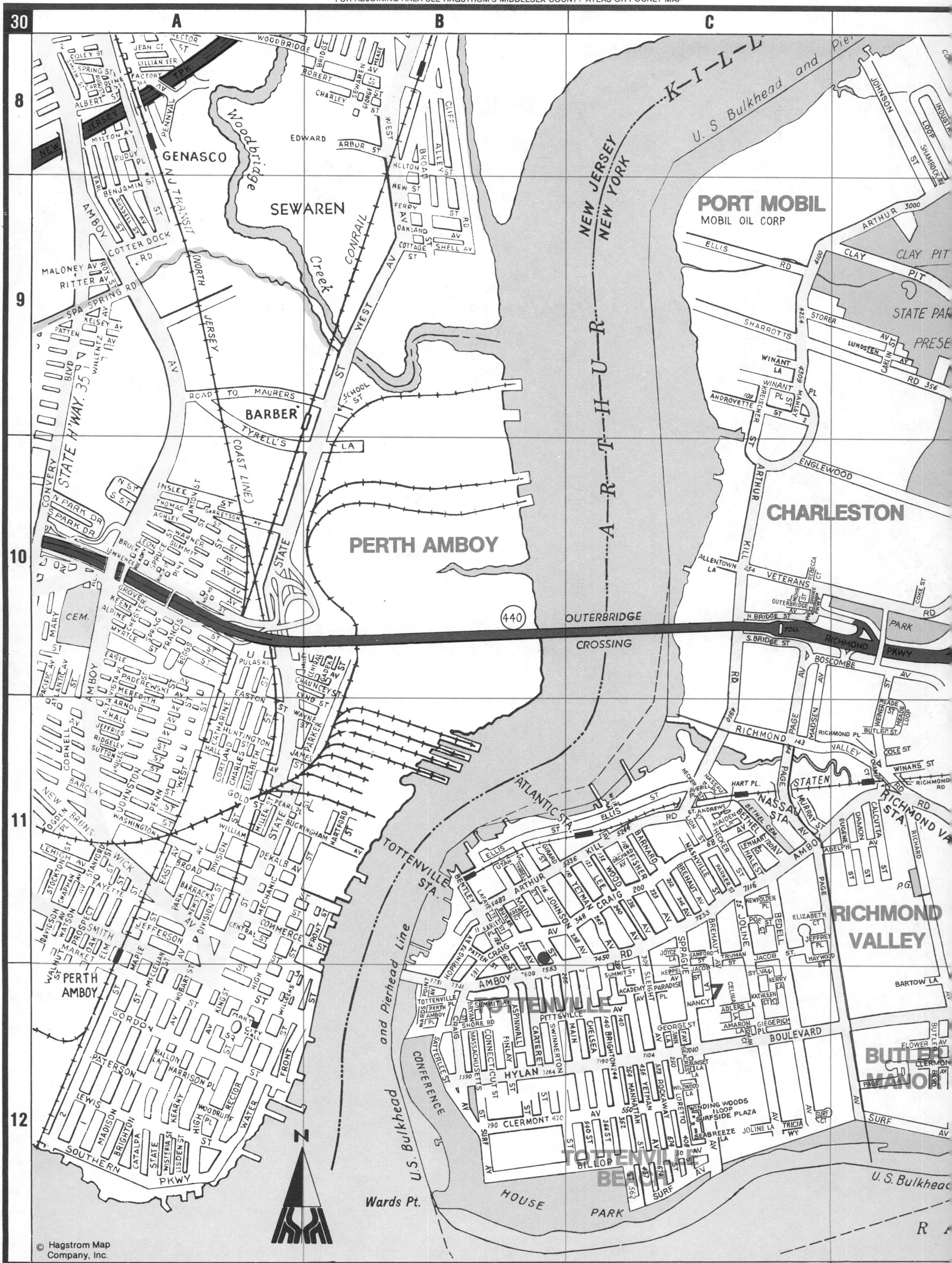

RICHMOND PKWY

RICHMOND VALLEY STA.

STATEN STA.

NASSAU STA.

RICHMOND VALLEY

BUTLER MANO

ATLANTIC STA.

TOTTENVILLE STA.

TOTTENVILLE

PITTSVILLE

U.S. Bulkhead and Pierhead Line

CONFERENCE

PERTH AMBOY

N

Wards Pt.

HOUSE PARK

BILLOP

TOTTENVIL BEA

U.S. Bulkhead

© Hagstrom Map
Company, Inc.

E   F   G   30

1. PRINCE LA
2. WHIRT LA
3. CANDON CT
4. PHYLLIS CT
5. ASHLEY LA
6. SANDYWOOD LA

8

9

ROSSVILLE

CITY PARK

SOUTH SHORE GOLF COURSE (PUBLIC)

12

ARDEN HEIGHTS

WOODROW

ANNADALE

ANNADALE STA.

HUGUENOT

HUGUENOT STA.

PARK

PRINCE'S BAY

PLEASANT PLAINS

PLEASANT PLAINS STA.

CEMETERY

MOUNT LORETTO

WOLFE'S POND PARK

BLUE HERON POND PARK

12

HUGUENOT BEACH

St. JOSEPH'S BY THE SEA H.S.

Arbutus Lake

9

TRENTON

PRINCE'S BAY STA.

PRINCESBAY BOATSMENS ASSN.

PRINCE'S BAY

Seguine Pt.

U.S. Bulkhead

U.S. Pierhead

10

11

12

ISLAND

WEIR AV

AMBOY

U.S. Pierhead

RITAN   BAY

A T L A N T I C   O C E A N

© Hagstrom Map Company, Inc.

FOR ADJOINING AREA SEE MAP NO.31

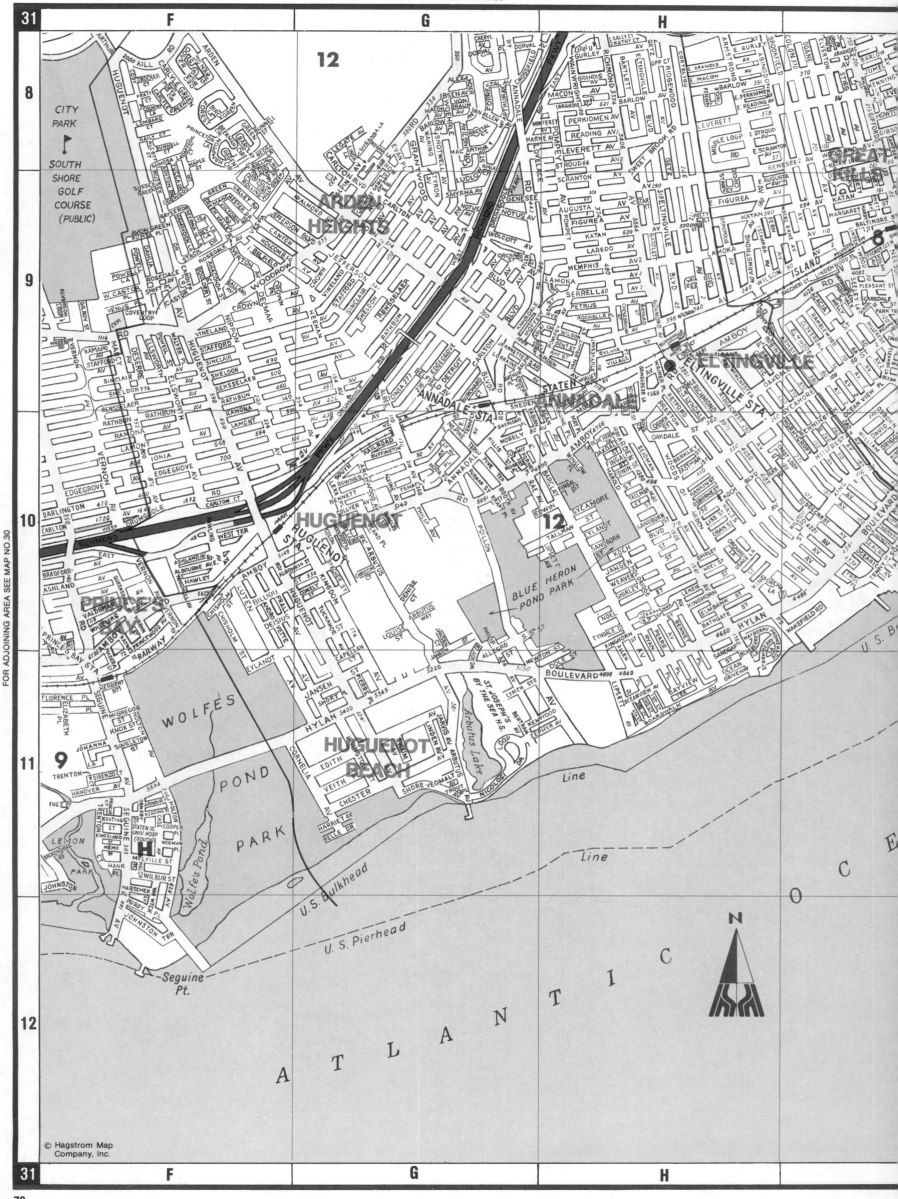

J   K   L   M   31   8

OCEANVIEW CEM.

OAKWOOD

OAKWOOD
BEACH

CEDAR
GROVE
BEACH

EVERGREEN
PARK

TERRACE
STA.

BAY
TERRACE

6

OAKWOOD
BEACH
SEWAGE
TREATMENT
PLANT

9

GREAT
GATEWAY NATIONAL RECREATION AREA

KILLS

PARK

U.S. Bulkhead
Line

U.S. Bulkhead

GREAT KILLS
YACHT CLUB

PARKING
FIELD

RICHMOND COUNTY
YACHT CLUB

GREAT

KILLS

HARBOR

U.S. Pierhead & Bulkhead Line

Line

Line

GREAT KILLS
BEACH

CROOKES
POINT

10

A   N

U.S. Pierhead

U.S. Pierhead

11

12

© Hagstrom Map
Company, Inc.

J   K   L   M   31

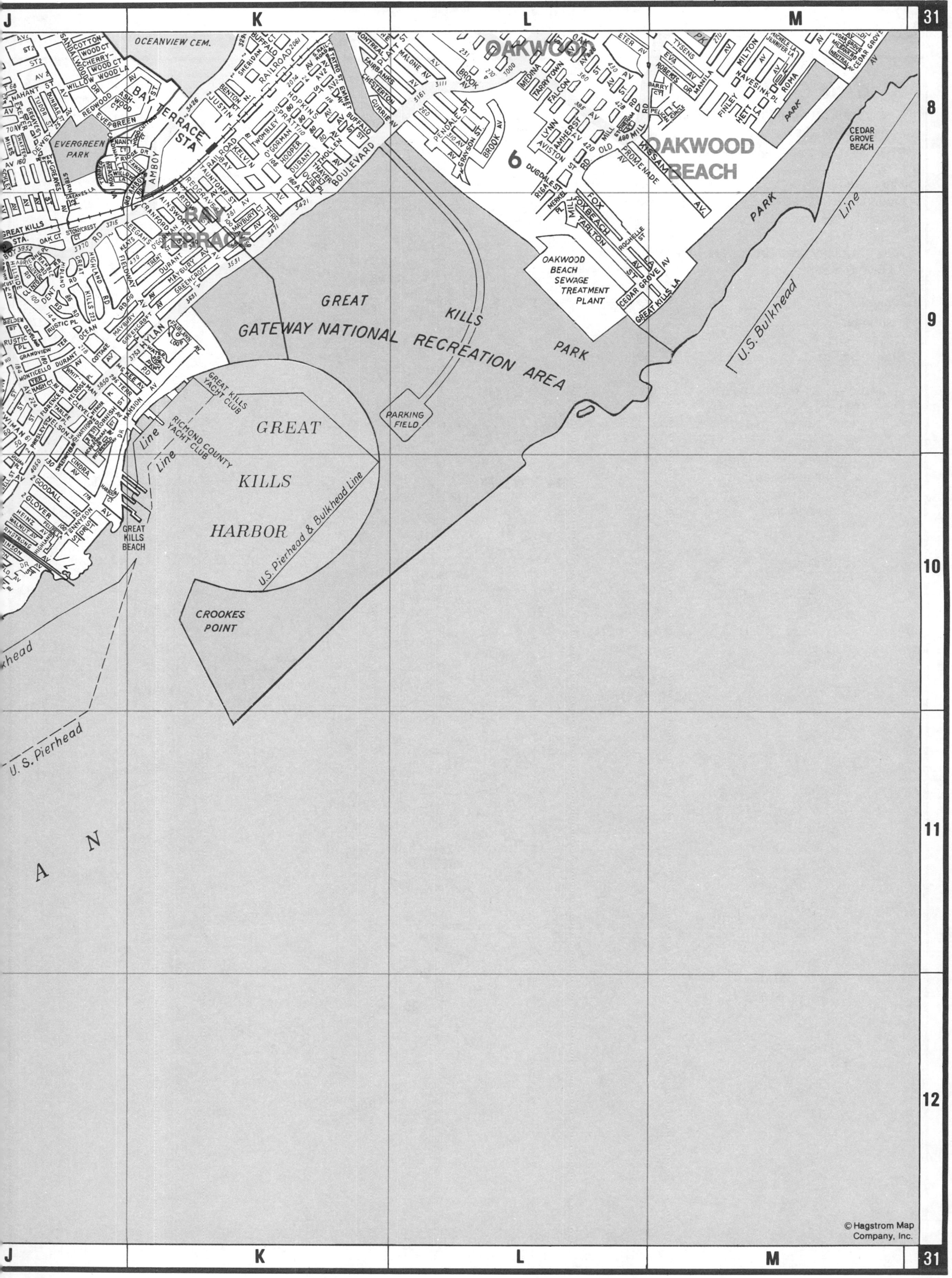

Statistics

New York City population (1990 census)
All Five Boroughs 7,322,564
Bronx 1,203,789
Brooklyn 2,300,664
Manhattan 1,487,536
Queens 1,951,598
Staten Island 378,977

New York City area (in square miles)
All Five Boroughs 307
Bronx 43
Brooklyn 72
Manhattan 24
Queens 109
Staten Island 59

.....and did you know New York City has
6,400   miles of streets
230   miles of subway lines
57   bridges
578   miles of waterfront
14.3   miles of beaches
1,543   parks and playgrounds
comprising 26,000+ acres

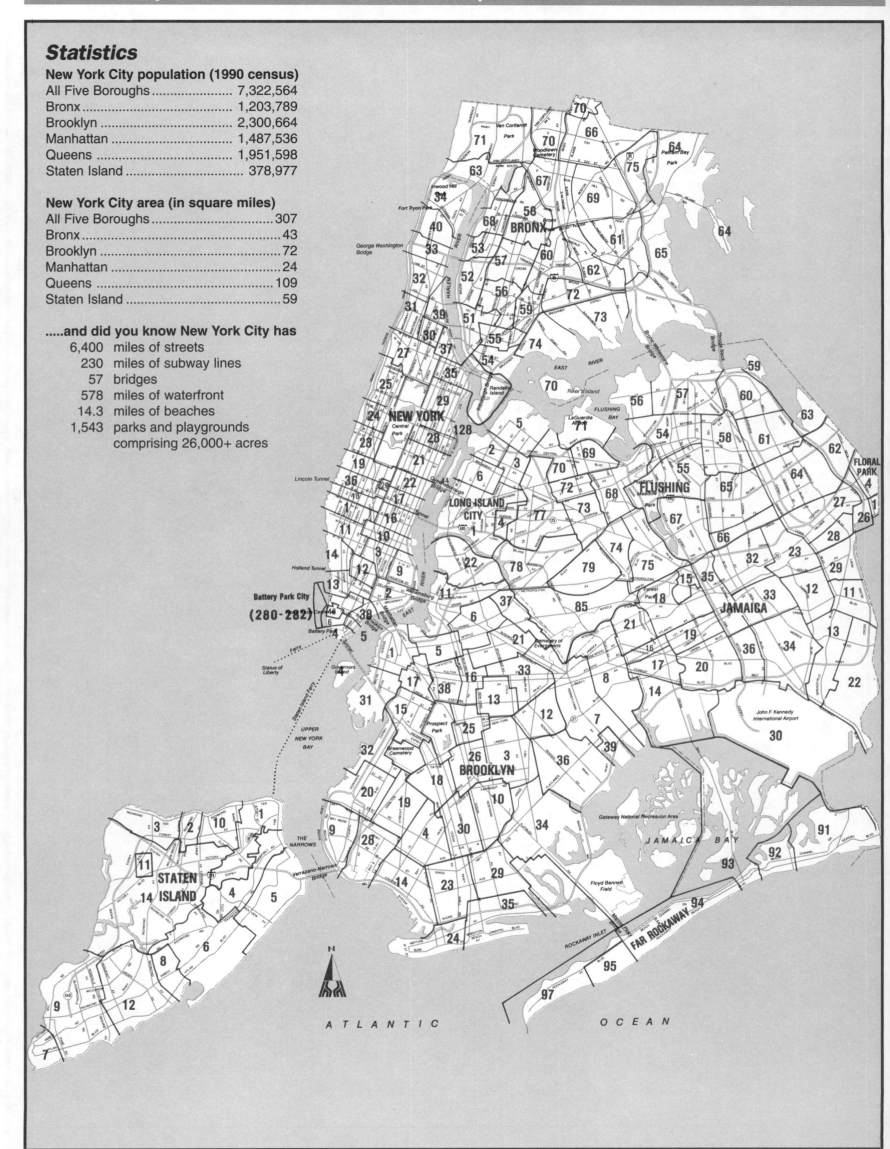

BOROUGH OF MANHATTAN

Post Office Station Zone Number and Name	Map	Grid
1-General Post Office, J.A. Farley Building 421 Eighth Av	1	C 18
2-Knickerbocker, 128 E Broadway	1	E 21
3-Cooper, 93 Fourth Av	1	D 19
4-Bowling Green, 25 Broadway	1	D 22
5-Wall Street, 73 Pine St	1	D 22
6-Trinity (see Bowling Green)	1	D 22
7-Church Street, 90 Church St	1	D 21
9-Peter Stuyvesant, 432 E 14th St	1	E 19
10-Madison Square, 149 E 23rd St	1	D 19
11-Old Chelsea, 217 W 18th St	1	C 19
*12-Prince, 103 Prince St	1	D 20
13-Canal Street, 350 Canal St	1	D 21
14-Village, 201 Varick St	1	C 20
16-Murray Hill, 115 E 34th St	1	D 18
17-Grand Central, 450 Lexington Av	1	D 17
18-Midtown, 221 W 38th St	1	C 18
19-Radio City, 322 W 52nd St	1	C 17
*20-Rockefeller Center, 610 Fifth Av	1	D 17
21-Lenox Hill, 217 E 70th St	2	E 16
22-Franklin D Roosevelt, 909 Third Av	1	E 17
23-Ansonia, 1990 Broadway	2	C 16
24-Planetarium, 127 W 83rd St	2	C 15
25-Cathedral, 215 W 104th St	2	B 14
26-Morningside, 232 W 116th St	2	C 13
27-Manhattanville, 365 W 125th St	2	C 12
28-Gracie, 229 E 85th St	2	E 15
29-Hell Gate, 153 E 110th St	2	D 13
30-College, 217 W 140th St	2	C 11
31-Hamilton Grange, 521 W 146th St	2	B 11
32-Audubon, 511 W 165th St	3	B 9
33-Washington Bridge, 555 W 180th St	3	B 9
34-Inwood, 90 Vermilyea Av	4	B 7
35-Triborough, 167 E 124th St	2	D 12
36-Times Square, 340 W 42nd St	1	C 17
37-Lincolnton, 2266 Fifth Av	2	D 11
38-Peck Slip, 1-15 Peck Slip	1	E 21
39-Colonial Park, 99 Macombs Pl	3	C 10
40-Fort George, 4558 Broadway	4	B 8
41-Custom House Building (see Bowling Green)	1	D 22
44-Island, 694 Main St, Roosevelt Island	2	F 16
45-Federal Reserve (see Peck Slip)	1	E 21
47-Offices of New York State Agencies, World Trade Center	1	D 22
48-World Trade Center, 2 World Trade Center	1	D 22
*128-Yorkville, 1591 Third Av	2	E 15
280-North Battery Park City (see Church St)	1	D 21
281-World Financial Center (see Church St)	1	D 21
282-South Battery Park City (see Church St)	1	D 21
463-Kingsbridge, 5517 Broadway, Bronx (use for Marble Hill also)	4	C 6

NOTE: For ZIP Code add 10 before three digit zone numbers, 100 before two digit numbers, and 1000 before single digit numbers.

BOROUGH OF THE BRONX

Post Office Station Zone Number and Name	Map	Grid
51-General Post Office, 558 Grand Concourse	3	D 10
52-High Bridge, 1315 Inwood Av	3	D 9
53-Morris Heights, 2024 Jerome Av	4	D 7
54-Mott Haven, 517 E 139th St	3	E 11
55-Hub, 633 St. Ann Av	3	E 10
56-Morrisania, 442 E 167th St	4	E 9
57-Tremont, 575 E Tremont Av	4	E 7
58-Fordham, 465 E 188th St	4	E 6
59-Boulevard, 1132 Southern Blvd	3	F 9
60-West Farms, 362 Devoe Av	4	G 7
61-Westchester, 2619 Ponton Av	7	J 6
62-Parkchester, 1449 West Av	7	H 7
63-Kingsbridge, 5517 Broadway	4	C 6
64-City Island, 199 City Island Av	6	M 4
65-Throgs Neck, 3630 E Tremont Av	7	L 6
66-Wakefield, 4165 White Plains Rd	5	E 3
67-Williamsbridge, 711 E Gun Hill Rd	5	F 4
68-Jerome Avenue, 2549 Jerome Av	4	D 6
69-Baychester, 1525 E Gun Hill Rd	6	H 4
70-Woodlawn, 4364 Katonah Av	5	D 3
71-Riverdale, 5951 Riverdale Av	5	A 3
72-Soundview, 1687 Gleason Av	7	H 8
73-Cornell, 1950 Lafayette Av	7	J 8
74-Boulevard-Carriers, 1132 Southern Blvd	3	F 9
75-Co-Op City, 3300 Conner St	6	H 4

NOTE: For ZIP Code add 104 before zone numbers.

BOROUGH OF QUEENS

LONG ISLAND CITY

Post Office Station Zone Number and Name	Map	Grid
1-General Post Office, 46-02 21st St	11	E 10
2-Astoria, 27-40 21st St	8	F 8
3-Steinway, 43-04 Broadway	8	F 9
4-Sunnyside, 45-15 44th St	11	F 10
5-Woolsey, 22-68 31st St	8	G 8
6-Broadway, 21-17 Broadway	8	F 9

NOTE: For ZIP Code add 1110 before zone numbers.

JAMAICA

Post Office Station Zone Number and Name	Map	Grid
11-Cambria, 229-01 Linden Blvd	15	O 13
12-St. Albans, 195-04 Linden Blvd	15	N 13
13-Springfield Gardens, 218-10 Merrick Blvd	15	N 13
14-Howard Beach, 160-50 Cross Bay Blvd	14	K 15
15-Kew Gardens, 83-30 Austin St	12	K 12
16-Ozone Park, 91-11 Liberty Av	14	J 13
17-Ozone Park, 91-11 Liberty Av	14	J 13
18-Richmond Hill, 122-01 Jamaica Av	12	K 12
18-Parcel Post, 133-03 Jamaica Av	12	L 12
19-South Richmond Hill, 117-04 101st Av	14	K 13
20-South Ozone Park, 126-15 Foch Blvd	15	L 14
21-Woodhaven, 86-42 Forest Pkwy	14	J 13
22-Rosedale, 145-06 243rd St	15	O 14
23-Hollis, 197-40 Jamaica Av	13	N 11
*24-Borough Hall, 120-55 Queens Blvd	12	K 11
25-St. Albans Veterans Administration Extended Care Center, 179th St & Linden Blvd	15	N 13
26-Bellerose, 237-15 Braddock Av	13	O 11
27-Queens Village, 209-20 Jamaica Av	13	N 11
28-Queens Village, 209-20 Jamaica Av	13	N 11
29-Queens Village, 209-20 Jamaica Av	13	N 11
30-John F Kennedy International Airport, Building 250, N Boundary Rd	15	M 15
31-Postmaster & General Delivery, 88-40 164th St	12	L 12
32-Jamaica (Main Office), 88-40 164th St	12	L 12
33-Jamaica (Main Office), 88-40 164th St	12	M 12
34-Rochdale Village, 165-100 Baisley Blvd	15	M 13
35-Archer Av Station, Jamaica, 147-21 Archer Av	12	L 12
36-South Ozone Park, 126-15 Foch Blvd	14	L 14
39-St. John's University, 81-10 Utopia Pkwy	13	M 11
46-Creedmore State Psychiatric Hospital, 80-45 Winchester Blvd (Queens Village)	13	O 10

NOTE: For ZIP Code add 114 before zone numbers.

FLUSHING

Post Office Station Zone Number and Name	Map	Grid
51-Official Mail	9	K 9
52-Flushing Box Mail and General Delivery	9	K 9
54-Linden Hill, 29-50 Union St	9	K 8
54-Station "B", 136-50 Roosevelt Av	9	K 9
55-Flushing (Main Office), 41-65 Main St	9	K 9
56-College Point, 120-07 15th Av	9	J 8
57-Whitestone, 14-44 150th St	9	L 8
58-Station "A", 40-03 164th St	9	L 9
59-Fort Totten, U.S. Government Res	10	M 7
60-Bayside (Section #1), 212-35 42nd Av	10	M 9
60-Bay Terrace, 212-35 26th Av	10	M 8
61-Bayside (Section #2), 212-35 42nd Av	10	M 9
62-Little Neck (Section #1), 250-10 Northern Blvd	10	O 9
62-Horace Harding, 56-01 Marathon Pkwy	10	O 9
63-Little Neck (Section #2), 250-10 Northern Blvd	10	O 9
64-Oakland Gardens, 61-43 Springfield Blvd	10	N 9
65-Fresh Meadows, 192-20 Horace Harding Expwy	13	M 10
65-Pomonok, 158-05 71st Av	12	L 10
66-Utopia, 182-04 Union Tpk	13	M 11
67-Station "C", 75-23 Main St	12	L 11
68-Corona, 103-28 Roosevelt Av	9	J 9
69-East Elmhurst (Section #1), 91-07 25th Av	8	H 9
70-East Elmhurst (Section #2), 91-07 25th Av	8	H 9
70-Trainsmeadow, 75-77 31st Av	8	G 9
71-La Guardia Airport, Main Terminal	8	H 8
72-Jackson Heights, 78-02 37th Av	11	H 10
73-Corona-Elmhurst, 59-01 Junction Blvd	11	J 10
73-Elmhurst "A", 80-27 Broadway	11	H 10
74-Rego Park, 89-12 Eliot Av	11	H 10
75-Forest Hills, 106-28 Queens Blvd	12	J 11
75-Parkside, 101-19 Metropolitan Av	12	J 12
77-Woodside, 39-25 61st St	11	G 10
78-Maspeth, 55-02 69th St	11	G 11
79-Middle Village, 71-35 Metropolitan Av	11	H 12
85-Ridgewood, 60-60 Myrtle Av	11	G 12
85-Fresh Pond, 60-80 Woodbine St	11	G 12
85-Glendale, 69-36 Myrtle Av	11	H 12

NOTE: For ZIP Code add 113 before zone numbers.

FAR ROCKAWAY

Post Office Station Zone Number and Name	Map	Grid
91-General Post Office, 18-36 Mott Av	16	O 17
92-Arverne, 329 Beach 59th St	18	M 18
93-Rockaway Beach, 90-14 Rockaway Beach Blvd	18	L 18
94-Rockaway Park, 113-25 Beach Channel Dr	18	K 19
95-Fort Tilden, Fort Tilden Military Res	17	H 20
*97-Rockaway Point, 33 Beach 209th St (open summer only)	17	G 20

NOTE: For ZIP Code add 116 before zone numbers.

FLORAL PARK

Post Office Station Zone Number and Name	Map	Grid
1-Floral Park, 35 Tulip Av, Floral Park	13	P 11
2-General Delivery, 35 Tulip Av	13	P 11
4-Glen Oaks, 256-29 Union Tpk	13	P 10
5-Glen Oaks, 256-29 Union Tpk	13	P 10

NOTE: For ZIP Code add 1100 before zone numbers.

BOROUGH OF BROOKLYN

Post Office Station Zone Number and Name	Map	Grid
1-General Post Office, 271 Cadman Plz E	20	C 13
3-Rugby, 726 Utica Av	23	F 15
4-Parkville, 6618 Twentieth Av	22	C 17
5-Pratt, 524 Myrtle Av	20	D 13
6-Metropolitan, 47 Debevoise St	19	E 12
7-East New York, 2645 Atlantic Av	21	G 14
8-New Lots, 1223 Sutter Av	21	H 14
9-Fort Hamilton, 8801 Fifth Av	22	A 17
10-Vanderveer, 2319 Nostrand Av	22	E 16
11-Williamsburg, 263 S 4th St	19	D 12
12-Brownsville, 167 Bristol St	21	F 14
13-St. John's Place, 1234 St John's Pl	21	E 14
14-Bath Beach, 1865 Benson Av	24	C 18
15-Van Brunt, 275 9th St	20	C 14
16-Brevoort, 1205 Atlantic Av	21	E 13
17-Times Plaza, 542 Atlantic Av	20	D 13
18-Kensington, 419 McDonald Av	22	E 15
19-Blythebourne, 1200 51st St	22	C 16
20-Bay Ridge, 5501 Seventh Av	22	B 16
21-Bushwick (see Metropolitan)	21	F 13
22-Greenpoint, 66 Meserole Av	19	E 11
23-Gravesend, 344 Av U	24	D 18
24-Coney Island, 2727 Mermaid Av	24	C 19
25-Lefferts, 315 Empire Blvd	20	E 14
26-Flatbush, 2273 Church Av	22	D 15
28-Dyker Heights, 8320 Thirteenth Av	24	B 17
29-Homecrest, 2370 E 19th St	24	E 18
30-Midwood, 1288 Coney Island Av	22	D 16
31-Red Hook, 615 Clinton Av	20	B 14
32-Bush Terminal, 824 Third Av	20	B 15
33-Stuyvesant, 1915 Fulton St	21	F 13
34-Ryder, 1739 E 45th St	23	F 17
35-Bay, 2628 E 18th St	25	E 18
36-Canarsie, 102-01 Flatlands Av	23	G 15
37-Wyckoff Heights, 86 Wyckoff Av	19	F 12
38-Adelphi, 950 Fulton St	20	D 13
39-Starrett City (see Canarsie)	23	G 15

NOTE: For ZIP Code add 112 before two digit zone numbers and 1120 before single digit zone numbers.

BOROUGH OF STATEN ISLAND

Post Office Station Zone Number and Name	Map	Grid
1-St. George, 45 Bay St	27	O 1
2-Port Richmond, 364 Richmond Av	26	K 2
3-Mariners Harbor, 2980 Richmond Ter	26	J 2
4-Stapleton, 160 Tompkins Av	27	O 2
5-Rosebank, 567 Tompkins Av	27	O 4
6-New Dorp, 2562 Hylan Blvd	29	M 7
7-Tottenville, 228 Main St	30	B 11
8-Great Kills, 15 Nelson Av	31	J 9
9-Princes Bay, 655-230 Rossville Av	30	E 11
10-West New Brighton, 1015 Castleton Av	27	L 2
12-Eltingville, 4455 Amboy Rd	31	H 9
14-General Post Office, 550 Manor Rd	27	L 4
14-New Springville, 2845 Richmond Av	28	H 6

NOTE: For ZIP Code add 103 before two digit zone numbers and 1030 before single digit zone numbers.

*Finance Station (customer service only)

Selected Points of Interest

Colleges & Universities

Point of Interest	Map	Grid
Barnard College, M	2	B 13
Baruch College (CUNY), M	1	D 19
Bronx Community College (CUNY), Bx	4	C 7
Brooklyn College (CUNY), Bk	22	E 16
City College (CUNY), M	2	C 11
College of Aeronautics, Q	8	H 9
College of Mount Saint Vincent, Bx	5	A 3
College of Staten Island (CUNY), SI	28	J 5
Columbia University, M	2	B 13
• Cooper Union, M	1	D 19
† CUNY Graduate Center, M	1	D 17
Fashion Institute of Technology, M	1	C 18
Fordham University, Bx	4	E 6
Fordham University, M	2	C 16
Herbert H Lehman College (CUNY), Bx	4	D 6
Hostos Community College (CUNY), Bx	3	D 11
Hunter College (CUNY), M	2	D 16
John Jay College of Criminal Justice (CUNY), M	2	C 16
Kingsborough Community College (CUNY), Bk	25	F 19
La Guardia Community College, Q	11	E 10
Long Island University, Bk	20	C 13
Manhattan College, Bx	5	B 4
Manhattan Community College (CUNY), M	1	C 21
• Medgar Evers Community College, Bk	20	E 14
New School for Social Research, M	1	D 19
New York University, M	1	D 20
Pace University, M	1	D 21
Parsons School of Design, M	1	D 19
Polytechnic University, Bk	20	C 13
Pratt Institute, Bk	20	D 13
Queens College (CUNY), Q	12	K 10
Queensborough Community College (CUNY), Q	10	N 9
Rockefeller University, M	2	E 16
St. John's University, Q	12	M 11
SUNY Health Science Center (Downstate), BK	21	E 15
SUNY Maritime College, Bx	7	N 7
Teacher's College, M	2	B 12
Wagner College, SI	27	N 3
Yeshiva University, M	3	C 8
York College (CUNY), Q	12	L 12

Hospitals

Point of Interest	Map	Grid
Bayley Seton, SI	27	O 3
Bellevue, M	1	E 18
Beth Israel Hospital North, M	2	E 15
Beth Israel Medical Center, M	1	E 19
Bird S Coler Memorial, M	2	F 15
Bronx-Lebanon, Bx	3	E 9
Bronx Municipal Hospital Center, Bx	7	H 5
Bronx Psychiatric Center, Bx	7	J 5
Brooklyn Hospital Center, Bk	20	D 13
Columbia-Presbyterian Medical Center, M	3	B 9
Coney Island, Bk	24	D 19
Elmhurst Hospital Center, Q	11	H 10
Goldwater Memorial, M	1	F 17
Harlem, M	2	D 11
Interfaith Medical Center, Bk	20	D 14
Kings County, Bk	21	E 15
Kingsborough Psychiatric Center, Bk	21	E 15
Kingsbrook Jewish Medical Center, Bk	21	E 15
Lenox Hill, M	2	D 15
Lincoln Medical Center, Bx	3	E 11
Long Island Jewish-Hillside Medical Center, Q	10	P 9
Manhattan Children's Psychiatric Center, M	2	F 13
Manhattan Eye, Ear and Throat, M	2	E 16
Manhattan Psychiatric Center, M	2	F 13
Memorial Sloan-Kettering Cancer Center, M	2	E 16
Metropolitan, M	2	E 14
Montefiore Hospital and Medical Center, Bx	5	D 4
Mount Sinai Medical Center, M	2	D 14
New York Downtown Hospital, M	1	D 21
New York Eye and Ear Infirmary, M	1	E 19
New York Hospital-Cornell Medical Center, M	2	E 16
New York Hospital Medical Center of Queens, Q	12	K 10
New York University Medical Center, M	1	E 18
North Central Bronx, Bx	5	D 4
North General, M	2	D 12
Queens Children's, Q	13	O 10
Queens Childrens Psychiatric Center, Q	13	O 10
Queens Hospital Center, Q	13	L 11
St. Albans Veterans Administration Extended Care Center, Q	15	N 13
St. Barnabas Hospital for Chronic Diseases, Bx	4	E 7
St. Lukes Hospital Center, M	2	B 13
St. Lukes Roosevelt Hospital Center, M	2	C 16
St. Vincent's, M	1	C 19
South Beach Psychiatric Center, SI	29	N 6
Staten Island University North	29	N 6
Staten Island University South	30	F 11
US Veterans, Bx	4	C 6
US Veterans, M	1	E 18
Veterans Administration, Bk	22	B 17
Woodhull Medical and Mental Health Center, Bk	19	E 12

Museums & Libraries

Point of Interest	Map	Grid
• Abigail Adam Smith Museum, M	2	E 16
• African American Institute 833 United Nations Plaza, M	1	E 17
• American Academy of Arts and Letters Broadway & 155th St, M	3	B 10
• American Craft Museum 40 W 53rd St, M	1	D 17
• American Museum of Immigration Liberty Island, New York Bay		
American Museum of Natural History Central Park W & 79th St, M	2	C 15
• American Museum of the Moving Image 36-01 35th Av, Q	8	F 9
• Bronx Museum of the Arts 165th St & Grand Concourse, Bx	3	D 9
• Brooklyn Children's Museum 145 Brooklyn Av, Bk	20	D 14
• Brooklyn Historical Society, Bk	19	C 13
Brooklyn Museum 200 Eastern Pkwy, Bk	20	E 14
Brooklyn Public Library - Central Branch Grand Army Plz at Flatbush Av & Eastern Pkwy, Bk	20	E 14
• Center for Inter-American Relations 680 Park Av, M	2	D 16
• Children's Museum of Manhattan, M	2	B 15
• Children's Museum of the Arts, M	1	D 20
• Chinese Museum 8 Mott St, Chinatown, M	1	E 21
• City Island Historical Nautical Museum 190 Fordham St, Bx	6	M 4
The Cloisters Fort Tryon Park, Washington Heights, M	4	B 7
• Cooper-Hewitt Museum Fifth Av & 91st St, M	2	D 14
• Donnell Library Center- New York Public Library 20 W 53rd St, M	1	D 17
• Dyckman House Broadway & 204th St, M	4	B 7
• Ellis Island Immigration Museum Ellis Island, New York Bay		
El Museo del Barrio 1230 Fifth Av, M	2	D 14
• Forbes Galleries, M	1	D 19
• Fordham Library Center 2556 Bainbridge Av, Bx	4	D 6
Fort Wadsworth Military Museum, SI	29	P 5
• Fraunces Tavern, M	1	D 22
• Frick Collection and Museum 1 E 70th St, M	2	D 16
• Guggenheim, Solomon R. Museum 1071 Fifth Av, M	2	D 15
• Gugenheim Museum SOHO, M	1	D 20
Hall of Science Flushing Meadows-Corona Park, Q	12	J 10
Hayden Planetarium Central Park W & 81st St, M	2	C 15
Hispanic Museum Broadway & 155th St, M	3	B 10
• International Center of Photography 1130 Fifth Av, M	2	D 14
Intrepid Sea-Air-Space Museum 12th Av & W 46th St (Pier 86), M	1	B 17
• Jamaica Arts Center 161-04 Jamaica Av, Q	12	L 12
• Jefferson Market Library- New York Public Library Av of the Americas & 10th St, M	1	D 19
• Jewish Museum Fifth Av & 92nd St, M	2	D 14
Leffert's Homestead 95 Prospect Park West, Bk	20	D 14
Library and Museum of the Performing Arts at Lincoln Center-New York Public Library 111 Amsterdam Av, M	2	C 19
• Library of the Blind and Physically Handicapped 166 Av of the Americas, M	1	D 20
• Long Island Historical Society 128 Pierrepont St, Bk	20	C 13
• Lower East Side Tenement Museum 97 Orchard St., M	1	E 20
Metropolitan Museum of Art Fifth Av & 82nd St, M	2	D 15
• Morris Jumel Mansion, M	3	C 10
• Museum for African Art, M	1	D 20
• Museum of American Financial History, M	1	D 22
• Museum of Archeology 631 Howard Av, SI	27	M 4
Museum of Bronx History Bainbridge Av & E 208th St, Bx	5	E 5
• Museum of Jewish Heritage, M	1	D 22
Museum of Modern Art 11 W 53rd St, M	1	D 17
Museum of Television and Radio 25 W 52nd St, M	1	D 17
Museum of the City of New York 1220 Fifth Av, M	2	D 14
National Museum of the American Indian- Smithsonian Institution Alexander Hamilton U.S. Custom House 1 Bowling Green, M	1	D 22
New York Aquarium for Wildlife Conservation Surf Av & W 8th St, Bk	24	D 19
• New York City Fire Museum 278 Spring St, M	1	C 20
• New York City Police Museum 235 E 20th St, M	1	E 19
• New York Historical Society Central Park W & 77th St, M	2	C 15
New York Public Library 5th Av & 42nd St, M	1	D 18
• New York Transit Museum Boerum Pl and Schermerhorn St, Bk	20	C 13
• Pierpont Morgan Library 29 E 36th St, M	1	D 18
• Queens Central Library, Q	13	M12
Queens Museum of Art Flushing Meadows-Corona Park, Q	12	J 10
Schomburg Center for Research in Black Culture-New York Public Library 515 Malcolm X Blvd & 135th St, M	3	C 11
• Science, Industry & Business Library- New York Public Library Madison Av & E 34 St, M	1	D 18
• South Street Seaport Museum, M	1	E 22
The Studio Museum 14 W 125th St, M	2	C 12
• Whitney Museum of American Art 945 Madison Av, M	2	D 15

Parks and Recreation

Beaches

Point of Interest	Map	Grid
Brighton, Bk	24	E 19
Coney Island, Bk	24	C 19
Far Rockaway, Q	18	N18
Great Kills, SI	31	K10
Huguenot, SI	31	G11
Jacob Riis Park, Q	17	H20
Manhattan, Bk	24	E 19
Midland, SI	29	N 7
New Dorp, SI	29	N 8
Oakwood, SI	31	M 9
Orchard, Bx	6	L 3
Oriental, Bk	25	F 19
Plumb, Bk	25	F 19
Rockaway, Q	18	K19
South, SI	29	P 6
Tottenville, SI	30	C12
Wolf's Pond Park, SI	30	F 11

Parks

Point of Interest	Map	Grid
Alley, Q	10	N 9
Alley Pond, Q	10	N 9
Astoria, Q	8	F 8
Baisley Pond, Q	15	M14
Battery, M	1	D22
Blue Heron Pond, SI	31	G10
Botanical Gardens, Bk	20	D14
Bronx, Bx	4	F 6
Brookville, Q	15	O14
Canarsie Beach, Bk	23	G16
Carl Schurz, M	2	E15
Central, M	2	C15
City Hall, M	1	D21
Claremont, Bx	4	D 8
Clay Pits Pond, SI	30	D 9
Clearview, Q	10	M 8
Clove Lakes, SI	27	L 3
Crocheron, Q	10	N 8
Crotona, Bx	4	E 8
Cunningham, Q	13	M10
Douglaston, Q	10	O 9
Dreirer-Offerman, Bk	24	C19
Dyker Beach, Bk	24	B 18
East River, M	1	F 20
Ferry Point, Bx	7	L 7
Flushing Meadows-Corona, Q	12	J 10
Forest, Q	12	J 12
Fort Greene, Bk	20	D13
Fort Tryon, M	4	B 8
Fort Washington, M	4	A 8
Frank M Charles Memorial, Q	14	K15
Gateway National Recreation Area, Bk, Q, SI	16, 25, 31	
Great Kills, SI	31	K 9
High Rock, SI	29	L 6
Highbridge, M	3	C 9
Highland, Bk-Q	14	G13
Inwood Hill, M	4	B 7
Isham, M	4	B 7
Jackie Robinson, M	3	C11
Jacob Riis, Q	17	H20
Juniper Valley, Q	11	H11
Kissena, Q	12	L10
La Tourette, SI	28	J 6
Macombs Dam (John Mullaly), Bx	3	D 9
Marcus Garvey, M	2	D12
Marine, Bk	25	F18
Morningside, M	2	C13
New York Botanical Gardens, Bx	4	E 5
Owis Head, Bk	22	A16
Parade Grounds, Bk	22	D15
Pelham Bay, Bx	4	J 2
Prospect, Bk	20	D14
Queens Botanical Gardens, Q	9	K 9
Randall's Island, M	2	F12
Richmond County, SI	29	L 5
Riverbank State, M	2	B11
Riverdale, Bx	5	A 5
Riverside, M	2	B15
Roberto Clemente State, Bx	4	C 8
Roy Wilkins-Southern Queens, Q	15	N13
St. Mary's, Bx	3	F11
Seaside-Asser Levy Park & Aquarium, Bk	24	D19
Seton Falls, Bx	5	G 3
Silver Lake, SI	27	N 3
Sound View, Bx	7	H 9
Springfield, Q	15	N14
Sunset, Bk	22	B15
Van Cortlandt, Bx	5	C 3
Wards Island, M	2	F14
Wave Hill, Bx	5	A 4
Willow Brook, SI	28	H 4
Wolfes Pond, SI	30	F11

Sports Facilities

Point of Interest	Map	Grid
Aqueduct Race Track, Q	14	K14
Baker Field, M	4	B 6
Belmont Park Race Track, Nassau County	13	P11
Chelsea Piers Sports & Entertainment Complex, M	1	B19
Downing Stadium, M	2	F13
Forest Hills Stadium, Q	12	J11
Madison Square Garden, M	1	C18
Rockefeller Center Skating Rink, M	1	D17
Shea Stadium, Q	9	J 9
USTA National Tennis Center, Q	9	J 9
Wollman Memorial Skating Rink, M	2	D16
Yankee Stadium, Bx	3	D10

Theaters & Concert Halls

Point of Interest	Map	Grid
† Alice Tully Hall Lincoln Center, Broadway & W 65th St, M	2	
• Alvin Alley Dance Theater 1515 Broadway & 44th St, M	1	C17
• Ambassador Theater 215 W 49th St, M	1	C17
† Avery Fisher Hall Lincoln Center, Broadway & W 65th St, M	2	
• Barrymore Theater 243 W 47th St, M	1	C17
• Belasco Theater 111 W 44th St, M	1	C17
† Biltmore Theater 261 W 47th St, M	1	
† Booth Theater 222 W 45th St, M	1	
† Broadhurst Theater 235 W 44th St, M	1	
† Broadway Theater 1681 Broadway, M	1	
Brooklyn Academy of Music 30 Lafayette St, Bk	20	D13
• Brooklyn Center for the Performing Arts (Brooklyn College) Nostrand Av & Av H, Bk	22	E16
† Brooks Atkinson 256 W 47th St, M	1	
† Carnegie Hall 881 Seventh Av, M	1	
† City Center Theater 131 W 55th St, M	1	
• Colden Center Queens College, Q	12	L10
• Douglas Fairbanks Theater 432 W 42nd St, M	1	C17
† Edison Theater 240 W 47th St, M	1	
† Eugene O'Neill Theater 230 W 49th St, M	1	
• Folksbiene Theater 123 E 55th St, M	1	C17
† Ford Center for the Performing Arts, 213 W 42nd St, M	1	
† 45th Street Theater 354 W 45th St, M	1	
† Gershwin Theater 222 W 51st St, M	1	
† Golden Theater 255 W 45th St, M	1	
• Harmony Theater 161 W 22nd St, M	1	C19
• Harold Clurman Theater 412 W 42nd St, M	1	C17
† Helen Hayes Theater 240 W 44th St, M	1	
† Imperial Theater 249 W 45th St, M	1	
• Intar 420 W 42nd St, M	1	C17
• Judith Anderson Theater 422 W 42nd St, M	1	C17
† Julliard Theater 144 W 66th St, M	2	
† Longacre Theater 220 W 48th St, M	1	
† Lunt-Fontanne Theater 205 W 46th St, M	1	
† Lyceum Theater 149 W 45th St, M	1	
† Madison Square Garden 32nd & 33rd Sts bet 7th & 8th Av, M	1	
† Majestic Theater 245 W 44th St, M	1	
• Mark Hellinger Theater 237 W 51st St, M	1	C17
† Martin Beck Theater 302 W 45th St, M	1	
† Metropolitan Opera House Lincoln Center, Broadway & W 64th St, M	2	
† Minskoff Theater Broadway & W 45th St, M	1	
† Mintzi E Newhouse Theater Lincoln Center, 150 W 65th St, M	1	
† Music Box Theater 239 W 45th St, M	1	
† Neil Simon Theater 250 W 52nd St, M	1	
† New Victory Theater 209 W 42nd St, M	1	
• New York Experience Theater 1221 Av of the Americas, M	1	C17
† Palace Theater 1564 Broadway, M	1	
• The Paramount Madison Square Garden, M	1	C18
• Playhouse Theater 1 and 2 359 W 48th St, M	1	C17
• Playwrights Horizon Theater 416 W 42nd St, M	1	C17
† Plymouth Theaters 236 W 45th St, M	1	
† Radio City Music Hall 1260 Av of the Americas, M	1	
• The Ritz 260 W 54th St, M	1	C17
† Royale Theater 242 W 45th St, M	1	
† St. James Theater 246 W 44th St, M	1	
• Samuel Beckett Theater 410 W 42nd St, M	1	C17
† Shubert Theater 225 W 44th St, M	1	
• South Street Theater 424 W 42nd St, M	1	C17
† Town Hall 123 W 43rd St, M	1	
† Virginia Theater 245 W 52nd St, M	1	
† Vivian Beaumont Theater Lincoln Center, 150 W 65th St, M	1	
• West Side Arts Theater 407 W 43rd St, M	1	C17
† Winter Garden Theater 1634 Broadway, M	1	

Transportation Facilities

Point of Interest	Map	Grid
Air Pegasus VIP Heliport Twelfth Av & W 30th St, M	1	B18
• Circle Line Sightseeing Yachts Pier 83 at W 42nd St, M	1	B17
Downtown Manhattan Heliport Pier 6 & East River, M	1	E22
East 60th Street Metroport E 60th St & Franklin D Roosevelt Dr, M	2	E16
Ellis Island Ferry (Circle Line) Battery Park, M	1	D22
Flushing Airport, Q	9	K 8
George Washington Bridge Bus Terminal 178th St & Broadway, M	3	B 9
Grand Central Terminal (MTA Metro-North Railroad) Lexington Av & 42nd St, M	1	D17
• Hudson River Day Line (to Bear Mt, West Point, Poughkeepsie) Pier 81 at W 41st St, M	1	B18
Island Helicopter Sightseeing 34th St & East River Dr, M	1	E18
John F Kennedy International Airport, Q	15	M15
La Guardia Airport Jackson Heights, Q	9	H 8
New York Waterway Ferries World Financial Center, M	1	C22
Whitehall St., M	1	D22
E 34th St, M	1	E18
W 34th St, M	1	B18
Passenger Ship Terminal 47th-52nd Sts & Twelfth Av, M	1	B17
PATH (Port Authority Trans-Hudson Railway) World Trade Center, M	1	D22
Av of the Americas/33rd St, M	1	D18
Pennsylvania Station (Amtrak-MTA Long Island Rail Road-NJ Transit) Seventh Av & 33rd St, M	1	C18
Port Authority Bus Terminal Eighth Av & 41st St, M	1	C18
Seaplane Terminal 23rd St & East River, M	1	E19
Staten Island Ferry Terminal Battery Park, S Ferry, M	1	D22
Staten Island Railway St. George, SI	27	O 1
Statue of Liberty Ferry (Circle Line) Battery Park, M	1	D22
Wall Street Heliport Pier 6 & East River, M	1	E22

NOTES: • Not indicated on map due to scale.
† Specific location shown onTheater District Map, page 8.

Key to Borough Name Abbreviations

Bk	Brooklyn
Bx	Bronx
M	Manhattan
Q	Queens
SI	Staten Island

Neighborhood	Map	Grid
MANHATTAN		
BATTERY PARK CITY	1	C 22
BOWERY	1	E 20
CARNEGIE HILL	2	D 14
CHELSEA	1	C 19
CHINATOWN	1	D 21
CIVIC CENTER	1	D 21
CLINTON	1	B 17
EAST HARLEM	2	D 12
EAST VILLAGE	1	E 20
FASHION CENTER	1	C 18
FINANCIAL DISTRICT	1	D 22
FLATIRON	1	D 19
FORT GEORGE	4	B 8
GRAMERCY PARK	1	D 19
GREENWICH VILLAGE	1	D 20
HAMILTON HEIGHTS	3	B 11
HARLEM	2	C 12
INWOOD	4	B 7
KIPS BAY	1	D 18
LENOX HILL	2	D 16
LINCOLN SQUARE	2	B 16
LITTLE ITALY	1	D 20
LOWER EAST SIDE	1	E 20
MANHATTAN VALLEY	2	B 14
MANHATTANVILLE	2	B 12
MARBLE HILL	4	B 6
MIDTOWN	1	C 17
MIDTOWN SOUTH	1	C 18
MORNINGSIDE HEIGHTS	2	B 13
MURRAY HILL	1	D 18
NOHO	1	D 20
RANDALLS ISLAND (EAST RIVER)	2	F 12
ROOSEVELT ISLAND (EAST RIVER)	2	F 16
SHERMAN CREEK	4	B 7
SOHO	1	D 20
SPANISH HARLEM	2	D 13
THEATER DISTRICT	1	C 17
TIMES SQUARE	1	C 17
TRIBECA	1	D 21
TURTLE BAY	1	D 17
TWO BRIDGES	1	E 21
UNION SQUARE	1	D 19
UPPER EAST SIDE	2	D 15
UPPER WEST SIDE	2	B 15
WASHINGTON HEIGHTS	3	B 9
WEST VILLAGE	1	C 20
YORKVILLE	2	E 15
THE BRONX		
ALLERTON	5	G 5
BATHGATE	4	E 8
BAYCHESTER	6	H 4
BEDFORD PARK	4	E 6
BELMONT	4	E 6
BRONX PARK SOUTH	4	F 7
BRONX RIVER	4	G 8
BRONXDALE	5	F 5
BRUCKNER	7	H 8
CASTLE HILL	7	J 8
CITY ISLAND	6	M 4
CLAREMONT VILLAGE	3	E 9
CLASON POINT	7	J 9
CO-OP CITY	6	H 3
CONCOURSE	3	D 9
CONCOURSE VILLAGE	3	D 10
COUNTRY CLUB	7	K 6
CROTONA PARK EAST	4	F 8
EAST TREMONT	4	E 7
EASTCHESTER	6	G 2
EASTCHESTER BAY	7	L 6
EDENWALD	5	G 3
EDGEWATER PARK	7	M 6
FIELDSTON	5	B 4
FORDHAM	4	D 6
HARDING PARK	7	J 8
HART ISLAND	6	N 3
HIGHBRIDGE	3	C 9
THE HUB	3	E 10
HUNTS POINT	3	G 10
KINGSBRIDGE	5	B 5
KINGSBRIDGE HEIGHTS	4	C 6
LONGWOOD	3	F 10
MELROSE	3	E 10
MIDDLETOWN	7	J 6
MORRIS HEIGHTS	4	C 8
MORRIS PARK	7	H 6
MORRISANIA	3	E 9
MOTT HAVEN	3	E 11
MOUNT EDEN	3	D 8
MOUNT HOPE	4	D 8
NORTH RIVERDALE	5	A 3
NORWOOD	4	E 5
OLINVILLE	5	F 4
PARKCHESTER	7	H 7
PELHAM BAY	7	J 5
PELHAM GARDENS	6	H 5
PELHAM PARKWAY	4	G 6
PORT MORRIS	3	F 11
RIVERDALE	5	A 5
SCHUYLERVILLE	7	K 6
SOUNDVIEW	7	H 9
SOUTH RIVERDALE	4	A 5
SPENCER ESTATES	6	K 5
SPUYTEN DUYVIL	4	B 6
THROGS NECK	7	L 7
TREMONT	4	D 7
UNIONPORT	7	J 7
UNIVERSITY HEIGHTS	4	C 7
VAN CORTLANDT VILLAGE	5	C 5
VAN NEST	7	G 6
WAKEFIELD	5	F 2

Neighborhood	Map	Grid
WEST FARMS	4	G 7
WESTCHESTER SQUARE	7	J 6
WILLIAMSBRIDGE	5	F 4
WOODLAWN	5	D 3
QUEENS		
ARVERNE	18	M 18
ASTORIA	8	F 9
AUBURNDALE	9	L 9
BAY TERRACE	10	M 8
BAYSIDE	10	M 9
BAYSWATER	16	N 17
BEECHHURST	9	L 7
BELLAIRE	13	N 11
BELLE HARBOR	17	J 19
BELLEROSE	13	O 11
BLISSVILLE	11	E 10
BREEZY POINT	17	F 20
BRIARWOOD	12	L 12
BROAD CHANNEL	16	L 17
BROOKVILLE	15	N 14
CAMBRIA HEIGHTS	15	O 13
COLLEGE POINT	9	J 8
CORONA	12	J 10
DITMARS	8	F 8
DOUGLAS MANOR	10	N 8
DOUGLASTON	10	N 9
DUTCH KILLS	8	E 10
EAST ELMHURST	8	H 9
EDGEMERE	18	N 18
ELMHURST	11	H 10
FAR ROCKAWAY	16	N 18
FLORAL PARK	13	P 10
FLUSHING	12	K 9
FOREST HILLS	12	J 11
FRESH MEADOWS	13	M 10
GLEN OAKS	10	P 9
GLENDALE	11	H 12
HAMMELS	18	L 18
HILLCREST	12	L 11
HOLLIS	13	N 12
HOLLIS HILL	13	N 10
HOLLISWOOD	13	N 11
HOWARD BEACH	14	K 15
HUNTERS POINT	11	E 10
JACKSON HEIGHTS	8	H 9
JAMAICA	12	L 12
JAMAICA ESTATES	13	M 11
JAMAICA HILLS	12	L 11
KEW GARDENS	12	K 12
KEW GARDENS HILLS	12	K 11
LAURELTON	15	O 14
LINDEN HILL	9	K 8
LINDENWOOD	14	J 14
LITTLE NECK	10	O 8
LONG ISLAND CITY	11	E 10
MALBA	9	K 7
MASPETH	11	G 11
MIDDLE VILLAGE	11	H 11
MURRAY HILL	9	L 9
NEPONSIT	17	J 19
OAKLAND GARDENS	13	N 10
OZONE PARK	14	K 13
POMONOK	12	L 10
QUEENS VILLAGE	13	O 11
QUEENSBORO HILL	12	K 10
QUEENSBRIDGE	8	E 9
RAVENSWOOD	8	E 9
REGO PARK	12	J 11
RICHMOND HILL	12	K 12
RIDGEWOOD	11	G 12
ROCKAWAY PARK	18	K 19
ROSEDALE	15	O 14
ROXBURY	17	H 20
ST. ALBANS	15	N 13
SEASIDE	18	K 19
SOMERVILLE	18	M 18
SOUTH JAMAICA	15	M 13
SOUTH OZONE PARK	14	L 14
SPRINGFIELD GARDENS	15	N 14
STEINWAY	8	G 8
SUNNYSIDE	11	F 10
WEST MASPETH	11	F 11
WHITESTONE	9	K 7
WOODHAVEN	14	J 13
WOODSIDE	11	G 10
BROOKLYN		
BATH BEACH	24	B 18
BAY RIDGE	22	A 16
BEDFORD-STUYVESANT	21	E 13
BENSONHURST	24	C 17
BERGEN BEACH	23	G 17
BOERUM HILL	20	C 13
BOROUGH PARK	22	C 16
BRIGHTON BEACH	24	D 19
BROADWAY JUNCTION	21	G 13
BROOKLYN HEIGHTS	19	C 12
BROWNSVILLE	21	G 14
BUSHWICK	19	F 12
CANARSIE	23	G 15
CARROLL GARDENS	20	C 13
CITY LINE	21	H 14
CLINTON HILL	20	D 13
COBBLE HILL	20	C 13
CONEY ISLAND	24	C 19
CROWN HEIGHTS	21	E 14
CYPRESS HILLS	21	H 13
DITMAS PARK	22	D 16
DOWNTOWN BROOKLYN	19	C 13
DYKER HEIGHTS	22	B 17
EAST FLATBUSH	23	F 16
EAST NEW YORK	21	H 14
EAST WILLIAMSBURG	19	E 12
FARRAGUT	23	E 15
FLATBUSH	22	E 16

Neighborhood	Map	Grid
FLATLANDS	23	F 17
FORT GREENE	20	D 13
FORT HAMILTON	24	A 17
FULTON FERRY	19	C 12
GEORGETOWN	23	G 16
GERRITSEN BEACH	25	F 18
GOWANUS	20	C 14
GRAVESEND	24	C 18
GREENPOINT	19	E 11
GREENWOOD HEIGHTS	20	C 15
HIGHLAND PARK	21	H 13
HOMECREST	24	D 18
KENSINGTON	22	D 16
MANHATTAN BEACH	25	E 19
MAPLETON	22	C 17
MARINE PARK	25	E 17
MIDWOOD	22	E 17
MILL BASIN	23	G 17
MILL ISLAND	23	G 17
NEW LOTS	21	H 14
NEW UTRECHT	22	C 17
NORTHSIDE	19	D 11
OCEAN HILL	21	F 13
OCEAN PARKWAY	24	D 17
PAERDEGAT BASIN	23	G 16
PARK SLOPE	20	C 14
PARKVILLE	22	D 16
PROSPECT HEIGHTS	20	D 13
PROSPECT PARK SOUTH	22	D 15
PROSPECT-LEFFERTS GARDENS	20	D 15
RED HOOK	20	B 14
REMSEN VILLAGE	23	F 15
RUGBY	21	E 15
SEA GATE	24	B 19
SHEEPSHEAD BAY	25	D 18
SOUTHSIDE	19	D 12
SPRING CREEK	21	H 15
STARRETT CITY	21	H 15
STUYVESANT HEIGHTS	21	E 13
SUNSET PARK	22	B 16
VINEGAR HILL	19	C 12
WEEKSVILLE	21	F 14
WILLIAMSBURG	19	D 12
WINDSOR TERRACE	20	D 15
WINGATE	21	E 14
STATEN ISLAND		
ANNADALE	31	G 9
ARDEN HEIGHTS	31	G 9
ARLINGTON	26	F 2
ARROCHAR	29	O 5
BAY TERRACE	31	K 9
BLOOMFIELD	26	G 3
BULLS HEAD	26	H 4
BUTLER MANOR	30	D 12
CASTLETON CORNERS	27	L 4
CHARLESTON	30	C 10
CHELSEA	28	G 5
CLIFTON	27	O 3
CONCORD	27	N 4
DONGAN HILLS	29	M 6
EGBERTVILLE	28	K 6
ELM PARK	26	K 3
ELTINGVILLE	31	H 9
EMERSON HILL	27	M 4
FOX HILLS	27	O 4
FRESH KILLS	28	F 6
GRANITEVILLE	26	J 3
GRANT CITY	29	M 7
GRASMERE	29	O 5
GREAT KILLS	31	J 9
GREENRIDGE	28	F 8
GRYMES HILL	27	N 3
HEARTLAND VILLAGE	28	J 6
HOWLAND HOOK	26	G 2
HUGUENOT	31	G 10
HUGUENOT BEACH	31	G 11
LIGHTHOUSE HILL	28	K 7
LIVINGSTON	27	L 1
MARINERS HARBOR	26	J 2
MIDLAND BEACH	29	N 7
MOUNT LORETTO	30	D 11
NEW BRIGHTON	27	N 1
NEW DORP	29	L 7
NEW DORP BEACH	29	M 8
NEW SPRINGVILLE	28	H 5
OAKWOOD	29	L 8
OAKWOOD BEACH	29	M 8
OLD PLACE	26	G 2
OLD TOWN	29	N 5
PARK HILL	27	N 4
PLEASANT PLAINS	30	E 11
PORT IVORY	26	H 1
PORT MOBIL	30	C 9
PORT RICHMOND	26	K 2
PRINCE'S BAY	30	F 10
RANDALL MANOR	27	M 2
RICHMOND VALLEY	30	D 11
RICHMONDTOWN	28	K 7
ROSEBANK	27	O 4
ROSSVILLE	30	E 8
ST. GEORGE	27	O 1
SHORE ACRES	27	P 4
SOUTH BEACH	29	O 6
STAPLETON	27	O 2
SUNNYSIDE	27	M 4
TODT HILL	29	L 5
TOTTENVILLE BEACH	30	C 12
TRAVIS	28	G 6
WEST BRIGHTON	27	L 2
WESTERLEIGH	26	K 3
WILLOWBROOK	26	J 4
WOODROW	30	E 9

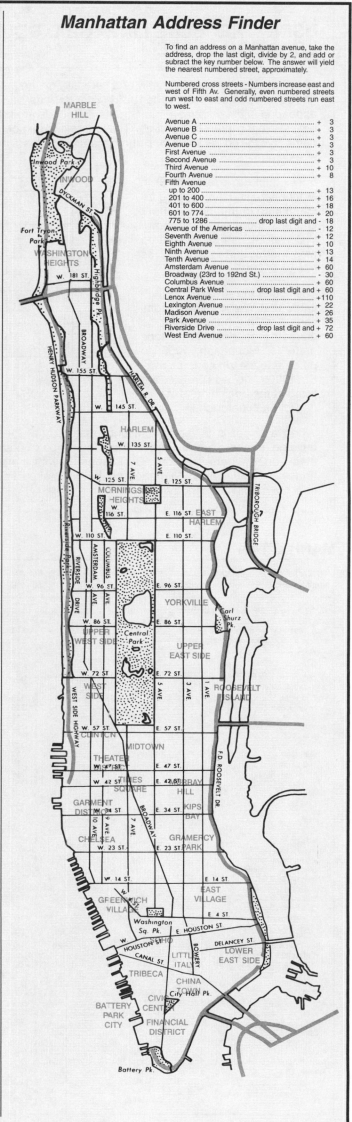

Manhattan Address Finder

To find an address on a Manhattan avenue, take the address, drop the last digit, divide by 2, and add or subtract the key number below. The answer will yield the nearest numbered street, approximately.

Numbered cross streets - Numbers increase east and west of Fifth Av. Generally, even numbered streets run west to east and odd numbered streets run east to west.

Avenue A	+ 3
Avenue B	+ 3
Avenue C	+ 3
Avenue D	+ 3
First Avenue	+ 3
Second Avenue	+ 3
Third Avenue	+ 10
Fourth Avenue	+ 8
Fifth Avenue	
up to 200	+ 13
201 to 400	+ 16
401 to 600	+ 18
601 to 774	+ 20
775 to 1286	drop last digit and - 18
Avenue of the Americas	- 12
Seventh Avenue	+ 12
Eighth Avenue	+ 10
Ninth Avenue	+ 13
Tenth Avenue	+ 14
Amsterdam Avenue	+ 60
Broadway (23rd to 192nd St.)	- 30
Columbus Avenue	+ 60
Central Park West	drop last digit and + 60
Lenox Avenue	+110
Lexington Avenue	+ 22
Madison Avenue	+ 26
Park Avenue	+ 35
Riverside Drive	drop last digit and + 72
West End Avenue	+ 60

USING THE "BLUE LINE" GRID SQUARE LOCATION SYSTEM

Blue lines are drawn horizontally and vertically on the map, forming grid squares. These squares can be identified by letters and numbers appearing in the map margins. Streets and roads are listed alphabetically in the index by borough. The letters and numbers after the name give the postal zone, map number and grid square in which the street appears.

For example, to locate Wall St. in Manhattan, find the heading for Manhattan in the index. The 1 D22 after the street name shows that Wall St. can be located on map 1 within grid square D22, as shown to the right.

The 5 after the street name indicates that Wall St. is in postal zone 5. This number can be added to the appropriate zip code prefix for Manhattan, 1000, to determine the zip code for Wall St., 10005. Zip code prefixes are listed at the beginning of the index for each borough.

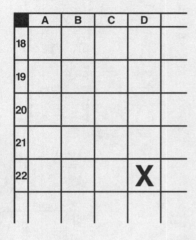

When a street is in more than one postal zone, the house or building numbers are divided to show the range of addresses for each zone. Where the word "OUT" appears with a number, that house or building and any higher number for that particular street is in the postal zone indicated.

ABBREVIATIONS USED ON HAGSTROM MAPS

Al	Alley	Pa	Path
Av	Avenue	Pk	Park
Blvd	Boulevard	Pkwy	Parkway
Boro	Borough	Pl	Place
Cem	Cemetery	PLGD/PG	Playground
Cir	Circle	Plz	Plaza
Cl	Close	Rd	Road
CO	County	Riv	River
Cr	Creek	RR	Railroad
Cres	Crescent	S	South
Ct	Court	Sq	Square
Dr	Drive	St	Saint
E	East	St	Street
Expwy	Expressway	Sta	Station
Ft	Fort	Ter	Terrace
GC	Golf Club	Term	Terminal
Hts	Heights	Tpk	Turnpike
Hwy	Highway	Tr	Trail
Isl, I	Island	Twp	Township
La	Lane	W	West
Mt	Mount	Wk	Walk
N	North		

NOTES: Numbered streets are indexed after the alphabetical listing.
"*" indicates that street name is not shown on map due to lack of space.

MANHATTAN
STREET INDEX AND POSTAL ZONES

STREET NAME AND HOUSE NUMBERS	ZONE NO.	MAP NO.	MAP GRID
NOTE: To obtain ZIP code for Manhattan, add 10 before three digit postal zone numbers, 100 before two digit postal zone numbers and 1000 before single digit postal zone numbers.			
A			
A Philip Randolph Sq	2		C13
Abingdon Sq	14	1	C19
Abraham Kazan St	2	1	F20
Academy St	34	4	B 7
Adam Clayton Powell Jr Blvd	2		C13
1800-2000	26	2	C13
2001-2259	27	2	C12
2260-2499	30	3	C11
2500-OUT	39	3	C10
Adm George Dewey Promenade	4	1	D22
Adrian Av	463	4	B 6
African Sq	27	2	C12
Albany St	0	0	D 0
1-99	6	1	D22
350-OUT	280	1	C22
Alex Rose Pl	33	4	B 8
Alexander Hamilton Sq	31	3	B11
Allard K Lowenstein Plz *(West side of United Nations Plz at E 45th St)	17	1	E17
Allen St	2	1	E21
American Express Plz *(125 Broad St)	4	1	D22
Amsterdam Av		2	B16
1-339	23	2	B16
340-639	24	2	B14
641-1139 & 640-1098	25	2	B14
1141-1479 & 1100-1478	27	2	B12
1480-1880	31	3	B11
1881-2268	32	3	B10
2269-2565	33	3	B 9
2566-OUT	40	4	B 8
Ann St	38	1	D21
Archbishop Fulton J Sheen Pl	17	1	D17
Arden St	40	4	B 7
Asser Levy Pl	10	1	E19
Astor Pl	3	1	D20
Astor Plz (1515 Broadway)	18	1	C17
Attorney St	2	1	E20
Audubon Av		3	B 9
1-160	32	3	B 9
161-439	33	4	B 8

STREET NAME AND HOUSE NUMBERS	ZONE NO.	MAP NO.	MAP GRID
440-OUT	40	4	B 8
Avenue A	9	1	E19
Avenue B	9	1	E19
Avenue C	9	1	E19
Avenue D	9	1	F19
Avenue of the Americas (6th Av)		1	D20
1-204	13	1	D20
205-415 & 206-334	14	1	D20
417-649 & 336-650	11	1	D19
651-773	10	1	D19
774-960	1	1	D18
961-1080	18	1	D18
1081-1219	36	1	D17
1220-1279	20	1	D17
1280-OUT	19	1	D17
1290 only	104	1	D17
1301 only	184	1	D17
1345 only	105	1	D17
Avenue of the Finest	38	1	E21
B			
Bache Plz	38	1	D21
Bank St	14	1	C20
Banker Trust Plz *(130 Liberty St)	6	1	D22
Barclay St	7	1	D21
Barrow St	14	1	C20
Baruch Dr	2	1	F20
Baruch Pl	2	1	F20
Battery Park Plz *(Pearl & State Sts)	4	1	D22
Battery Pl		1	D22
1-23	4	1	D22
24-OUT	280	1	D22
Baxter St	13	1	D21
Bayard St		1	E21
1-38	2	1	E21
39-OUT	13	1	D21
Beach St	13	1	C21
Beak St	34	4	B 7
Beaver St		1	D22
1-53 & 2-74	4	1	D22
55-OUT & 76-OUT	5	1	D22
Bedford St	14	1	C20
Beekman Pl	22	1	E17
Beekman St	38	1	D21
Bennett Av		4	B 8
1-131	33	4	B 8
132-OUT	40	4	B 8
Benson St	13	1	D21

STREET NAME AND HOUSE NUMBERS	ZONE NO.	MAP NO.	MAP GRID
Bethune St	14	1	C20
Bialystoker Pl	2	1	F20
Bleecker St		1	D20
1-226	12	1	D20
227-OUT	14	1	C20
Bloomfield St	14	1	B19
Bogardus Pl	40	4	B 8
Bond St	12	1	D20
Bowery		1	E21
1-279 (odd)	2	1	E21
2-148 (even)	13	1	E20
150-364 (even)	12	1	E20
281-OUT & 366-OUT	3	1	D20
Bowling Green	4	1	D22
Bradhurst Av		3	C11
1-63	30	3	C11
64-OUT	39	3	C10
Bridge St	4	1	D22
Broad St		1	D22
1-23	5	1	D22
24-OUT	4	1	D22
Broadway		1	D22
1-27 & 2-70	4	1	D22
29-171 (odd)	6	1	D22
72-148 (even)	5	1	D22
120 only	271	1	D22
150-222 (even)	38	1	D22
173-331 & 224-334	7	1	D21
233 only	279	1	D21
333-487 & 336-486	13	1	D21
489-697 & 488-694	12	1	D20
699-901 & 696-900	3	1	D19
902-1139	10	1	D19
1140-1330	1	1	D18
1331-1450	18	1	C18
1451-1589 & 1452-1592	36	1	C17
1591-1809 & 1594-1810	19	1	C17
1811-2160	23	2	C16
2161-2459	24	2	B15
2461-2959 & 2460-2918	25	2	B14
2961-3299 & 2920-3298	27	2	B12
3300-3699	31	3	B11
3700-4100	32	3	B10
4101-4379	33	4	B 8
4380-4759	40	4	B 8
4760-5170	34	4	B 7
5171-5510	463	4	C 6
Broadway Al *(From E 26th St to E 27th St bet 2nd and 3rd Av)	16	1	E18
Broadway Pl *(W 46th St & Broadway)	36	1	C17

STREET NAME AND HOUSE NUMBERS	ZONE NO.	MAP NO.	MAP GRID
Broadway Ter	40	4	B 8
Broome St		1	D20
109-338	2	1	E20
339-OUT	13	1	D20
Burling Slip	5	1	E22
C			
Cabrini Blvd		4	B 9
1-250	33	4	B 9
251-OUT	40	4	B 8
Canal St		1	C20
1-151 & 2-142	2	1	E21
153-OUT & 144-OUT	13	1	D20
Cannon St	2	1	F20
Cardinal Hayes Pl	7	1	D21
Cardinal Stepinac Pl	36	1	B18
Carlisle St	6	1	D22
Carmine St	14	1	C20
Cathedral Pkwy		2	B13
1-399 & 2-348	26	2	C13
401-OUT & 350-OUT	25	2	B13
Catherine La	13	1	D21
Catherine Slip	38	1	E21
Catherine St	38	1	E21
Cedar St		1	D22
1	5	1	D22
3-27 (odd)	38	1	D22
29-87 & 2-88	5	1	D22
89-OUT	6	1	D22
Central Park N	26	2	C13
Central Park S (Olmsted Way)	19	2	C16
Central Park W		2	C16
1-160	28	2	C16
161-310	24	2	C15
311-OUT	25	2	C14
Centre Market Pl	13	1	D20
Centre St		1	D21
1-73 & 2-68	7	1	D21
75-OUT & 70-OUT	13	1	D21
Chambers Ct	281	1	C21
Chambers St	7	1	C21
Charles La	14	1	C20
Charles St	14	1	C20
Charlton St	14	1	C20
Chase Manhattan Plz	5	1	D22
Chatham Sq	38	1	E21
Chelsea Sq	11	1	C19
Cherokee Pl	21	2	E15
Cherry St	2	1	E21
Chisum Pl	37	3	D11

STREET NAME AND HOUSE NUMBERS	ZONE NO.	MAP NO.	MAP GRID
Chittenden Av	33	4	B 8
Christopher St	14	1	C20
Chrystie St	2	1	E21
Church St		1	D22
1-17 (odd)	6	1	D22
2-18 (even)	48	1	D22
19-225 & 20-168	7	1	D21
227-OUT & 170 out	13	1	D21
Circle Line Plz *(west end of 42nd St & 12th Ave)	36	1	B17
City Hall	7	1	D21
Claremont Av	27	2	B13
Clarkson St	14	1	C20
Cleveland Pl	12	1	D20
Cliff St	38	1	D22
Clinton St	2	1	E21
Coenties Al	4	1	D22
Coenties Slip	4	1	D22
Collister St	13	1	C21
Col Charles Young Triangle	39	3	C10
Col Robert Magaw Pl	33	4	B 8
Columbia St	2	1	F20
Columbus Av		2	C15
1-339	23	2	C16
340-639	24	2	C15
640-OUT	25	2	C14
Columbus Cir		2	C16
1-10	19	2	C16
11-OUT	23	2	C16
Commerce St	14	1	C20
Confucius Plz	2	1	E21
Convent Av		2	C12
1-116	27	2	C12
117-OUT	31	3	C11
Convent Hill	27	2	C12
Cooper Sq	3	1	D20
Cooper St	34	4	B 7
Cornelia St	14	1	C20
Cortlandt Al	13	1	D21
Cortlandt St	7	1	D22
Crosby St		1	D20
1-40	13	1	D20
41-OUT	12	1	D20
Cumming St	34	4	B 7
D			
Dag Hammarskjold Plz (305-311 E 47th St)	17	1	E17
David B Friedland Sq *(Broadway, St Nicolas & W 170th St)	32	3	B 9

STREET NAME AND HOUSE NUMBERS	ZONE NO.	MAP NO.	MAP GRID
David Ben-Gurion Pl *(E 43rd St, bet Fifth & Vanderbilt Aves)	17	1	D17
Delancey St	2	1	E20
Delancey St S	2	1	E20
Depew Pl	17	1	D17
Desbrosses St	13	1	C21
Dey St	7	1	D22
Diamond & Jewelry Way *(W 47th St, bet Fifth Av & Av of the Americas)	36	1	D17
Division St	2	1	E21
Dominick St	13	1	C20
Dongan Pl	40	4	B 7
Donnellon Sq	31	3	C11
Dorrence Brook Sq *(W 136th St, St Nicolas & Edgecomb Aves)	30	3	C11
Douglas MacArthur Plz	17	1	E17
Dover St	38	1	E21
Downing St	14	1	C20
Doyers St	13	1	E21
Duane St		1	D21
1-125	7	1	D21
49-89 (odd)	278	1	D21
126-OUT	13	1	D21
Duffy Sq	36	1	C17
Duke Ellington Blvd (W 106th St)	25	2	B13
Dutch St	38	1	D22
Dyckman St		4	B 7
1-99	34	4	B 7
100-217	40	4	B 7
218-OUT	34	4	B 7
Dyer Av	18	1	C18

E

STREET NAME AND HOUSE NUMBERS	ZONE NO.	MAP NO.	MAP GRID
East Broadway		1	E21
1-15 & 2-10	38	1	E21
17-OUT & 12-OUT	2	1	E21
East End Av		2	E15
1-23 & 2-18	21	2	E15
25-155 & 20-160	28	2	E15
157-OUT & 162-OUT	128	2	E15
East Houston St		1	D20
1-91 & 2-88	12	1	D20
93-OUT & 90-OUT	2	1	E20
East River Dr (see Franklin D Roosevelt Dr)		2	E13
East River Piers		1	D22
6	4	1	E22
9 & 11 & 13 & 14	5	1	E22
15-18	38	1	E22
35 & 43	2	1	F21
East Rd (Roosevelt Island)	44	1	F17
East Side Express Hwy (South St Viaduct)	5	1	E22
East Tower Dr	23	2	B16
East 1st St		1	E20
1-73	3	1	E20
74-198 & 75-119	9	1	E20
East 2nd St		1	E20
1-87 & 2-98	3	1	E20
89-299 & 100-398	9	1	E20
East 3rd St		1	E20
1-99	3	1	E20
100-OUT	9	1	E20
East 4th St		1	E20
2-20 (even)	12	1	D20
22-130 & 1-133	3	1	E20
132-OUT & 135-OUT	9	1	E20
East 5th St		1	E20
200-399	3	1	E20
500-799	9	1	E20
East 6th St		1	E20
200-399	3	1	E20
400-999	9	1	E20
East 7th St		1	E20
1-89	3	1	E20
90-299	9	1	E20
East 8th St		1	D19
1-199	3	1	E19
200-OUT	9	1	E19
East 9th St		1	D19
1-399	3	1	D19
400-OUT	9	1	E19
East 10th St		1	D19
1-244	3	1	D19
245-OUT	9	1	E19
East 11th St		1	D19
1-399	3	1	D19
400-OUT	9	1	E19
East 12th St		1	D19
1-399	3	1	D19
400-OUT	9	1	E19
East 13th St		1	D19
1-399	3	1	D19
400-OUT	9	1	E19
East 14th St		1	D19
1-399	3	1	D19
400-OUT	9	1	E19
East 15th St		1	D19
1-399	3	1	D19
400-OUT	9	1	E19
East 16th St		1	D19
1-399	3	1	D19
400-OUT	9	1	E19
East 17th St	3	1	D19
121 only	211	1	E19
East 18th St	3	1	D19
East 19th St	3	1	D19
East 20th St		1	D19
1-399	3	1	D19
400-OUT (even)	9	1	D19
401-OUT (odd)	10	1	D19
East 21st St	10	1	D19
East 22nd St	10	1	D19
East 23rd St	10	1	D19
East 24th St	10	1	D19
East 25th St	10	1	D18
East 26th St		1	D18
1-399 (odd)	10	1	D18
401-OUT (odd)	16	1	E18
All even numbers	10	1	D18
East 27th St	16	1	D18
East 28th St	16	1	D18
East 29th St	16	1	D18
East 30th St	16	1	D18
East 31st St	16	1	D18
East 32nd St	16	1	D18
East 33rd St	16	1	D18
East 34th St	16	1	D18
East 35th St	16	1	D18
East 36th St	16	1	D18
East 37th St	16	1	D18
East 38th St	16	1	D18
East 39th St	16	1	D18
East 40th St	16	1	D18
East 41st St	17	1	D18
49 only	165	1	D18
125 only	168	1	D18
East 42nd St	17	1	D17
60 only	165	1	D17
122 only	168	1	D17
135 only	174	1	D17
East 43rd St	17	1	D17
1 only	175	1	D17
9 only	173	1	D17
130 only	174	1	D17
East 44th St	17	1	D17
18 only	173	1	D17
East 45th St	17	1	D17
5 only	176	1	D17
East 46th St	17	1	D17
East 47th St	17	1	D17
East 48th St	17	1	D17
East 49th St	17	1	D17
East 50th St	22	1	D17
East 51st St	22	1	D17
East 52nd St	22	1	D17
55 only	55	1	D17
East 53rd St	22	1	D17
East 54th St	22	1	D17
East 55th St	22	1	D17
East 56th St	22	1	D17
East 57th St	22	1	D17
East 58th St	22	1	D17
150 only	155	1	D17
East 59th St	22	2	D16
East 60th St	22	2	D16
East 61st St	21	2	D16
East 62nd St	21	2	D16
East 63rd St	21	2	D16
East 64th St	21	2	D16
East 65th St	21	2	D16
East 66th St	21	2	D16
East 67th St	21	2	D16
East 68th St	21	2	D16
East 69th St	21	2	D16
East 70th St	21	2	D16
East 71st St	21	2	D16
East 72nd St	21	2	D16
East 73rd St	21	2	D16
East 74th St	21	2	D15
East 75th St	21	2	D15
East 76th St	21	2	D15
East 77th St	21	2	D15
500 only	162	2	D15
East 78th St	21	2	D15
East 79th St	21	2	D15
East 80th St	21	2	D15
East 81st St	28	2	D15
East 82nd St	28	2	D15
East 83rd St	28	2	D15
East 84th St	28	2	D15
East 85th St	28	2	D15
East 86th St	28	2	D15
East 87th St	128	2	D15
East 88th St	128	2	D15
East 89th St	128	2	D15
East 90th St	128	2	D14
East 91st St	128	2	D14
East 92nd St	128	2	D14
East 93rd St	128	2	D14
East 94th St	128	2	D14
East 95th St	128	2	D14
East 96th St	128	2	D14
East 97th St	29	2	D14
East 98th St	29	2	D14
East 99th St	29	2	D14
East 100th St	29	2	D14
East 101st St	29	2	D14
East 102nd St	29	2	D14
East 103rd St	29	2	D14
East 104th St	29	2	D14
East 105th St	29	2	D13
East 106th St	29	2	D13
East 107th St	29	2	D13
East 108th St	29	2	D13
East 109th St	29	2	D13
East 110th St	29	2	D13
East 111th St	29	2	D13
East 112th St	29	2	D13
East 113th St	29	2	E13
East 114th St	29	2	E13
East 115th St	29	2	D13
East 116th St	29	2	D13
East 117th St	35	2	D13
East 118th St	35	2	D13
East 119th St	35	2	D13
East 120th St	35	2	D12
East 121st St	35	2	D12
East 122nd St	35	2	D12
East 123rd St	35	2	D12
East 124th St	35	2	D12
East 125th St	35	2	D12
East 126th St	35	2	D12
East 127th St	35	2	D12
East 128th St	35	2	D12
East 129th St	35	2	D12
East 130th St	37	2	D12
East 131st St	37	2	D12
East 132nd St	37	2	D12
East 135th St	37	3	D11
East 138th St	37	3	D11
East 139th St	37	3	D11
Edgar Allan Poe St	24	2	B15
Edgar St	6	1	D22
Edgecombe Av		3	C11
1-231	30	3	C11
232-394	31	3	C10
395-OUT	32	3	C10
Edward L Morgan Pl	32	3	B10
Eighth Av		1	C19
1-79 & 2-66	14	1	C19
81-277 & 68-278	11	1	C19
279-499	1	1	C18
500-637	18	1	C18
638-789	36	1	C17
790-996	19	1	C17
Eldridge St	2	1	E21
Eleventh Av		1	B18
2 only	14	1	B19
3-200	11	1	B19
201-419 & 202-426	1	1	B18
421-533 & 428-538	18	1	B18
535-661 & 540-662	36	1	B17
663-OUT	19	1	B17
Elizabeth St		1	E21
1-136	13	1	E21
137-OUT	12	1	E20
Elk St	7	1	D21
Ellwood St	40	4	B 7
Emerson St	34	4	B 7
Ericsson Pl	13	1	D21
Esplanade Gardens Plz *(Lenox Av bet 147th and 145th Sts)	39	3	D11
Essex St	2	1	E21
Exchange Al	6	1	D22
Exchange Pl		1	D22
1-67 & 2-42	5	1	D22
69-OUT & 44-OUT	4	1	D22
Exchange Plz *(Broadway, Trinity Pl & Exchange Al)	6	1	D22
Exterior St	34	4	C 7
Extra Pl	3	1	E20

F

STREET NAME AND HOUSE NUMBERS	ZONE NO.	MAP NO.	MAP GRID
Fairview Av	40	4	B 8
Fashion Av (7th Av)		1	C18
282-461	1	1	C18
462-576	18	1	C18
577-599	36	1	C17
Father Demo Sq	14	1	C20
Father Fagan Sq	13	1	D20
Federal Plz	7	1	D21
26 only	278	1	D21
Federal Reserve Plz *(Liberty & Nassau Sts & Maiden La)	5	1	D22
Fifth Av		1	D18
1-133 (odd)	3	1	D19
2-152 (even)	11	1	D19
135-231 & 154-216	10	1	D18
218-370 (even)	1	1	D18
233-459 (odd)	16	1	D18
350 only	118	1	D18
372-498 (even)	18	1	D18
461-609 (odd)	17	1	D17
500 only	110	1	D17
502-594 (even)	36	1	D17
521 only	175	1	D17
551 only	176	1	D17
596-638 (even)	20	1	D17
611-787	22	1	D17
630 only	111	1	D17
640-770 (even)	19	1	D17
666 only	103	1	D17
745 only	151	1	D17
767 only	153	2	D16
788-990	21	2	D16
991-1059	28	2	D15
1060-1150	128	2	D14
1151-1415 & 1152-1312	29	2	D13
1314-1416 (even)	26	2	D13
1417-2119 & 1418-2116	35	2	D12
2121-OUT & 2118-OUT	37	3	D11
Finn Sq	13	1	D21
First Av		1	E20
1-343 (odd)	3	1	E20
2-346 (even)	9	1	E20
345 & 347-444	10	1	E19
445-699	16	1	E18
700-876	17	1	E17
877-1095 & 878-1100	22	1	E17
1097-1531 & 1102-1538	21	2	E16
1533-1679 & 1540-1666	28	2	E15
1681-1885 & 1668-1854	128	2	E14
1857-2257 & 1856-2254	29	2	E13
2259-OUT & 2256-OUT	35	2	E12
First Pl	280	1	D22
Fletcher St	38	1	D22
Foley Sq	7	1	D21
Forsyth St	2	1	E21
Fort Charles Pl	463	4	C 6
Fort George Av	40	4	B 8
Fort George Hill	40	4	B 8
Fort Washington Av		3	B 8
1-300	32	3	B10
301-599	33	4	B 8
600-OUT	40	4	B 8
Fourth Av	3	1	D20
Frank D'Amico Plz *(bet Hester St & Canal St at Forsyth St)	2	1	E21
Frankfort St	38	1	D21
Franklin D Roosevelt Dr		1	E19
1-611	2	1	F20
612-765	9	1	F20
800-1999	9	1	F20
2000-2599	10	1	E19
2600-3999	16	1	E18
4000-4899	17	1	E17
4900-5999	22	1	E17
6000-7999	21	2	E16
8000-8699	28	2	E15
8700-9599	128	2	E14
9600 - 115-99	29	2	E13
116-00 - 130-99	35	2	E12
Franklin Pl	13	1	D21
Franklin Sq *	38	1	E21
Franklin St	13	1	D21
Frawley Cir	29	2	D13
Frederick Douglass Blvd		2	C13
2031-2223 & 2032-2226	26	2	C13
2225-2481 & 2228-2488	27	2	C12
2483-2727 & 2490-2728	30	3	C11
2729-OUT	39	3	C10
Frederick Douglass Cir	26	2	C13
Freedom Pl	23	2	B16
Freeman Al	2	1	E20
Front St		1	E22
1-73 & 2-76	4	1	D22
75-151 & 78-154	5	1	D22
153-OUT & 156-OUT	38	1	E22
Fulton St		1	D21
1-167 & 2-158	38	1	D22
169-OUT & 160-OUT	7	1	D21

G

STREET NAME AND HOUSE NUMBERS	ZONE NO.	MAP NO.	MAP GRID
Gansevoort St	14	1	C19
Gateway Plz	280	1	C22
Gay St	14	1	C20
Gold St	38	1	D22
Gouverneur La	5	1	D22
Gouverneur Slip E	2	1	F21
Gouverneur Slip W	2	1	F21
Gouverneur St	2	1	F21
Gracie Sq	28	2	E15
Gracie Ter	28	2	E15
Gramercy Park		1	D19
1-37	3	1	D19
38-OUT	10	1	D19
Gramercy Park E	3	1	D19
Gramercy Park W	3	1	D19
Grand Army Plz	20	2	D16
Grand St		1	E20
1-235	13	1	D20
236-OUT	2	1	E20
Great Jones Al	12	1	D20
Great Jones St	12	1	D20
Greeley Sq	1	1	C18
Greene St		1	D21
1-55	13	1	D21
56-228	12	1	D20
229-OUT	3	1	D20
Greenwich Av		1	C19
All odd numbers	14	1	C19
All even numbers	11	1	C19
Greenwich St		1	C21
1-40	4	1	D22
41-169 & 42-164	6	1	D22
171-301 & 166-292	7	1	D21
303-549 & 294-552	13	1	C21
551-OUT & 554-OUT	14	1	C20
Grove Pl	14	1	C20
Grove St	14	1	C20
Gustave Hartman Sq	2	1	E20
Gustave Levy Pl *(bet 5th Av & Madison Av from 98th St to 102nd St)	29	2	D14

H

STREET NAME AND HOUSE NUMBERS	ZONE NO.	MAP NO.	MAP GRID
Hamill Pl *(at Foley Sq bet Centre St and Worth St)	7	1	D21
Hamilton Pl	31	3	B11
Hamilton Ter	31	3	C11
Hancock Pl	27	2	C12
Hancock Sq	27	2	C12
Hanover Plz *(bounded by Beaver, Hanover & Pearl Sts)	5	1	D22
Hanover Sq		1	D22
1-7 (odd) & 2	4	1	D22
9-OUT & 4-OUT (even)	5	1	D22
Hanover St		1	D22
1-OUT (odd) & 2-6 (even)	5	1	D22
8-OUT (even)	4	1	D22
Harkness Plz *(W 62nd St, bet Columbus Av & Broadway)	23	2	C16
Harlem River Dr	39	3	C10
Harlem River Driveway		3	C 9
151-00-160-99	39	3	C10
161-00-172-99	32	3	C 9
173-00-186-99	33	4	C 8
187-00-192-99	40	4	C 8
193-00-OUT	34	4	C 8
Harrison St	13	1	C21
Harry Blumenstein Plz *(Broome & Pitt Sts)	2	1	E20
Harry Delancey Plz	2	1	E20
Harry Howard Sq	13	1	D21
Haven Av		3	B 9
1-162	32	3	B 9
163-OUT	33	3	B 9
Haven Plz *(bet Szold Pl & Av C, at E 12th St)	9	1	E19
Henderson Pl	28	2	E15
Henry Hudson Pkwy	34	4	B 7
Henry Hudson Pkwy		2	B15
Henry J Browne Blvd	24	2	C14
Henry Phipps Plz *(E 26th to 29th Sts, bet First & Second Aves)	16	1	E18
Henry St		1	E21
1-11	38	1	E21
12-OUT	2	1	E21
Henshaw St	34	4	B 7
Herald Sq	1	1	D18
Hester St		1	D21
45-149 & 42-134	2	1	E21
151-OUT & 136-OUT	13	1	D21
Hillside Av	40	4	B 8
Hogan Pl	13	1	D21
Holland Tunnel Plz *(Varick St, bet Laight & Vestry Sts)	13	1	D21
Holy Rosary Sq *(Pleasant Av & E 119th St)	35	2	E13
Horatio St	14	1	C19
Houston St (see East or West Houston Sts)			
Howard Sq	13	1	D21
Howard St	13	1	D21
Hubert St	13	1	C21
Hudson River Piers (see N River Piers)			
Hudson St		1	D20
1-339 & 2-344	13	1	D21
341-OUT & 346-OUT	14	1	C20

I

STREET NAME AND HOUSE NUMBERS	ZONE NO.	MAP NO.	MAP GRID
Independence Plz	13	1	C21
Independence Plz N	13	1	C21
Independence Plz S	7	1	C21
Indian Rd	34	4	B 6
Insurance Plz *(101 Murray St)	7	1	C21
Inwood Plz	34	4	B 7
Irving Pl	3	1	D19
Isham St	34	4	B 7

J

STREET NAME AND HOUSE NUMBERS	ZONE NO.	MAP NO.	MAP GRID
Jackson Sq	14	1	C19
Jackson St	2	1	F20
Jacobus Pl	463	4	B 6
James St	38	1	E21
Jane St	14	1	C19
Jay St	13	1	C21
Jefferson St	2	1	E21
Jersey St	12	1	D20
Joe Louis Plz *(W 31st to 33rd Sts, bet Seventh & Eighth Aves)	1	1	C18
John Delury Sr. Plz *(triangular area at intersection of Fulton St and Gold St)	38	1	D22
John P Ladson Pl *(Lenox Av, Central Park N to W 111th St)	26	2	D13
John St	38	1	D22
Jones Al	12	1	D20
Jones St	14	1	C20
J P Ward St	6	1	D22
Jumel Pl	32	3	C 9
Jumel Ter	32	3	C10

K

STREET NAME AND HOUSE NUMBERS	ZONE NO.	MAP NO.	MAP GRID
Kenmare St	12	1	D20
Kent Pl *(connects Pearl St with Cardinal Hayes Pl)	7	1	D21
Kimlau Sq	38	1	E21
King St		1	C20
1-5	12	1	D20
6-OUT	14	1	C20

L

STREET NAME AND HOUSE NUMBERS	ZONE NO.	MAP NO.	MAP GRID
La Guardia Pl	12	1	D20
La Salle St	27	2	B12
Lafayette Plz	33	4	B 8
Lafayette St		1	D21
1-39 & 2-34	7	1	D21
41-193 & 36-192	13	1	D21
194-372	12	1	D20

STREET NAME AND HOUSE NUMBERS	ZONE NO.	MAP NO.	MAP GRID
373-OUT	3	1	D20
Laight St	13	1	C21
Langston Hughes Pl	35	2	D12
Laurel Hill Ter		4	C 8
1-120	33	4	C 8
121-OUT	40	4	C 8
Legion Mem Sq	5	1	D22
Lenox Av (Malcolm X Blvd)		2	D13
1-199	26	2	D13
201-399 & 200-402	27	2	D12
401-699 & 404-698	37	3	D11
700-OUT	39	3	D11
Lenox Ter	37	3	D11
Leonard St	13	1	D21
Leroy St	14	1	C20
Lewis St	2	1	F20
Lexington Av		1	D18
1-79	10	1	D18
80-353	16	1	D18
354-538	17	1	D17
380 only	168	1	D17
405 only	174	1	D17
420 only	170	1	D17
480 only	167	1	D17
500 only	172	1	D17
539-765 & 540-762	22	1	D17
767-1171 & 764-1162	21	2	D16
1173-1291 & 1164-1288	28	2	D15
1293-1489 & 1290-1486	128	2	D14
1491-1869 & 1488-1870	29	2	D13
1871-2169	35	2	D12
2170-OUT	37	2	D12
Liberty Pl	38	1	D22
Liberty Plz *(77-79 Liberty St)	6	1	D22
Liberty St		1	D22
1-76	5	1	D22
33 only	45	1	D22
77- 199	6	1	D22
200-OUT	281	1	C22
Lieut William Tighe Triangle *(Dyckman St & Broadway)	34	4	B 7
Lillian Wald Dr *(Lillian Wald Houses)	9	1	F20
Lincoln Pl *(E 113th St west of 3rd Av)	35	2	D13
Lincoln Sq	23	2	C16
Lispenard St	13	1	D21
Little West 12th St	14	1	B19
Livingston Pl *(see Nathan D Perlman Plz)	3	1	E19
Louise Nevelson Plz *(William St, bet Maiden La & Liberty St)	5	1	D22
Ludlow St	2	1	E21
Luis Muñoz Marin Blvd	29	2	D13

M

STREET NAME AND HOUSE NUMBERS	ZONE NO.	MAP NO.	MAP GRID
MacDougal Al	11	1	D20
MacDougal St		1	D20
1-7 (odd)	13	1	D20
2-154 (even) & 9-141 (odd)	12	1	D20
143-OUT (odd) & 156-OUT (even)	11	1	D20
Machito Sq *(Third Av & E 111th St)	29	2	E13
Macombs Pl	39	3	C10
Madison Av		1	D18
1-61	10	1	D18
63-277 (odd) & 62-280 (even)	16	1	D18
279-429 (odd) & 282-430 (even)	17	1	D17
305 only	165	1	D17
342 only	173	1	D17
431-651	22	1	D17
616-628 (even)	153	2	D16
653-1047 (odd) & 652-1056 (even)	21	2	D16
1049-1209 & 1058-1188	28	2	D15
1211-1379 & 1190-1378	128	2	D14
1380-1767	29	2	D13
1768-2056	35	2	D12
2057-OUT	37	2	D12
Madison Sq Plz	10	1	D18
Madison St		1	E21
1-67 & 2-72	38	1	E21
69-OUT & 74-OUT	2	1	E21
Magaw Pl	33	4	B 8
Maher Cir	32	3	C10
Maiden La		1	D22
102-134 (even)	5	1	D22
all other numbers	38	1	D22
Main St (Roosevelt Island)	44	2	F16
Mangin St	7	1	F20
Manhattan Al *(connects Reade St with *Republican Al)	7	1	D21
Manhattan Av		2	C14
1-239	25	2	C14
241-479 & 240-488	26	2	C13
481-OUT & 490-OUT	27	2	C12
Manhattan Pl	7	1	D21
Manhattan Plz *(W 42nd & 43rd Sts, bet Ninth & Tenth Aves)	36	1	B17
Marble Hill Av	463	4	C 6
Marble Hill La	463	4	C 6
Margaret Corbin Dr	40	4	B 7
Margaret Corbin Plz	40	4	B 8
Marginal St	2	1	F21
Market Slip	2	1	E21
Market St	2	1	E21
Marketfield St	4	1	D22
Martin Luther King Jr Blvd E	35	2	D12
Martin Luther King Jr Blvd W	27	2	B12
Martin R. Celic Plz *(SW corner of Pitt St and Delancey St)	2	1	E20
Martin Sq	34	4	B 7
McKenna Sq	32	3	B 9
McNally Plz	33	4	C 8
Mercer St		1	D21
1-63	13	1	D21
64-260	12	1	D20
261-OUT	3	1	D20
Mill La	4	1	D22
Mill Rock Plz *(1797-1811 First Av)	128	2	E14
Milligan Pl	11	1	C19
Minetta La	12	1	D20
Minetta Pl	12	1	D20
Minetta St	12	1	D20
Mitchell Pl	17	1	E17
Mitchell Sq	32	3	B 9
Monroe St	2	1	E21
Mgr Francis J Kett Plz *(Tenth Av, bet W 204th & W 205th Sts)	34	4	B 7
Montefiore Sq	31	3	B11
Montgomery St	2	1	F21
Moore St	4	1	D22
Morningside Av		2	C13
1-58	26	2	C13
59-OUT	27	2	C12
Morningside Dr		2	C13
1-59	25	2	C13
60-OUT	27	2	C13
Morris St		1	D22
1-9 (odd)	4	1	D22
all other numbers	6	1	D22
Morton St	14	1	C20
Mosco St	13	1	E21
Motorgate Plz (Roosevelt Island)	44	2	F16
Mott St		1	E21
1-173 & 2-168	13	1	E21
175-OUT & 170-OUT	12	1	D20
Mount Carmel Sq *(Pleasant Av & E 116th St)	29	2	E13
Mount Morris Park W	27	2	D12
Mulberry St		1	D21
1-177	13	1	D21
178-OUT	12	1	D20
Mulry Sq	14	1	C19
Murray St		1	C21
1-199	7	1	D21
200-399	281	1	C21
Museum Mile (Fifth Av)		2	D15
991-1059	28	2	D15
1060-1150	128	2	D14
1151-1415	29	2	D14

N

STREET NAME AND HOUSE NUMBERS	ZONE NO.	MAP NO.	MAP GRID
Nagle Av		4	B 8
1-169	40	4	B 8
170-OUT	34	4	B 7
Nassau St		1	D22
1-47 & 2-40	5	1	D22
13-25 (odd)	271	1	D22
49-OUT & 42-OUT	38	1	D22
Nathan Cummings Plz *(E 100th St bet Park & Madison Aves)	29	2	D14
Nathan D Perlman Pl	3	1	E19
Nelson & Winnie Mandela Cor *(E 42nd St & Second Av, SE Corner)	17	1	E18
Nevada Plz *(W 69th & 70th Sts, bet Broadway & Amsterdam Av)	23	2	B16
New St		1	D22
1-11 & 2-28	5	1	D22
13-OUT & 30-OUT	4	1	D22
New York Plz	4	1	D22
Ninth Av		1	C19
1-43	14	1	C19
44-227	11	1	C19
228-449	1	1	C18
450-559	18	1	C18
560-700	36	1	C17
701-925	19	1	C17
3700-4199	34	4	C 7
Norfolk St	2	1	E20
North End Av	281	1	C21
North Moore St	13	1	C21
North River Piers		1	C21
A	4	1	D22
21-34	13	1	C21
40-57	14	1	C20
58-64	11	1	B19
65-75	1	1	B18
76-80	18	1	B18
81-88	36	1	B17
90-99	19	1	B17

O

STREET NAME AND HOUSE NUMBERS	ZONE NO.	MAP NO.	MAP GRID
Odell M Clark Pl *(W 138th St, bet Lenox Av & Adam Clayton Powell Jr Blvd)	30	3	C11
Old Broadway	27	2	B12
Old Slip	5	1	D22
Oliver St	38	1	E21
Orchard St	2	1	E21
Overlook Ter		4	B 8
1-65	33	4	B 8
66-OUT	40	4	B 8

P

STREET NAME AND HOUSE NUMBERS	ZONE NO.	MAP NO.	MAP GRID
Pace Plz	38	1	D21
Paladino Av	35	2	E12
Paramount Plz *(1633 Broadway)	19	1	C17
Park Av		2	D15
1-99	16	1	D18
100-298	17	1	D17
101 only	178	1	D17
200 only	166	1	D17
228 & 230 only	169	1	D17
245 only	167	1	D17
250 only	177	1	D17
255 only	169	1	D17
277 only	172	1	D17
299 only	171	1	D17
300-519	22	1	D17
345 only	154	1	D17
375 only	152	1	D17
521-923 & 520-914	21	2	D16
925-1059 & 916-1058	28	2	D15
1061-1245 & 1060-1240	128	2	D14
1247-1637 & 1242-1636	29	2	D13
1639-1919 & 1638-1914	35	2	D12
1921-2299 & 1916-2298	37	2	D12
Park Av Plz *(55 E 52nd St)	22	1	D17
Park Av S		1	D19
200-250	3	1	D19
251-363 & 252-384	10	1	D19
386-OUT & 365-OUT	16	1	D18
Park Pl	7	1	D21
Park Pl W	281	1	C21
Park Row		1	D21
44-166 (even)	7	1	D21
All other numbers	38	1	D21
Park St	13	1	D21
Park Ter E	34	4	B 7
Park Ter W	34	4	B 7
Patchin Pl	11	1	C19
Payson Av	34	4	B 7
Pearl St		1	D22
1-117 & 2-100	4	1	D22
119-197 & 102-194	5	1	D22
199-463 & 196-462	38	1	D22
464-OUT	7	1	D21
Peck Slip	38	1	E21
Pedestrian St	2	1	F20
Pell St	13	1	E21
Pennsylvania Plz	1	1	C18
1 only	119	1	C18
2 only	121	1	C18
Peretz Sq	9	1	E20
Perry St	14	1	C20
Pershing Sq	17	1	D18
Peter Cooper Rd	10	1	E19
Peter Minuit Plz	4	1	D22
Pike Slip	2	1	E21
Pike St	2	1	E21
Pine St		1	D22
1-19 (odd) & 16-98 (even)	5	1	D22
2-14	271	1	D22
70 only	270	1	D22
Pinehurst Av N	33	3	B 9
Pinehurst Av S	33	3	B 9
Pitt St	2	1	E20
Platt St	38	1	D22
Plaza Lafayette	33	3	B 9
Pleasant Av		2	E13
263-299 & 264-296	29	2	E13
300-OUT	35	2	E13
Police Plz	38	1	E21
Pomander Wk	25	2	B14
Post Av	34	4	B 7
Prince St	12	1	D20
Printing House Sq *(Park Row & Nassau St)	38	1	D21

Q

STREET NAME AND HOUSE NUMBERS	ZONE NO.	MAP NO.	MAP GRID
Queensboro Bridge Plz *(E 58th & 59th Sts and Second Av)	22	2	E16

R

STREET NAME AND HOUSE NUMBERS	ZONE NO.	MAP NO.	MAP GRID
Raoul Wallenberg Wk *(west side of United Nations Plz, E 42nd to 47th Sts)	17	1	E17
Reade St		1	D21
1-83	7	1	D21
84-OUT	13	1	D21
Rector Pl	280	1	C22
Rector St	6	1	D22
Reinhold Niebuhr Pl	27	2	B12
Renwick St	13	1	C20
Republican Al *(connects Elk St with *Manhattan Al)	7	1	D21
Ridge St	2	1	E20
River Rd (Roosevelt Island)	44	2	F16
River Ter	281	1	C21
Riverside Dr		2	B16
1-40	23	2	B16
41-190	24	2	B15
191-439	25	2	B14
440-569	27	2	B12
475 only	115	2	B12
570-762	31	3	B11
763-1150	32	3	B10
1151-1599	33	4	B 8
1600-1780	40	4	B 8
1781-OUT	34	4	B 7
Riverside Dr E	27	2	B12
Riverside Dr W	27	2	B12
Riverview Ter	22	2	E16
Rivington St	2	1	E20
Robert F Wagner Sr Pl	38	1	E21
Rockefeller Plz	20	1	D17
30 only	112	1	D17
45 only	111	1	D17
75 only	19	1	D17
Ronald E McNair Pl	35	2	E12
Roosevelt Sq	27	2	C12
Rose St *(connects Frankfort St with Av of the Finest)	38	1	D21
Ruppert Plz *(1751-1763 Second Av)	128	2	E14
Rutgers Slip	2	1	E21
Rutgers St	2	1	E21
Rutherford Pl	3	1	E19
Ryders Al	38	1	D21

S

STREET NAME AND HOUSE NUMBERS	ZONE NO.	MAP NO.	MAP GRID
St. Andrew's Plz	7	1	D21
St. Clair Pl	27	2	B12
St. James Pl	38	1	E21
St. Johns La	13	1	D21
St. Lukes Pl	14	1	C20
St. Marks Pl		1	E19
1-85 (exc 83)	3	1	E19
84-OUT (exc 85)	9	1	E19
St. Nicholas Av		2	C13
1-201 & 2-198	26	2	C13
203-455 & 200-456	27	2	C12
457-699 & 458-690	30	3	C11
701-861 & 692-860	31	3	C10
862-1259	32	3	B 9
1260-1539	33	4	B 8
1540-OUT	40	4	B 8
St. Nicholas Pl		3	C10
1-60	31	3	C10
61-OUT	32	3	C10
St. Nicholas Ter		2	C12
1-55	27	2	C12
56-OUT	31	3	C11
St. Paul's Pl *(E 117th St, bet Park & Lexington Aves)	35	2	D13
Sakharov Bonner Cor *(Third Av & 67th St, SW corner)	21	2	D16
Samuel A Spiegel Sq	2	1	F20
Samuel Dickstein Plz	2	1	E20
Samuel Marx Triangle *(Adam Clayton Powell Jr Blvd, St. Nicolas Av & W 115th St)	26	2	C13
Schomberg Plz *(E 110th to 111th Sts, bet Fifth & Madison Ave)	29	2	D13
Scott Sq	34	4	C 7
Seaman Av	34	4	B 7
Seaport Plz *(199 Water St)	38	1	D22
Second Av		1	E20
1-343	3	1	E20
344-459	10	1	E19
460-746	16	1	E18
747-922	17	1	E17
923-1141 & 924-1138	22	1	E17
1143-1541 & 1140-1536	21	2	E16
1543-1679 & 1538-1680	28	2	E15
1681-1863 & 1682-1854	128	2	E14
1865-2259 & 1856-2258	29	2	E13
2260-OUT	35	2	E12
Second Pl	280	1	D22
Seminary Rd *(W 122nd St, bet Claremont Av & Amsterdam Av)	27	2	B12
Seventh Av		1	C19
1-243 & 2-240	11	1	C19
245-461 & 242-460	1	1	C18
450 only	123	1	C18
462-576	18	1	C18
577-720	36	1	C17
721-941	19	1	C17
888 only	106	1	C17
Seventh Av S	14	1	C20
Sheridan Sq	14	1	C20
Sheriff St	2	1	F20
Sherman Av		4	B 7
1-84	40	4	B 7
85-299	34	4	B 7
Sherman Plz *(2039-2049 Broadway)	23	2	B16
Sherman Sq	23	2	B16
Shinbone Al	12	1	D20
Sickles St	40	4	B 7
Sixth Av (see Avenue of the Americas)		1	D19
Sniffen Ct	16	1	D18
South End Av	280	1	D22
South Ferry	4	1	D22
South Ferry Plz	4	1	D22
South Pinehurst Av	33	3	B 9
South St		1	D22
1-39	4	1	D22
40-75	5	1	E22
76-202	38	1	E21
203-OUT	2	1	E21
South Street Seaport	38	1	E22
South Street Viaduct	38	1	E21
South William St	4	1	D22
Spring St		1	C20
1-220	12	1	D20
221-OUT	13	1	C20
Spruce St	38	1	D21
Staff St	34	4	B 7
Stanton St	2	1	E20
Staple St	13	1	D21
State St	4	1	D22
State St Plz *(1-6 State St)	4	1	D22
Steve Flanders Sq *(West side of Broadway & Murray St)	7	1	D21
Stevens Plz *(1181 Av of the Americas)	36	1	C17
Stone St	4	1	D22
Straus Sq	2	1	E21
Stuyvesant Oval	9	1	E19
Stuyvesant Sq	3	1	E19
Stuyvesant St	3	1	D19
Suffolk St	2	1	E20
Sullivan St	12	1	D20
Sunken Plz *(Rockefeller Center)	20	1	D17
Sutton Pl	22	2	E17
Sutton Pl S	22	1	E17
Sutton Sq	22	1	E17
Sylvan Ct	35	2	D12
Sylvan Pl	35	2	D12
Sylvan Ter	32	3	C10
Szold Pl	9	1	F19

T

STREET NAME AND HOUSE NUMBERS	ZONE NO.	MAP NO.	MAP GRID
Taras Shevchenko Pl	3	1	E20
Temple St	6	1	D22
Tenth Av		1	B19
1-59	14	1	B19
61-235 & 60-240	11	1	B19
237-449 & 242-448	1	1	B18
450-555	18	1	B18
557-703 & 556-684	36	1	B17
705-905 & 686-906	19	1	B17
3700-4099	34	4	B 7
Terrace View Av	463	4	B 6
Teunissen Pl	463	4	B 6
Thames St	6	1	D22
Thayer St	40	4	B 7
Theatre Al	38	1	D21
Thelonius Sphere Monk Cir *(W 63rd St, off W End Av)	23	2	B16
Third Av		1	D18
1-243	3	1	D19
244-356	10	1	D18
357-618	16	1	D18
605 only	158	1	E18
619-796	17	1	D17
797-1009	22	1	D17
964 only	155	1	D17
1010-1409	21	2	D16
1410-1549	28	2	D15
1550-1709	128	2	D14
1711-2123 & 1710-2120	29	2	D13
2125-2399 & 2122-2398	35	2	D12
Third Pl	280	1	D22
Thomas St		1	D21
1-42	7	1	D21
43-OUT	13	1	D21
Thompson St		1	D20
1-49	13	1	D20
50-OUT	12	1	D20
Tiemann Pl	27	2	B12
Times Sq	36	1	C17
Times Sq Plz *(1475 Broadway)	36	1	C17
Trans-Manhattan Expwy	33	3	B 9
Trimble Pl	7	1	D21
Trinity Pl	6	1	D22
Tudor City Pl	17	1	E18
Tunnel Entrance St	16	1	E18
Tunnel Exit St	16	1	E18
Twelfth Av		1	B17
1-99	14	1	B19
100-164	11	1	B19
165-360	1	1	B18
361-499	18	1	B18
500-639	36	1	B17
640-874	19	1	B17
2240-2351	27	2	B12
2352-OUT	31	3	B11

U

STREET NAME AND HOUSE NUMBERS	ZONE NO.	MAP NO.	MAP GRID
Union Sq	3	1	D19
Union Sq E	3	1	D19
Union Sq W	3	1	D19
United Nations Headquarters	17	1	E17
United Nations Plz	17	1	E17
University Pl	3	1	D19
University Plz *(110-118 Bleecker St)	12	1	D20

V

STREET NAME AND HOUSE NUMBERS	ZONE NO.	MAP NO.	MAP GRID
Van Corlear Pl	463	4	B 6
Vandam St	13	1	C20
Vanderbilt Av	17	1	D17
Vanderbilt Concourse *(Grand Central Station)	17	1	D17
Varick St		1	D21
1-169 & 2-172	13	1	D21
171-OUT & 174-OUT	14	1	C20
Verdi Sq	23	2	B16
Vermilyea Av	34	4	B 7
Vesey St		1	D21
1-198	7	1	D21
200-399	281	1	C21
Vestry St	13	1	C21
Vietnam Veterans Plz	4	1	D22
Village Sq	11	1	D19
Vincent F Albano Sq *(Tudor City Pl & E 41st St)	17	1	E18

W

STREET NAME AND HOUSE NUMBERS	ZONE NO.	MAP NO.	MAP GRID
Wadsworth Av		3	B 9
1-279	33	3	B 9
280-OUT	40	4	B 8
Wadsworth Ter	40	4	B 8
Walker St	13	1	D21
Wall St	5	1	D22
Wall St Plz *(88 Pine St)	5	1	D22
Wanamaker Pl	3	1	D19
Warren St		1	C21
1-99	7	1	C21
200-399	281	1	C21
Washington Mews	3	1	D20
Washington Pl		1	D20
1-60	3	1	D20
61-90	11	1	D20
91-OUT	14	1	C20
Washington Sq E	3	1	D20
Washington Sq N		1	D20
1-13	3	1	D20
14-27	11	1	D20
Washington Sq S	12	1	D20
Washington Sq W	11	1	D20
Washington St		1	C20
1-39 & 2-32	4	1	D22
41-169 & 34-170	6	1	D22
171-286	7	1	D21
287-531	13	1	C21
532-OUT	14	1	C20
Washington Ter	33	4	B 8
Water St		1	D22
1-69 & 2-56	4	1	D22
55 only	41	1	D22
71-153 & 58-152	5	1	D22
154-299	38	1	E22
300-OUT	2	1	E21
Waterside Plz	10	1	E18
Watts St	13	1	C21
Waverly Pl		1	D20
1-99	3	1	D20
101-133 & 100-130	11	1	D20
135-OUT & 132-OUT	14	1	C20
W.C. Handy's Pl	19	1	C17
Weehawken St	14	1	C20
Wesley Williams Pl *(W 135th St, bet Lenox Av & Adam Clayton Powell Jr Blvd)	30	3	C11
West Broadway		1	D20
1-95	7	1	D21
97-373 & 96-368	13	1	D21
375-OUT & 370-OUT	12	1	D20
West End Av		2	B16
1-341	23	2	B16
343-637 & 342-640	24	2	B15
639-OUT & 642-OUT	25	2	B14
West Houston St		1	C20
1-177 & 2-170	12	1	D20
179-OUT & 172-OUT	14	1	C20
West Rd (Roosevelt Island)	44	1	E17
West St		1	D22
1-20	4	1	D22
21-114	6	1	D22
115-185	7	1	C21
186-324	13	1	C21
325-OUT	14	1	C20
West Thames St	280	1	C22
West 3rd St	12	1	D20
West 4th St		1	D20
1-151 & 2-154	12	1	D20
153-OUT & 156-OUT	14	1	C19
West 8th St	11	1	D19
West 9th St	11	1	D19
West 10th St		1	C20
1-127	11	1	D19
128-OUT	14	1	C20
West 11th St		1	C20
1-199	11	1	D19
200-OUT	14	1	C20
West 12th St		1	C20
1-229	11	1	D19
230-OUT	14	1	C19
West 13th St		1	C19
1-299	11	1	D19
300-OUT	14	1	C19
West 14th St		1	C19
1-299	11	1	D19
300-OUT	14	1	C19
West 15th St	11	1	B19
West 16th St	11	1	B19
West 17th St	11	1	B19
West 18th St	11	1	B19
West 19th St	11	1	B19
West 20th St	11	1	B19
West 21st St		1	B19
1-99	10	1	D19
100-OUT	11	1	B19
West 22nd St		1	B19
1-99	10	1	D19
100-OUT	11	1	B19
West 23rd St		1	B19
1-99	10	1	D19
100-OUT	11	1	B19
West 24th St		1	B19
1-99	10	1	D19
100-OUT	11	1	B19
West 25th St		1	B18
1-99	10	1	D18
100-OUT	1	1	B18
West 26th St		1	B18
1-99	10	1	D18
100-OUT	1	1	B18
West 27th St	1	1	B18
West 28th St	1	1	B18
West 29th St	1	1	B18
West 30th St	1	1	B18
West 31st St	1	1	C18
West 32nd St	1	1	B18
West 33rd St	1	1	B18
West 34th St	1	1	B18
250 only	119	1	C18
West 35th St	1	1	B18
238 only	122	1	C18
West 36th St	18	1	B18
West 37th St	18	1	B18
West 38th St	18	1	C18
West 39th St	18	1	C18
West 40th St	18	1	B18
West 41st St	36	1	B18
West 42nd St	36	1	B17
West 43rd St	36	1	B17
West 44th St	36	1	B17
West 45th St	36	1	B17
West 46th St	36	1	B17
West 47th St	36	1	B17
West 48th St		1	B17
1-145 (odd)	20	1	D17
All other numbers	36	1	B17
West 49th St		1	B17
1-139	20	1	D17
140-OUT	19	1	B17
West 50th St		1	B17
1-157 & 2-134	20	1	D17
159-OUT & 136-OUT	19	1	B17
West 51st St		1	B17
2-146 (even)	20	1	D17
All other numbers	19	1	B17
West 52nd St	19	1	B17
West 53rd St	19	1	B17
West 54th St	19	1	B17
West 55th St	19	1	B17
West 56th St	19	1	B17
West 57th St	19	1	B17
250 only	107	1	C17
West 58th St	19	1	B17
West 59th St	19	2	B16
West 60th St	23	2	B16
West 61st St	23	2	B16
West 62nd St	23	2	B16
West 63rd St	23	2	B16
West 64th St	23	2	B16
West 65th St	23	2	B16
West 66th St	23	2	B16
West 67th St	23	2	B16
West 68th St	23	2	B16
West 69th St	23	2	B16
West 70th St	23	2	B16
West 71st St	23	2	B16
West 72nd St	23	2	B16
West 73rd St	23	2	B16
West 74th St	23	2	B15
West 75th St	23	2	B15
West 76th St	23	2	B15
West 77th St	24	2	B15
West 78th St	24	2	B15
West 79th St	24	2	B15
West 80th St	24	2	B15
West 81st St	24	2	B15
West 82nd St	24	2	B15
West 83rd St	24	2	B15
West 84th St	24	2	B15
West 85th St	24	2	B15
West 86th St	24	2	B15
West 87th St	24	2	B15
West 88th St	24	2	B15
West 89th St	24	2	B15
West 90th St	24	2	B14
West 91st St	24	2	B14
West 92nd St	25	2	B14
West 93rd St	25	2	B14
West 94th St	25	2	B14
West 95th St	25	2	B14
West 96th St	25	2	B14
West 97th St	25	2	B14
West 98th St	25	2	B14
West 99th St	25	2	B14
West 100th St	25	2	B14
West 101st St	25	2	B14
West 102nd St	25	2	B14
West 103rd St	25	2	B14
West 104th St	25	2	B14
West 105th St	25	2	B13
West 106th St	25	2	B13
West 107th St	25	2	B13
West 108th St	25	2	B13
West 109th St	25	2	B13
West 110th St (see Cathedral Pkwy)			
West 111th St		2	B13
1-399	26	2	D13
500-OUT	25	2	B13
West 112th St		2	B13
1-399	26	2	D13
500-OUT	25	2	B13
West 113th St		2	B13
1-399	26	2	C13
400-OUT	25	2	B13
West 114th St		2	B13
1-399	26	2	C13
400-OUT	25	2	B13
501-599 (odd)	27	2	B13
West 115th St		2	B13
1-399	26	2	D13
400-499 & 600-699	25	2	B13
500-599	27	2	B13
West 116th St		2	B13
1-399	26	2	D13
400- 499 & 600-699	27	2	B13
West 117th St	26	2	D13
West 118th St		2	D13
1-399	26	2	D13
400-OUT	27	2	C13
West 119th St		2	D13
1-399	26	2	D13
400-OUT	27	2	B13
West 120th St	27	2	B12
West 121st St	27	2	B12
West 122nd St	27	2	B12
West 123rd St	27	2	B12
West 124th St	27	2	D12
West 125th St	27	2	C12
West 126th St	27	2	B12
West 127th St	27	2	C12
West 128th St	27	2	C12
West 129th St	27	2	B12
West 130th St		2	B12
1-99	37	2	D12
100-OUT	27	2	C12
West 131st St		2	B12
1-99	37	2	D12
100-OUT	27	2	B12
West 132nd St		2	B12
1-99	37	2	D12
100-OUT	27	2	B12
West 133rd St		2	B12
100-349	30	2	C12
350-OUT	27	2	B12
West 134th St		2	B12
1-99	37	2	D12
100-399	30	2	C12
400-699	31	2	B12
West 135th St		3	B11
1-99	37	3	D11
100-399	30	3	C11
400-699	31	3	B11
West 136th St		3	B11
100-399	30	3	C11
400-699	31	3	B11
West 137th St		3	B11
1-99	37	3	D11
100-399	30	3	C11
600-OUT	31	3	B11
West 138th St		3	B11
1-97	37	3	D11
98-399	30	3	C11
400-OUT	31	3	B11
West 139th St		3	B11
1-99	37	3	D11
100-399	30	3	C11
500-OUT	31	3	B11
West 140th St		3	B11
100-399	30	3	C11
400-OUT	31	3	B11
West 141st St		3	B11
1-99	37	3	D11
100-399	30	3	C11
400-OUT	31	3	B11
West 142nd St		3	B11
1-99	37	3	D11
100-399	30	3	C11
400-OUT	31	3	B11
West 143rd St		3	B11
1-99	37	3	D11
100-399	30	3	C11
400-OUT	31	3	B11
West 144th St		3	B11
100-399	30	3	C11
400-OUT	31	3	B11
West 145th St		3	B11
101-355 & 100-358	39	3	C11
341-OUT (odd) & 360-OUT (even)	31	3	B11
West 146th St		3	B11
1-349	39	3	C11
350-OUT	31	3	B11
West 147th St		3	B11
1-349	39	3	C11
350-OUT	31	3	B11
West 148th St		3	B11
1-349	39	3	C11
350-OUT	31	3	B11
West 149th St		3	B10
1-349	39	3	C10
350-OUT	31	3	B10
West 150th St		3	B10
1-349	39	3	C10
350-OUT	31	3	B10
West 151st St		3	B10
1-349	39	3	C10
350-OUT	31	3	B10
West 152nd St		3	B10
1-349	39	3	C10
350-OUT	31	3	B10
West 153rd St		3	B10
1-349	39	3	C10
350-OUT	31	3	B10
West 154th St		3	C10
1-349	39	3	C10
350-OUT	32	3	C10
West 155th St		3	B10
1-349	39	3	C10
350-OUT	32	3	B10
West 156th St	32	3	B10
West 157th St	32	3	B10
West 158th St	32	3	B10
West 159th St	32	3	B10
West 160th St	32	3	B10
West 161st St	32	3	B10
West 162nd St	32	3	B10
West 163rd St	32	3	B10
West 164th St	32	3	B 9
West 165th St	32	3	B 9
West 166th St	32	3	B 9
West 167th St	32	3	B 9
West 168th St	32	3	B 9
West 169th St	32	3	B 9
West 170th St	32	3	B 9
West 171st St	32	3	B 9
West 172nd St	32	3	B 9
West 173rd St	32	3	B 9
West 174th St	33	3	B 9
West 175th St	33	3	B 9
West 176th St	33	3	B 9
West 177th St	33	3	B 9
West 178th St	33	3	B 9
West 179th St	33	3	B 9
West 180th St	33	4	B 8
West 181st St	33	4	B 8
West 182nd St	33	4	B 8
West 183rd St	33	4	B 8
West 184th St	33	4	B 8
West 185th St	33	4	B 8
West 186th St	33	4	B 8
West 187th St	33	4	B 8
West 188th St	40	4	B 8
West 189th St	40	4	B 8
West 190th St	40	4	B 8
West 191st St	40	4	B 8
West 192nd St	40	4	B 8
West 193rd St	40	4	B 8
West 196th St	40	4	B 8
West 201st St	34	4	C 7
West 202nd St	34	4	C 7
West 203rd St	34	4	C 7
West 204th St	34	4	B 7
West 205th St	34	4	C 7
West 206th St	34	4	C 7
West 207th St	34	4	B 7
West 208th St	34	4	C 7
West 211th St	34	4	B 7
West 212th St	34	4	B 7
West 213th St	34	4	B 7
West 214th St	34	4	B 6
West 215th St	34	4	B 6
West 216th St	34	4	C 6
West 217th St	34	4	B 6
West 218th St	34	4	C 6
West 219th St	34	4	C 6
West 220th St	34	4	C 6
West 225th St	463	4	C 6
West 227th St	463	4	B 6
West 228th St	463	4	C 6
White St	13	1	D21
Whitehall St	4	1	D22
Willett St	2	1	F20
William St		1	D22
1-9 & 2-6	4	1	D22
11-83 & 8-78	5	1	D22
85-OUT & 80-OUT	38	1	D22
Wooster St		1	D21
1-55 & 2-58	13	1	D21
57-OUT & 60-OUT	12	1	D20
World Financial Center	281	1	C22
World Trade Center	48	1	D22
N.Y.S. Agencies	47	1	D22
Worth St	13	1	D21

Y

STREET NAME AND HOUSE NUMBERS	ZONE NO.	MAP NO.	MAP GRID
York Av		2	E16
1101-1509 & 1100-1512	21	2	E16
1511-1655 & 1514-1656	28	2	E15
1657-OUT & 1658-OUT	128	2	E14
York St	13	1	D21

STREET INDEX AND POSTAL ZONES — THE BRONX

NOTE: To obtain ZIP code for The Bronx, add 104 before postal zone numbers.

A

STREET NAME AND HOUSE NUMBERS	ZONE NO.	MAP NO.	MAP GRID
Abbot St	70	5	E 2
Acorn Pl	65	7	M 7
Adams Pl		4	E 7
1-2289	57	4	E 7
2290-OUT	58	4	E 7
Adams St	60	4	G 7
Adee Av	65	7	M 6
Adee Av		5	F 5
1-899	67	5	F 5
900-OUT	69	5	F 5
Adler Pl	75	6	H 3
Admiral La	73	7	K 9
Agar Pl	65	6	K 5
Alan Pl	65	7	N 7
Albany Cres	63	4	C 6
Alcott Pl	75	6	H 3
Alden Pl	57	4	E 7
Alderbrook Rd	71	5	A 4
Aldrich St	75	6	H 4
Aldus St	59	3	F 9
Alexander Av	54	3	E11
Allen Pl	75	6	H 3
Allerton Av		5	F 5
1-899	67	5	F 5
900-OUT	69	6	G 5
Amethyst St	62	4	G 7
Ampere Av	65	6	K 5
Amundson Av	66	6	G 2
Anderson Av	52	3	D 9
Andrews Av	53	4	C 7
Andrews Av N		4	C 7
1-2249	53	4	C 7
2250-OUT	68	4	C 7
Andrews Av S	53	4	C 8
Anthony Av	57	4	D 8
Anthony J Griffin Pl	51	3	D11
Antin Pl	62	4	G 6
Aqueduct Av E		4	D 7
1-2275	53	4	D 7
2276-2353	68	4	D 7
Aqueduct Av W	68	4	D 6
Archer Rd	62	7	H 7
Archer St		7	H 7
1-1879	60	7	H 7
1880-OUT	62	7	H 7
Arlington Av		5	A 4
1-3899	63	5	B 5
3900-OUT	71	5	A 4
Armand Pl	63	5	C 5
Arnow Av		5	F 5
600-899	67	5	F 5
900-OUT	69	5	G 5
Arnow Pl	61	6	J 5
Arthur Av		4	E 7
1700-2299	57	4	E 7
2300-OUT	58	4	E 7
Arthur H Murphy Sq	57	4	E 7
Asch Loop	75	6	H 3
Aster Pl	65	7	M 7
Astor Av		6	G 5
700-899	67	6	G 5
900-OUT	69	6	G 5
Austin Pl	55	3	F11
Avenue Saint John	55	3	F10

B

STREET NAME AND HOUSE NUMBERS	ZONE NO.	MAP NO.	MAP GRID
B St *(off Baisley Av bet Crosby Av and Hobart Av)	61	7	K 6

STREET NAME AND HOUSE NUMBERS	ZONE NO.	MAP NO.	MAP GRID
Babe Ruth Plz	51	3	D10
Bagley St *(off Hutchinson River Pkwy)	65	7	K 8
Bailey Av	63	4	C 6
Bailey Pl	63	5	C 5
Bainbridge Av		5	D 4
1-3029	58	4	D 6
3030-OUT	67	5	E 5
Baisley Av		7	K 6
1-3099	61	7	K 6
3100-OUT	65	7	K 6
Baker Av	60	4	G 7
Balcom Av		7	J 6
1-1299	65	7	K 6
1300-OUT	61	7	J 6
Baldwin St	70	5	E 2
Balsam Pl	65	7	M 7
Bantam Pl	69	6	H 4
Banyer Pl	73	7	H 8
Barker Av	67	5	F 5
Barkley Av	65	7	K 7
Barn Hill Sq	68	4	D 6
Barnes Av		5	F 2
1-2199	62	4	G 6
2200-3899	67	5	F 5
3900-4599	66	5	F 3
4600-OUT	70	5	F 2
Barnett Pl *(off Barnes Av bet Rhinelander Av & Morris Park Av)	62	7	G 6
Barrett Av	73	7	J 8
Barretto St		3	G 9
1-899	74	3	G 9
900-OUT	59	3	G 9
Barry St	74	3	G10
Bartholdi St	67	5	F 4
Bartow Av		6	H 4
1-1999	69	6	H 4
2000-OUT	75	6	H 4
Bassett Av		6	H 5
1-1699	61	6	H 5
1700-2099	75	6	J 4
Bassford Av		4	E 7
1-2289	57	4	E 7
2290-OUT	58	4	E 7
Bathgate Av		4	E 8
1-2289	57	4	E 8
2290-OUT	58	4	E 7
Bay St	64	6	M 4
Baychester Av		6	H 4
1-3200	75	6	J 4
3201-3499	69	6	G 3
3500-OUT	66	6	G 3
Baychester Av	65	5	F 2
Bayshore Av	65	6	K 5
Bayview Av	65	6	K 5
Beach Av		7	H 8
1-199	73	7	J 9
1000-1399	72	7	H 8
1400-OUT	60	4	G 7
Beach St	64	6	M 4
Beaumont Av		4	E 7
1111-2299	57	4	E 7
2300-OUT	58	4	E 7
Beck St		3	F10
1-809	55	3	F10
810-OUT	59	3	F10
Bedford Park Blvd		5	D 5
1-199	68	5	D 5
200-OUT	58	5	D 5
Bedford Park Blvd W	68	5	D 5
Beech Pl	65	7	M 7
Beech Ter	54	3	F11
Beech Tree La	64	6	J 2
Beekman Av	54	3	F11
Belden St	64	6	M 4
Bell Av	66	6	G 2
Bellamy Loop	75	6	H 3
Belmont Av		4	E 7
1-2299	57	4	E 7
2300-OUT	58	4	E 7
Belmont St	57	4	E 8
Benchley Pl	75	6	H 3
Benedict Av	62	7	H 7
Benson St	61	7	J 6
Bergen Av	55	3	E11
Bernard S Deutsch Plz	53	4	C 8
Betts Av	73	7	K 9
Bevy Pl	65	7	N 7
Billingsley Ter	53	4	C 8
Birchall Av	62	4	G 6
Bivona St	75	6	G 3
Blackrock Av		7	J 7
1-2299	72	7	J 7
2300-OUT	62	7	J 7
Blackstone Av		5	B 5
1-3899	63	5	B 5
3900-OUT	71	5	B 5
Blackstone Pl	71	5	B 5
Blair Av	65	7	M 6
Blondell Av	61	7	J 6
Bogart Av	62	4	G 6
Boller Av		6	G 3
1-3499	75	6	J 4
3500-OUT	66	6	G 3
Bolton Av	73	7	J 8
Bolton St	62	4	G 6
Bonner Pl	56	3	D 9
Boone Av		4	G 8
1-1459	59	4	G 8
1460-OUT	60	4	F 8
Boscobel Pl	52	4	C 8
Boston Close	69	6	G 3
Boston Rd		5	F 5
1-1432	56	3	E 9
1433-2163	60	4	F 8
2164-2199	62	4	F 6
2201-2733 (odd)	67	5	F 5
2200-2748 (even)	67	5	F 5
2735-3599 (odd)	69	6	G 4
2750-3798 (even)	69	6	G 4
3601-4339 (odd)	66	6	G 3
3800-4340 (even)	75	6	G 3
Botanical Sq	58	4	E 6
Bouck Av	69	6	G 4
Bowne St	64	6	M 4
Boyd Av	66	5	F 2
Boynton Av		4	G 8
1-999	73	3	H 9
1000-OUT	72	4	G 8
Bradford Av	61	7	K 6
Bradley St	70	5	E 2
Bradley Ter	63	4	B 6
Brady Av	62	4	G 6
Brandt Pl	53	4	C 8
Bridge St	64	6	L 3
Briggs Av	58	4	D 6
Brinsmade Av	65	7	K 7
Bristow St	59	4	F 8
Britton St	67	5	F 5
Broadway		5	B 3
5171-5970	63	5	C 5
5971-OUT	71	5	B 3
Bronx and Pelham Pkwy	62	4	G 6
Bronx Blvd		5	E 2
1-3899	67	5	E 4
3900-4399	66	5	E 3
4400-OUT	70	5	E 2
Bronx Park Av	60	4	G 7
Bronx Park E		5	F 5
1-2199	62	4	G 6
2200-OUT	67	5	F 5
Bronx Park S	60	4	F 7
Bronx River Av		3	G 9
1-999	73	3	G 9
1000-1499	72	3	G 9
1500-OUT	60	4	G 7
Bronx River Pkwy	62	4	G 8
Bronx River Pkwy	62	5	E 3
Bronxdale Av	62	4	G 6
Bronxwood Av		5	F 3
1-3899	69	5	F 5
3900-OUT	66	5	F 3
Brook Av		4	E 8
1-439	54	3	E11
440-738	55	3	E10
739-1016	51	3	E 9
1017-1504	56	3	E 9
1505-OUT	57	4	E 8
Broun Pl	75	6	H 3
Brown Pl	54	3	E12
Bruckner Blvd		3	F10
1-419	54	3	F11
420-799	55	3	G10
800-1408 (even)	74	3	G 9
801-1409 (odd)	59	3	G 9
1410-2498 (even)	73	7	H 8
1411-2499 (odd)	72	7	H 8
2500-OUT (even)	65	7	K 7
2501-2899 (odd)	72	7	K 7
2901out (odd)	61	7	K 6
Bruckner Expwy		6	J 5
Bruner Av		5	F 2
1-3599	69	6	G 4
3600-OUT	66	5	F 2
Brush Av	65	7	K 7
Bryant Av		4	F 8
1-949	74	3	G 9
950-1453	59	3	G 9
1454-OUT	60	4	F 8
Buchanan Pl	53	4	D 7
Buck St	61	7	H 6
Buckley St	64	6	M 4
Buhre Av	61	6	J 5
Bullard Av		5	E 2
1-4399	66	5	E 2
4400-OUT	70	5	E 2
Burke Av		5	F 5
1-899	67	5	F 5
900-OUT	69	5	G 4
Burnett Pl	74	3	G10
Burnside Av E		4	D 7
1-199	53	4	D 7
200-OUT	57	4	D 7
Burnside Av W	53	4	C 7
Burr Av	61	6	J 5
Bush St		4	D 7
1-199	53	4	D 7
200-OUT	57	4	D 7
Bussing Av	66	5	F 3
Bussing Pl	66	5	F 2
Butler Pl		7	J 6
1-2399	62	7	J 7
2400-OUT	61	7	J 6
Buttrick Av	65	7	L 7
Byron Av	66	5	E 2

C

STREET NAME AND HOUSE NUMBERS	ZONE NO.	MAP NO.	MAP GRID
Caesar Pl	73	7	J 8
Calhoun Av	65	7	K 6
Cambreleng Av		4	E 7
1-2289	57	4	E 7
2290-OUT	58	4	E 7
Cambridge Av	63	5	B 5
Cameron Pl	53	4	D 7
Camp St	66	5	F 2
Campbell Dr	65	6	K 5
Canal Pl	51	3	D11
Canal St W	51	3	D11
Cannon Pl	63	5	C 5
Capuchin Way	67	5	F 4
Carlisle Pl	67	5	F 4
Carpenter Av		5	E 2
1-3899	67	5	E 4
3900-4399	66	5	E 3
4400-OUT	70	5	E 2
Carroll Pl	56	3	D 9
Carroll St	64	6	M 4
Carter Av	57	4	E 8
Carver Loop	75	6	H 3
Casals Pl	75	6	H 3
Casanova St	74	3	G10
Casler Pl	65	7	N 7
Castle Hill Av		7	J 7
1-999	73	7	K 8
1000-1105	72	7	J 7
1106-OUT	62	7	H 6
Catalpa Pl	65	7	M 7
Cauldwell Av		3	F10
1-736	55	3	F10
737-OUT	56	3	E 9
Cayuga Av	71	5	B 4
Cedar Av		4	C 7
1800-2059	53	4	C 7
2060-OUT	68	4	C 7
Cedar La	51	3	D10
Cedar Pl	65	7	M 7
Centre St	65	7	M 6
Centre St	64	6	M 4
Chaffee Av	65	7	M 7
Charlotte St	60	4	F 8
Chatterton Av		7	J 7
1-2338	72	7	J 7
2339-OUT	62	7	J 7
Chesbrough Av	61	7	J 6
Chester St	69	6	G 3
Chestnut Dr	67	5	F 5
Chestnut St	67	5	F 4
Chisholm St	59	3	F 9
Choctaw Pl	61	6	H 5
Church Sq	72	7	J 7
Cicero Av	73	7	J 8
Cincinnatus Av	73	7	K 8
City Island Av	64	6	M 4
City Island Rd	64	6	K 3
Claflin Av	68	4	C 6
Claremont Pkwy	57	4	E 8
Clarence Av	65	7	L 6
Clason Point La N *(Clason Point Gardens)	73	7	H 8
Clason Point La S *(Clason Point Gardens)	73	7	H 8
Clay Av		4	E 8
1-1505	56	3	E 9
1506-OUT	57	4	E 8
Clementine St	66	6	H 2
Clifford Pl	53	4	D 8
Clinton Av		4	E 8
1-1499	56	3	E 9
1500-OUT	57	4	E 8
Clinton Pl	53	4	D 7
Close Av		4	G 8
1-999	73	4	G 9
1000-OUT	72	4	G 8
Coddington Av	61	7	K 6
Colden Av		5	F 4
1-2199	62	7	H 6
2200-OUT	69	5	F 4
Coles La	58	4	D 6
Colgate Av		4	G 8
1-999	73	4	G 9
1000-OUT	72	4	G 8
College Av		3	E 9
1-927	51	3	E11
928-1449	56	3	E 9
1450-OUT	57	4	D 8
College Rd	71	5	B 4
Collis Pl	65	7	M 7
Colonial Av	61	6	J 5
Columbus Sq	58	4	E 6
Commerce Av		7	J 6
1-1299	62	7	J 7
1300-OUT	61	7	J 6
Commonwealth Av		7	H 8
1-999	73	7	J 9
1000-1419	72	7	H 8
1420-OUT	60	4	G 7
Compton Av	73	7	J 9
Concord Av		3	F11
1-413	54	3	F11
414-OUT	55	3	F10
Concourse Village E	51	3	D10
Concourse Village W	51	3	D10
Connell Pl	65	6	K 5
Conner St		6	G 2
1-2299	66	6	G 2
2300-OUT	75	6	H 2
Continental Av	61	6	J 5
Co-Op City Blvd	75	6	H 3
Cooper Pl	75	6	H 3
Corlear Av	63	5	B 5
Cornell Av	73	7	K 9
Cornell Pl	61	7	K 6
Cpl Irwin Fischer Pl	52	3	C 9
Cpl Walter J Fufidio Sq	74	3	G10
Corsa Av	69	6	G 4
Coster St	74	3	G10
Cottage Pl	56	4	E 8
Country Club Rd	65	6	K 5
Courtlandt Av	51	3	E10
Crames Sq	59	3	G 9
Cranford Av		5	F 2
1-849	70	5	F 2
850-OUT	66	5	F 2
Craven St	74	3	G10
Crawford Av	66	6	G 3
Crescent Av	58	4	E 7
Creston Av		4	D 7
1-2293	53	4	D 7
2294-OUT	68	4	D 7
Crimmins Av	54	3	F11
Croes Av		7	H 8
1-999	73	7	H 8
1000-OUT	72	7	H 8
Croes Pl *(Clason Point Gardens)	73	7	H 9
Cromwell Av		3	D 9
1-889	51	3	D10
890-OUT	52	3	D 9
Crosby Av	61	7	K 6
Cross Bronx Expwy		4	E 8
1-100	52	4	D 8
101-759	57	4	E 8
760-1199	60	4	F 8
1200-2498 (even)	72	4	G 7
1201-1899 (odd)	60	4	G 7
1901-2499 (odd)	62	7	H 7
2500-OUT	65	7	K 7
Cross St	64	6	M 4
Crotona Av		4	E 7
1-1499	56	4	F 8
1500-2289	57	4	E 8
2290-OUT	58	4	F 7
Crotona Park E	60	4	F 8
Crotona Park N		4	E 8
1-759	57	4	E 8
760-OUT	60	4	F 8
Crotona Park S	56	4	E 8
Crotona Pkwy	60	4	F 8
Crotona Pl	56	4	E 8
Cruger Av		5	F 5
1-2199	62	4	G 6
2200-OUT	67	5	F 5
Cypress Av	54	3	F11
Cypress Pl	54	3	F11
Cyrus Pl	58	4	E 6

D

STREET NAME AND HOUSE NUMBERS	ZONE NO.	MAP NO.	MAP GRID
Daisy Pl	65	7	M 7
Daly Av	60	4	F 8
Daniel St	61	7	J 6
Dare Pl	65	7	N 7
Dark St	66	6	G 2
Darrow Pl	75	6	H 3
Dash Pl	63	5	B 5
David Sheridan Plz	71	5	B 3
Davidson Av		4	D 8
1-2270	53	4	D 8
2271-OUT	68	4	D 7
Davis Av	65	7	L 7
Dawson St		3	F10
1-809	55	3	F10
810-OUT	59	3	F10
Dean Av	65	7	L 6
Debs Pl	75	6	H 3
Decatur Av		4	D 6
1-3029	58	4	D 6
3030-OUT	67	5	E 5
De Foe Pl	75	6	H 3
De Kalb Av	67	5	D 4
De Kruif Pl	75	6	H 3
Delafield Av	71	5	A 4
Delafield Av	71	5	B 5
Delafield La	71	5	B 5
Delafield Pl	71	5	A 3
Delancey Pl	62	4	G 6
Delanoy Av	69	6	H 4
Delavall Av	75	6	H 3
Demeyer St	69	6	J 4
Depot Pl	52	3	C 9
De Reimer Av		5	F 2
1-3499	75	6	G 3
3500-OUT	66	5	F 2
Devanney Sq	57	4	D 7
Devoe Av	60	4	G 7
Devoe Ter	68	4	C 6
Dewey Av	65	7	L 7
DeWitt Pl	69	6	G 4
Deyo St	69	6	G 4
Dickerson Av	63	5	D 5
Digney Av	66	5	F 3
Dill Pl	65	7	L 7
Ditmars St	64	6	M 4
Dock St	65	7	M 6
Dodgewood Rd	71	5	B 5
Dogwood Dr	62	7	H 7
Donizetti Pl	75	6	H 3
D'Onofrio Sq	69	5	F 4
Doris St	62	7	J 7
Dorothea Pl	58	4	D 6
Dorsey St	61	7	H 6
Douglas Av		5	B 5
1-3299	63	5	B 5
3300-OUT	71	5	B 5
Dr. Martin Luther King Jr Blvd		3	C 9
900-1522	52	3	C 9
1535-2240	53	4	C 8
2250-OUT	68	4	D 7
Dr. Theodore Kazimiroff Blvd	58	4	E 6
Drake Park S	74	3	H10
Drake St	74	3	G 9
Dreiser Loop	75	6	H 3
Dudley Av	61	7	K 6
Duncan St	69	5	F 4
Duncomb Av	67	5	E 5
Dupont St	74	3	G10
Duryea Av	66	6	G 2
Dwight Pl	65	6	K 5
Dyre Av	66	6	G 2

E

STREET NAME AND HOUSE NUMBERS	ZONE NO.	MAP NO.	MAP GRID
Eagle Av		3	E10
1-743 and 2-738	55	3	E10
745-OUT and 740-OUT	56	3	E10
Eames Pl	68	4	C 6
Earhart La	75	6	J 4
Earley St	64	6	M 4
East Av	62	7	H 7
East Bay Av	74	3	H10
East Burnside Av		4	D 7
1-199	53	4	D 7
200-OUT	57	4	D 7
East Clarke Pl	52	3	D 9
East Fordham Rd		4	E 6
1-199	68	4	D 6
200-OUT	58	4	E 6
East Gun Hill Rd		5	F 4
1-899	67	5	E 4
900-OUT	69	5	G 4
East Kingsbridge Rd		4	D 6
1-199	68	4	D 6
200-OUT	58	4	D 6
East Mosholu Pkwy N (odd only)	67	5	D 5
East Mosholu Pkwy S		5	D 5
2-48 (even only)	68	5	D 5
50-OUT (even only)	58	5	D 5
East Mount Eden Av		4	D 8
1-149	52	4	D 8
150-OUT	57	4	D 8
East Tremont Av		4	D 8
1-199	53	4	D 8
200-759	57	4	D 8
760-1879	60	4	F 7
1880-2399	62	7	H 7
2400-3400	61	7	H 6
3401-OUT	65	7	K 6
East 132nd St		3	E12
200-239	51	3	E12
240-OUT	54	3	E12
East 133rd St		3	F12
200-239	51	3	F12
240-OUT	54	3	F12
East 134th St		3	E11
200-239	51	3	E11
240-OUT	54	3	E11
East 135th St		3	E11
100-249	51	3	E11
250-OUT	54	3	E11
East 136th St		3	E11
100-269	51	3	E11
270-OUT	54	3	E11
East 137th St		3	E11
100-269	51	3	E11
270-OUT	54	3	E11
East 138th St		3	D11
100-269	51	3	D11
270-OUT	54	3	E11
East 139th St		3	E11
100-269	51	3	E11
270-OUT	54	3	E11
East 140th St		3	D11
100-289	51	3	D11
290-OUT	54	3	E11
East 141st St		3	E11
100-309	51	3	E11
310-OUT	54	3	E11
East 142nd St		3	E11
100-299	51	3	E11
300-OUT	54	3	E11
East 143rd St		3	E11
1-334	51	3	E11
335-OUT	54	3	E11
East 144th St		3	D11
1-339	51	3	D11
340-OUT	54	3	E11
East 145th St		3	E11
1-349	51	3	E11
350-599	54	3	E11
600-OUT	55	3	F11
East 146th St		3	D11
1-359	51	3	D11
360-OUT	55	3	E11
East 147th St	55	3	E11
East 148th St		3	E11
1-353	51	3	E11
354-OUT	55	3	E11
East 149th St		3	D11
1-350	51	3	D11
351-OUT	55	3	E10
East 150th St		3	E10
1-353	51	3	D10
354-OUT	55	3	F10
East 151st St		3	E10
1-353	51	3	E10
354-OUT	55	3	F10
East 152nd St		3	E10
1-353	51	3	E10
354-OUT	55	3	F10

STREET NAME AND HOUSE NUMBERS	ZONE NO.	MAP NO.	MAP GRID
East 153rd St		3	E10
1-353	51	3	D10
354-OUT	55	3	E10
East 154th St		3	E10
1-353	51	3	E10
354-OUT	55	3	E10
East 155th St	55	3	E10
East 156th St		3	E10
1-353	51	3	E10
354-1099	55	3	E10
1100-OUT	74	3	G10
East 157th St	51	3	D10
East 158th St		3	D10
1-569	51	3	D10
570-OUT	56	3	F10
East 159th St		3	D10
1-569	51	3	D10
570-OUT	56	3	E10
East 160th St		3	E10
1-569	51	3	E10
570-808	56	3	F10
809-OUT	59	3	F10
East 161st St		3	D10
1-569	51	3	D10
570-808	56	3	E10
809-OUT	59	3	F10
East 162nd St		3	D10
1-159	52	3	D10
160-809	51	3	E10
810-OUT	59	3	F 9
East 163rd St		3	D10
160-569	51	3	D10
570-811	56	3	E 9
812-OUT	59	3	F 9
East 164th St		3	D 9
1-159	52	3	D 9
160-809	56	3	E 9
810-OUT	59	3	F 9
East 165th St		3	D 9
1-159	52	3	D 9
160-809	56	3	E 9
810-OUT	59	3	F 9
East 166th St		3	D 9
1-159	52	3	D 9
161-809 & 160-812	56	3	E 9
811-OUT & 814-OUT	59	3	F 9
East 167th St		3	D 9
1-179	52	3	D 9
180-809	56	3	E 9
810-OUT	59	3	F 9
East 168th St		3	D 9
1-199 & 2-196	52	3	D 9
201-801 & 198-800	56	3	E 9
802-OUT	59	3	F 9
East 169th St		3	D 9
1-199	52	3	D 9
201-809 & 200-798	56	3	E 9
811-OUT & 800-OUT	59	3	F 9
East 170th St		3	D 9
1-199	52	3	D 9
200-796	56	3	E 9
797-OUT	59	4	F 8
East 171st St		4	D 8
1-199	52	4	D 8
200-OUT	57	4	E 8
East 172nd St		4	D 8
1-199	52	4	D 8
200-759	57	4	D 8
760-1099	60	4	F 8
1100-OUT	72	4	G 8
East 173rd St		4	D 8
100-759	57	4	D 8
760-1099	60	4	F 8
1100-OUT	72	4	G 8
East 174th St		4	D 8
1-100	52	4	D 8
101-759	57	4	D 8
760-1099	60	4	F 8
1100-OUT	72	4	G 8
East 175th St		4	D 8
1-149	53	4	D 8
150-759	57	4	D 8
760-OUT	60	4	F 8
East 176th St		4	D 8
1-153	53	4	D 8
154-759	57	4	D 8
760-OUT	60	4	F 8
East 177th St		4	D 8
1-199	53	4	D 8
200-759	57	4	D 8
760-1199	60	4	G 7
1200-2498 (even)	72	4	G 7
1201-1899 (odd)	60	4	G 7
1901-2499 (odd)	62	4	H 7
2500-OUT	65	4	L 6
East 178th St		4	D 7
1-199	53	4	D 7
200-759	57	4	E 7
760-OUT	60	4	F 7
East 179th St		4	D 7
1-199	53	4	D 7
200-759	57	4	E 7
760-OUT	60	4	F 7
East 180th St		4	D 7
1-199	53	4	D 7
200-759	57	4	E 7
760-OUT	60	4	F 7
East 181st St		4	D 7
1-199	53	4	D 7
200-759	57	4	E 7
760-OUT	60	4	F 7
East 182nd St		4	D 7
1-199	53	4	D 7
200-759	57	4	E 7
760-OUT	60	4	F 7
East 183rd St		4	D 7
1-199	53	4	D 7
200-759	58	4	E 7
760-OUT	60	4	F 7
East 184th St		4	D 7
1-199	68	4	D 7
200-OUT	58	4	E 7
East 185th St		4	E 7
200-759	58	4	E 7
760-OUT	60	4	F 7
East 186th St	58	4	E 7
East 187th St	58	4	E 7
East 188th St		4	D 6
1-199	68	4	D 6
200-OUT	58	4	E 6
East 189th St	58	4	E 6
East 190th St	68	4	D 6
East 191st St		4	D 6
1-199	68	4	D 6
200-OUT	58	4	E 6
East 192nd St		4	D 6
1-199	68	4	D 6
200-OUT	58	4	D 6
East 193rd St		4	D 6
1-199	68	4	D 6
200-OUT	58	4	D 6
East 194th St		4	D 6
200-2799	58	4	D 6
2800-OUT	61	6	J 5
East 195th St		4	D 6
200-2799	58	4	D 6
2800-OUT	61	6	J 5
East 196th St		4	D 6
1-199	68	4	D 6
200-2799	58	4	D 6
2800-OUT	61	6	J 5
East 197th St		4	D 6
1-199	68	4	D 6
200-2799	58	4	D 6
2800-OUT	61	6	J 5
East 198th St		4	D 6
1-199	68	4	D 6
200-OUT	58	4	D 6
East 199th St		5	D 5
1-199	68	5	D 5
200-OUT	58	4	E 6
East 201st St	58	5	D 5
East 202nd St		5	D 5
200-399	58	5	D 5
400-OUT	67	5	E 5
East 203rd St		5	D 5
200-399	58	5	D 5
400-OUT	67	5	E 5
East 204th St		5	D 5
1-199	68	5	D 5
200-269	58	5	D 5
270-OUT	67	5	E 5
East 205th St		5	D 5
1-149	68	5	D 5
150-219	58	5	D 5
220-OUT	67	5	E 5
East 206th St		5	D 5
150-219	58	5	D 5
220-OUT	67	5	E 5
East 207th St	67	5	E 5
East 208th St	67	5	D 5
East 209th St	67	5	E 5
East 210th St	67	5	D 5
East 211th St		5	E 4
1-899	67	5	E 4
900-OUT	69	5	F 4
East 212th St		5	D 4
1-899	67	5	D 4
900-OUT	69	5	F 4
East 213th St		5	D 4
1-899	67	5	D 4
900-OUT	69	5	F 4
East 214th St		5	F 4
1-899	67	5	F 4
900-OUT	69	5	F 4
East 215th St		5	F 4
1-899	67	5	F 4
900-OUT	69	5	F 4
East 216th St		5	E 4
1-899	67	5	F 4
900-OUT	69	5	F 4
East 217th St		5	F 4
1-899	67	5	F 4
900-OUT	69	5	F 4
East 218th St		5	F 4
1-899	67	5	F 4
900-OUT	69	5	F 4
East 219th St		5	F 4
1-899	67	5	F 4
900-OUT	69	5	F 4
East 220th St		5	E 4
1-899	67	5	F 4
900-OUT	69	5	F 4
East 221st St		5	E 4
1-899	67	5	F 4
900-OUT	69	5	F 4
East 222nd St		5	E 4
550-899	67	5	F 3
900-OUT	69	5	F 3
East 223rd St	66	5	E 3
East 224th St	66	5	E 3
East 225th St	66	5	E 3
East 226th St	66	5	E 3
East 227th St	66	5	E 3
East 228th St	66	5	E 3
East 229th St	66	5	E 3
East 230th St	66	5	E 3
East 231st St	66	5	E 3
East 232nd St	66	5	E 3
East 233rd St		5	D 3
1-549	70	5	D 3
550-OUT	66	5	E 3
East 234th St		5	D 3
1-549	70	5	D 3
550-OUT	66	5	E 3
East 235th St		5	D 3
1-549	70	5	D 3
550-OUT	66	5	E 3
East 236th St		5	D 3
1-549	70	5	D 3
550-OUT	66	5	E 3
East 237th St		5	D 3
1-549	70	5	D 3
550-OUT	66	5	E 2
East 238th St		5	D 3
1-699	70	5	D 3
700-OUT	66	5	E 2
East 239th St		5	D 3
1-699	70	5	D 3
700-OUT	66	5	E 2
East 240th St	70	5	D 3
East 241st St		5	D 2
1-869	70	5	D 2
870-OUT	66	5	E 2
East 242nd St	70	5	D 2
East 243rd St	70	5	E 2
Eastburn Av	57	4	D 8
Eastchester Pl	75	6	H 2
Eastchester Rd		6	G 4
1-2199	61	7	H 6
2200-3649	69	6	G 4
3650-OUT	66	5	F 3
Echo Pl		4	D 7
1-199	53	4	D 7
200-OUT	57	4	D 7
Edenwald Av	66	5	F 2
Edge St	65	7	M 6
Edgehill Av	63	4	B 6
Edgemere St	64	6	J 2
Edgewater Rd		3	G 9
1-999	74	3	G 9
1000-OUT	59	3	G 9
Edison Av		7	K 6
1-1099	65	7	K 6
1100-OUT	61	7	K 6
Edsall Av	63	4	B 6
Edson Av		6	G 3
1-3499	69	6	H 4
3500-OUT	66	6	G 3
Edward L Grant Hwy	52	3	C 9
Edwards Av	61	7	J 6
Effingham Av	73	7	K 8
Eger Pl	65	7	N 7
Einstein Loop	75	6	J 4
Einstein Loop E	75	6	J 4
Einstein Loop N	75	6	J 4
Einstein Loop S	75	6	J 4
Elder Av		4	G 8
1-999	73	3	G 9
1000-OUT	72	3	G 9
Elgar Pl	75	6	J 4
Elliot Pl	52	3	D 9
Ellis Av		7	H 7
1-2024	72	7	H 7
2025-OUT	62	7	J 7
Ellison Av	61	7	J 6
Ellsworth Av	65	7	L 6
Elm Dr	62	7	H 7
Elm Pl	58	4	D 6
Elm Pl	65	7	M 7
Elsmere Pl	60	4	F 7
Elton Av		3	E10
1-743	55	3	E10
744-OUT	51	3	E10
Ely Av		5	F 2
1-3499	69	6	H 4
3500-OUT	66	5	F 2
Emerson Av	65	7	L 8
Emmet St	58	4	E 6
Erdman Pl	75	6	J 4
Ericson Pl	61	7	J 6
Erskine Pl	75	6	J 4
Esplanade		6	G 5
1-2199	61	6	G 5
2200-OUT	69	6	G 5
Evelyn Pl	68	4	D 7
Evergreen Av		4	G 8
1-999	73	3	G 9
1000-OUT	72	4	G 8
Ewen Av	63	5	B 5
Exterior St		4	C 6
1-1000	51	3	D11
1601-2299	68	4	C 7
2300-OUT	63	4	C 6

F

STREET NAME AND HOUSE NUMBERS	ZONE NO.	MAP NO.	MAP GRID
Faile St		3	G 9
1-919	74	3	G10
920-OUT	59	3	G 9
Fairfax Av	65	7	K 6
Fairfield Av	63	4	B 6
Fairmount Av	65	7	K 6
Fairmount Pl		4	F 7
1-759	57	4	F 7
760-OUT	60	4	F 7
Faraday Av	71	5	B 3
Farragut St	74	3	J10
Father Zeiser Pl	68	4	C 7
Featherbed La	52	4	C 8
Fenton Av	69	6	G 4
Fern Pl	65	7	N 7
Ferris Av	65	7	K 7
Ferris Pl	61	7	J 6
Field Pl		4	D 7
1-199	68	4	D 7
200-OUT	58	4	D 7
Fielding St	69	6	H 4
Fieldston Rd		5	B 4
1-3999	63	5	B 5
4000-OUT	71	5	B 4
Fieldston Ter	71	5	B 4
Fillmore St	60	4	G 7
Findlay Av	56	3	E 9
Fink Av	61	7	J 6
Fish Av	69	6	G 4
Fleet Ct	73	7	K 9
Fletcher Pl	57	4	E 7
Flint Av	75	6	H 2
Folin St	57	4	D 7
Food Center Dr	74	3	H 9
Foote Av	65	7	K 7
Ford St	57	4	D 7
Fordham Pl	64	6	M 4
Fordham Plz	58	4	E 6
Fordham Rd (see E or W Fordham Rd)			
Fordham St	64	6	M 4
Forest Av		3	F10
1-745 & 2-742	55	3	F10
747-OUT & 744-OUT	56	3	F10
Forster Pl	71	5	B 3
Fort Independence St	63	5	C 5
Fort Schuyler Rd	61	7	J 6
Fowler Av	62	4	G 6
Fox St		3	F10
1-799	55	3	F10
800-OUT	59	3	F10
Fox Ter	69	6	G 4
Franklin Av	56	3	E 9
Freeman St	59	3	F 9
Frisby Av	61	7	J 6
Fteley Av		7	H 8
1-999	73	7	H 8
1000-OUT	72	7	H 8
Fuller St	61	7	H 6
Fulton Av		3	E 9
1-1505 & 2-1500	56	3	E 9
1507-OUT & 1502-OUT	57	4	E 8
Furman Av		5	E 2
1-4499	66	5	E 2
4500-OUT	70	5	E 2

G

STREET NAME AND HOUSE NUMBERS	ZONE NO.	MAP NO.	MAP GRID
Gale Pl	63	5	C 5
Garden Pl	70	5	E 2
Garden St		4	F 7
1-759	57	4	F 7
760-OUT	60	4	F 7
Garfield St	60	4	G 7
Garrett Pl	66	6	G 2
Garrison Av	74	3	G10
Gates Pl	67	5	D 4
Geo. Farkas Sq *(intersection of Fordham Rd & Grand Concourse)	68	4	D 6
George St *(off Dudley Av bet Mayflower Av & Edison Av)	61	7	J 6
Geranium Pl	65	7	N 7
Gerard Av		3	D10
1-871	51	3	D10
872-OUT	52	3	D 9
Gerber Pl	65	7	L 7
Gertland Pl	64	6	J 2
Giegerich Pl	65	7	N 7
Gifford Av	65	7	K 7
Gilbert Pl	74	3	G 9
Gildersleeve Av	73	7	J 9
Giles Pl	63	5	C 5
Gillespie Av	61	7	K 6
Gillespie Sq	56	3	E 9
Givan Av		6	G 4
1-1999	69	6	G 4
2000-OUT	75	6	H 3
Givan Sq	69	6	H 4
Gladstone Sq	59	3	F 9
Gleason Av		7	H 8
1-2037 (odd) & 2-2050 (even)	72	7	H 8
2039-OUT (odd) & 2052-OUT (even)	62	7	J 7
Glebe Av		7	J 7
1-2399	62	7	J 7
2400-OUT	61	7	J 6
Glennon Pl	65	7	N 7
Glover St	62	7	J 7
Goble Pl	52	4	D 8
Godwin Ter	63	4	C 6
Goodridge Av	71	5	B 4
Goulden Av	68	4	D 6
Gouverneur Av	63	5	C 5
Gouverneur Pl	56	3	E 9
Grace Av		6	H 4
1-3499	69	6	H 4
3500-OUT	66	6	G 3
Graff Av	65	7	L 7
Graff Av	65	7	K 7
Graham Pl *(off Morris Park Av bet Matthews & Muliner Av)	62	4	G 6
Graham Sq	51	3	E11
Grand Av		4	D 7
1-2270	53	4	D 7
2271-OUT	68	4	D 7
Grand Concourse		3	D 9
1-899 (odd)	51	3	D11
2-1036 (even)	51	3	D11
901-1679 (odd)	52	3	D 9
1038-1448 (even)	56	3	D 9
1450-2298 (even)	57	4	D 8
1681-2299 (odd)	53	4	D 8
2300-OUT (even)	58	4	D 8
2301-OUT (odd)	68	5	D 5
Grandview Pl	52	3	D 9
Grant Av		3	D 9
1-940	51	3	D10
941-OUT	56	3	D 9
Green Av	61	7	J 7
Greene Pl	65	7	K 6
Grenada Pl	66	5	F 3
Greystone Av		5	B 5
1-3900	63	5	B 5
3901-OUT	71	5	B 5
Grinnell Pl	74	3	G10
Griswold Av	65	6	K 5
Grosvenor Av	71	5	B 4
Grote St		4	F 7
1-759	57	4	E 7
760-OUT	60	4	F 7
Guerlain St		4	G 7
1-1879	60	4	G 7
1880-OUT	62	4	H 7
Guion Pl	60	4	G 7
Gun Hill Rd (see E or W Gun Hill Rd)			
Gunther Av		5	F 2
1-3499	69	6	H 4
3500-OUT	66	5	F 2

H

STREET NAME AND HOUSE NUMBERS	ZONE NO.	MAP NO.	MAP GRID
Hadley Av	71	5	A 5
Haight Av	61	7	H 6
Hall of Fame Ter	53	4	C 7
Hall Pl	59	3	F 9
Halleck St	74	7	H 9
Halperin Av	61	7	J 6
Halsey St	61	7	J 6
Hammersley Av	69	6	G 4
Hampden Pl	68	4	C 7
Harding Av	65	7	L 8
Harding Av	65	7	M 6
Harper Av	66	6	G 2
Harrington Av	61	7	J 6
Harrison Av	53	4	D 8
Harrod Av	72	4	G 8
Harrod Pl	72	4	G 8
Hart St	73	7	K 8
Haskin St	61	7	K 6
Haswell St	61	7	J 6
Hatting Pl	65	7	M 7
Havemeyer Av		7	J 7
1-999	73	7	J 7
1000-1039	72	7	J 7
1040-OUT	62	7	J 7
Haviland Av		7	J 7
1-2166	72	7	J 7
2167-OUT	62	7	J 7
Hawkins St	64	6	M 4
Hawkstone St	52	4	D 8
Hawthorne Dr	62	7	H 7
Hawthorne St	69	6	H 4
Hazel Pl	65	7	N 7
Heath Av	63	4	C 6
Heathcote Av	75	6	H 2
Hegney Pl		3	E10
1-743 & 2-738	55	3	E10
745-OUT & 740-OUT	51	3	E10
Hennessy Pl	53	4	C 7
Henry Hudson Pkwy		5	B 4
2600-3899	63	5	B 5
3900-OUT	71	5	B 4
Henry Hudson Pkwy E & W		5	B 5
2600-3899	63	5	B 5
3900-OUT	71	5	B 4
Henwood Pl	53	4	D 8
Hering Av		6	G 4
1-2199	61	7	H 6
2200-OUT	69	6	G 5
Herkimer Pl	70	5	D 3
Hermany Av	73	7	J 8
Herschell St	61	7	J 6
Hewitt Pl		3	F10
1-809	55	3	F10
810-OUT	59	3	F10
Hicks St	69	6	G 4
High Island	64	6	M 3
Highbridge St (now Cpl Irwin Fischer Pl)	52	3	C 9
Hill Av	66	5	F 2
Hillman Av	63	5	C 5
Hobart Av	61	6	J 5
Hoe Av		4	F 8
1-1459	59	3	F 9
1460-OUT	60	4	F 8
Hoffman St	58	4	E 7
Holland Av		5	F 5
1-2199	62	4	G 6
2200-OUT	67	5	F 5
Hollers Av	75	6	H 2
Holly Pl	65	7	M 7
Hollywood Av		7	L 6
1-1199	65	7	L 6

STREET NAME AND HOUSE NUMBERS	ZONE NO.	MAP NO.	MAP GRID
1200-OUT	61	7	K 6
Holt Pl	67	5	E 5
Home St		3	F 9
1-801	56	3	F 9
802-OUT	59	3	F 9
Homer Av	73	7	J 8
Hone Av		7	G 6
1-2199	61	7	H 6
2200-OUT	69	6	G 5
Honeywell Av	60	4	F 7
Hornaday Pl	60	4	F 7
Horton St	64	6	M 4
Hosmer Av	65	7	L 7
Howe Av	73	7	K 8
Hoxie St	70	5	F 2
Hubbell St	61	7	H 6
Hudson Manor Ter	63	5	B 5
Hudson River Rd	71	5	A 4
Hugh J Grant Cir		7	H 7
even numbers	72	7	H 7
odd numbers	62	7	H 7
Hughes Av		4	E 7
1-2270	57	4	E 7
2271-OUT	58	4	E 7
Huguenot Av	75	6	H 2
Hull Av	67	5	E 5
Hunt Av	62	4	G 6
Hunter Av		6	G 3
400-450	64	6	M 4
451-OUT	75	6	G 3
Huntington Av	65	7	K 7
Hunts Point Av	74	3	G 9
Husson Av	73	7	K 9
Hutchinson Av	75	6	H 2
Hutchinson River Pkwy		6	H 2
1-1499	65	7	K 7
1500-3999	61	7	J 6
4000-OUT	75	6	J 4
Hutchinson River Pkwy E		6	J 5
1600-3099	61	6	J 5
4100-4240	75	6	J 4
Hutchinson River Pkwy W	75	6	J 4
Hutton Sq	58	4	E 7
Huxley Av	71	5	B 3

I

STREET NAME AND HOUSE NUMBERS	ZONE NO.	MAP NO.	MAP GRID
Independence Av		5	B 5
1-3999	63	4	B 6
4000-OUT	71	5	B 5
Indian Rd	71	5	B 4
Indian Tr	65	7	M 7
Industrial St	61	7	J 6
Interstate Hwy 87 (see Major Deegan Expwy)	71	5	C 4
Interstate Hwy 95		6	J 5
Interstate Hwy 95		4	F 8
Interstate Hwy 295		7	K 7
Interstate Hwy 678		7	L 8
Interstate Hwy 695		7	L 6
Intervale Av	59	3	F 9
Inwood Av	52	3	D 9
Irvine St	74	3	G 9
Irwin Av	63	5	B 5
Iselin Av	71	5	B 4
Ittner Pl	57	4	E 8
Ives St	61	7	H 6
Ivy Pl	65	7	N 7

J

STREET NAME AND HOUSE NUMBERS	ZONE NO.	MAP NO.	MAP GRID
Jackson Av		3	F10
1-411	54	3	F11
412-746	55	3	F10
747-OUT	56	3	F10
Jarrett Pl	61	7	H 6
Jarvis Av	61	6	J 5
Jasamine Pl	65	7	N 7
Jay Pl	65	7	K 7
Jay St	65	7	K 8
Jefferson Pl	56	3	E 9
Jennings St		4	F 8
1-899	59	4	F 8
900-OUT	60	4	F 8
Jerome Av		5	D 5
1-1649	52	3	D 9
1650-2280	53	4	D 7
2281-3299	68	4	D 6
3300-3899	67	5	D 4
3900-OUT	70	5	D 3
Jesup Av	52	4	D 8
Jesup Pl	52	4	C 8
Johnson Av	63	4	B 6

K

STREET NAME AND HOUSE NUMBERS	ZONE NO.	MAP NO.	MAP GRID
Kappock St	63	4	B 6
Katonah Av	70	5	D 3
Kearney Av	65	6	K 5
Kearney Av	65	7	M 7
Kelly St		3	F 9
1-799	55	3	F10
800-OUT	59	3	F 9
Kennelworth Pl	65	6	K 5
Kepler Av	70	5	D 3
Kilroe St	64	6	L 3
Kimberly Pl	63	4	C 6
King Av	64	6	L 3
Kings College Pl	67	5	E 4
Kingsbridge Av	63	4	C 6
Kingsbridge Rd E		4	D 6
1-199	68	4	D 6
200-OUT	58	4	D 6

STREET NAME AND HOUSE NUMBERS	ZONE NO.	MAP NO.	MAP GRID
Kingsbridge Rd W		4	C 6
1-148	68	4	C 6
149-OUT	63	4	C 6
Kingsbridge Ter	63	4	C 6
Kingsland Av	69	6	H 4
Kingsland Pl	53	4	D 8
Kinsella St	62	7	G 6
Kirby St	64	6	M 4
Knapp St	69	6	G 4
Knolls Cres	63	4	B 6
Knox Pl	67	5	D 5
Kossuth Av	67	5	D 5

L

STREET NAME AND HOUSE NUMBERS	ZONE NO.	MAP NO.	MAP GRID
La Salle Av	61	7	K 6
Lacombe Av	73	7	J 9
Laconia Av		6	G 5
1-3899	69	6	G 5
3900-OUT	66	5	F 3
Ladd Rd	71	5	A 4
Lafayette Av		3	H 9
1-1450	74	3	G10
1451-2499	73	3	H 9
2500-OUT	65	7	K 7
Lafontaine Av	57	4	E 7
Lake View Pl	71	5	B 4
Lakewood Pl	61	7	H 6
Lamport Pl	65	7	L 7
Landing Rd	68	4	C 7
Lane Av	61	7	J 6
Latting St	61	7	J 6
Laurel Dr	62	7	H 7
Laurie Av	61	6	J 5
Lawton Av	65	7	L 7
Layton Av	65	7	K 6
Lebanon St	60	4	G 7
Leggett Av		3	F10
1-1079	55	3	F10
1080-OUT	74	3	G10
Leland Av		7	H 8
1-999	73	7	J 9
1000-1359	72	7	H 8
1360-OUT	60	7	H 7
Lester St	67	5	F 5
Libby Pl	61	7	J 6
Library Av	65	6	K 5
Liebig Av	71	5	B 3
Light St	66	6	G 2
Lincoln Av	54	3	E12
Linden Av	65	7	M 7
Linden Dr	62	7	H 7
Lisbon Pl	58	5	D 5
Little League Pl	61	7	J 6
Livingston Av	71	5	B 4
Locust Av	54	3	F11
Locust Point Dr	65	7	M 6
Lodovick Av	69	6	H 4
Logan Av	65	7	L 6
Logan Av	65	7	M 7
Lohengrin Pl	65	6	K 5
Longfellow Av		4	F 8
1-999	74	3	G 9
1000-1454	59	3	G 9
1455-OUT	60	4	F 8
Longstreet Av	65	7	M 7
Longwood Av		3	F10
1-1050	59	3	F10
1051-OUT	74	3	G10
Loomis St	61	6	H 5
Lorillard Pl	58	4	E 7
Loring Pl N		4	C 7
1-2249	53	4	C 7
2250-OUT	68	4	C 7
Loring Pl S	53	4	C 8
Lou Auger Sq	63	5	B 5
Lou Gehrig Plz	51	3	D10
Louis Nine Blvd	59	4	F 8
Lowell St	59	3	G 9
Lowerre Pl	66	5	E 3
Lucerne St	65	6	K 5
Lurting Av		7	H 6
1-2199	61	7	H 6
2200-OUT	69	6	G 5
Lustre St	66	6	G 2
Lydig Av		4	G 6
1-1023	62	4	G 6
1024-OUT	61	4	G 6
Lyman Pl	59	3	F 9
Lyon Av	62	7	J 7
Lyvere St	61	7	H 6

M

STREET NAME AND HOUSE NUMBERS	ZONE NO.	MAP NO.	MAP GRID
Mable Wayne Pl *	51	3	D10
Mac Donough Pl	65	6	K 5
Mace Av		5	F 5
1-899	67	5	F 5
900-OUT	69	5	G 5
Maclay Av		7	H 6
1-2399	62	7	H 6
2400-OUT	61	7	H 6
Macombs Rd		4	D 8
1-1603	52	4	D 8
1604-OUT	53	4	D 8
Macy Pl	55	3	F10
Magenta St		5	E 5
1-899	67	5	E 5
900-OUT	69	5	F 4
Magnolia Pl	65	7	M 7
Mahan Av	61	6	J 5
Main St	65	7	M 6

STREET NAME AND HOUSE NUMBERS	ZONE NO.	MAP NO.	MAP GRID
Maitland Av	61	7	J 6
Major Deegan Expwy		4	C 8
Major Deegan Expwy		3	D11
Major Deegan Expwy		5	C 5
Manhattan College Pkwy	71	5	B 5
Manida St	74	3	G10
Manning St	62	7	H 7
Manor Av	72	4	G 8
Mansion St	60	4	G 7
Mapes Av	60	4	F 7
Maple Av *(off Chaffee Av)	65	7	M 7
Maple Dr	62	7	H 7
Maran Pl	62	4	G 6
Marcy Pl		3	D 9
1-199	52	3	D 9
200-OUT	56	3	D 9
Marina Dr	65	7	L 7
Marine St	64	6	M 4
Marion Av	58	4	D 6
Marmion Av	60	4	F 8
Marolla Pl	66	6	G 3
Martha Av	70	5	D 2
Marvin Pl	61	7	H 6
Matilda Av		5	E 2
1-4399	66	5	E 2
4400-OUT	70	5	E 2
Matthews Av		5	F 5
1-2199	62	5	F 5
2200-OUT	67	4	G 6
Matthewson Rd	53	4	C 8
Mayflower Av	61	6	J 5
McClellan St		3	D 9
1-159	52	3	D 9
160-OUT	56	3	D 9
McCracken Av	53	4	C 8
McDonald St	61	6	H 5
McGraw Av		7	H 7
1-1859	72	7	H 7
1860-OUT	62	7	H 7
McKinley Sq	56	3	E 9
McOwen Av	75	6	H 2
Mead St	60	4	G 7
Meagher Av	65	7	M 7
Melrose Av		3	E10
1-742	55	3	E10
743-OUT	51	3	E10
Melville St	60	4	G 7
Merriam Av	52	3	C 9
Merrill St	60	4	G 7
Merritt Av		6	G 2
1-3599	75	6	H 3
3600-OUT	66	6	G 2
Merry Av	61	7	K 6
Metcalf Av		7	H 8
1-999	73	7	H 8
1000-OUT	72	7	H 8
Metropolitan Av	62	7	H 7
Metropolitan Oval *(Parkchester)	62	7	H 7
Meyers St	61	7	K 6
Mickle Av	69	6	G 4
Middletown Rd		7	J 6
1-3149	61	7	J 6
3150-OUT	65	6	K 5
Miles Av	65	7	L 7
Milton Pl	65	7	M 7
Minerva Pl	68	4	D 6
Minford Pl	60	4	F 8
Minnieford Av	64	6	M 3
Miriam St	58	4	D 6
Mitchell Pl	65	7	N 7
Mohegan Av	60	4	F 7
Monroe Av	57	4	D 8
Monsignor Cahill Pl	69	6	G 4
Monsignor Halpin Pl	65	7	M 7
Monterey Av	57	4	E 7
Montgomery Av	53	4	C 8
Montgomery Pl	61	7	H 6
Monticello Av	66	5	F 2
Morgan Av	69	6	H 4
Morris Av		4	D 6
1-928	51	3	E11
929-1449	56	3	D 9
1450-1799	57	4	D 8
1800-2293	53	4	D 7
2294-OUT	68	4	D 6
Morris Park Av		4	G 7
1-646	60	4	G 7
647-1023	62	4	H 6
1024-OUT	61	7	H 6
Morrison Av		4	G 8
1-999	73	3	H 9
1000-OUT	72	4	G 8
Morton Pl	53	4	D 8
Mosholu Av	71	5	B 4
Mosholu Pkwy	71	5	C 3
Mosholu Pkwy	71	5	E 5
Mount Eden Pkwy	57	4	D 8
Mount Hope Pl		4	D 8
1-199	53	4	D 8
200-OUT	57	4	D 8
Mulford Av	61	6	J 5
Muliner Av	62	4	G 6
Mullan Pl	65	7	M 7
Mulvey Av	66	6	G 2
Mundy La	66	5	F 2
Munn Av	62	7	J 7
Murdock Av		5	F 2
1-4799	66	5	F 2
4800-OUT	70	5	F 2

N

STREET NAME AND HOUSE NUMBERS	ZONE NO.	MAP NO.	MAP GRID
Napier Av	70	5	D 3
Naples Ter	63	5	C 5
Narragansett Av	61	6	H 5
Needham Av		6	G 3
1-1599	69	6	G 4
1600-2199	66	6	G 3
Neill Av		4	G 6
1-1023	62	4	G 6
1024-OUT	61	4	G 6
Nelson Av		4	C 8
1-1599	52	3	C 9
1600-OUT	53	4	C 8
Neptune Ct	73	7	K 9
Neptune La	73	7	K 9
Nereid Av		5	E 2
1-699	70	5	E 2
700-OUT	66	5	F 2
Netherland Av		4	B 6
1-3899	63	4	B 6
3900-OUT	71	5	A 4
Neumann Goldman Memorial Plz	67	5	E 5
New England Thruway		6	H 3
Newbold Av		7	H 7
1-1999	72	7	H 7
2000-OUT	62	7	H 7
Newell St	67	5	E 4
Newman Av	73	7	J 9
Newport Av	61	7	H 6
Noble Av		7	H 8
1-999	73	7	H 8
1000-1499	72	7	H 8
1500-OUT	60	4	G 7
Noell Av	75	6	H 2
North Botanical Sq	58	4	E 6
North Brother Island	54	3	G11
North Oak Dr	67	5	F 5
North St	68	4	D 7
Norton Av	73	7	K 8
Nuvern Av	66	6	G 2

O

STREET NAME AND HOUSE NUMBERS	ZONE NO.	MAP NO.	MAP GRID
Oak Av	65	7	M 7
Oak La	64	6	J 2
Oak Point Av	74	3	G10
Oak Ter	54	3	F11
Oak Tree Pl	57	4	E 7
Oakland Pl	57	4	E 7
Oakley St	69	6	G 4
O'Brien Av	73	7	J 9
O'Brien Sq	57	4	E 8
Odell St	62	7	H 7
Ogden Av	52	3	C 9
Ohm Av	65	6	K 5
Olinville Av	67	5	E 4
Oliver Pl	58	4	E 6
Olmstead Av		7	J 7
1-999	73	7	J 8
1000-1199	72	7	J 7
1200-OUT	62	7	H 7
One Lighting Pl	74	3	H10
Oneida Av	70	5	D 3
O'Neill Pl	69	6	H 4
Orloff Av	63	5	C 5
Osborne Pl	53	4	C 7
Osgood St	70	5	E 2
Osman Pl	70	5	F 2
Otis Av	65	7	K 6
Outlook Av	65	6	K 5
Overing St	61	7	H 6
Oxford Av	63	5	B 5

P

STREET NAME AND HOUSE NUMBERS	ZONE NO.	MAP NO.	MAP GRID
Paine St	61	7	K 6
Palisade Av		5	A 5
1-3899	63	5	A 5
3900-OUT	71	5	A 5
Palisade Pl	53	4	C 8
Palmer Av		6	G 3
2200-3399	75	6	J 4
3500-OUT	66	6	G 3
Park Av		3	D11
2300-3267	51	3	D11
3268-3799	56	3	E 9
3801-4545 & 3800-4552	57	4	E 8
4547-OUT & 4554-OUT	58	4	E 7
Park Dr	64	6	J 2
Park Dr	64	6	K 3
Parkchester Rd	62	7	H 7
Parker St	62	7	H 7
Parkside Pl	67	5	E 5
Parkview Av	61	6	J 5
Parkview Ter	68	4	D 6
Parsifal Pl	65	6	K 5
Patterson Av	73	7	J 9
Paul Av	68	5	D 5
Paulding Av		5	F 3
1-1549	61	6	H 6
1550-2199	62	7	H 6
2200-3899	69	5	F 4
3900-OUT	66	5	F 3
Paulis Pl	64	6	M 4
Pawnee Pl	61	6	H 5
Pearsall Av	69	5	G 4
Peartree Av	75	6	H 2
Pelham Bay Park W	75	6	H 2
Pelham Bridge Rd	64	6	K 3
Pelham Parkway N		4	G 6
1-899 (odd)	67	4	G 6
901-OUT	69	6	H 5
Pelham Parkway S		4	G 6
2-948 (even)	62	4	G 6
950-OUT (even)	61	6	H 5
Pell Pl	64	6	M 4
Penfield St	70	5	E 2
Pennyfield Av	65	7	M 7
Perot St	63	5	C 5
Perry Av		5	E 5
1-3029	58	5	E 5
3030-OUT	67	5	E 5
Peters Pl	70	5	E 3
Phelan Pl	53	4	C 8
Philip Av	65	7	L 7
Pierce Av		7	H 6
1-1023	62	7	H 6
1024-OUT	61	7	H 6
Pilgrim Av	61	6	J 5
Pilot St	64	6	M 4
Pinchot Pl	61	6	H 5
Pine Dr	62	7	H 7
Pinkney Av	75	6	H 2
Pitman Av	66	5	F 2
Plimpton Av	52	3	C 9
Ploughman's Bush	71	5	A 5
Plymouth Av	61	7	J 6
Poe Pl *(off Coles La)	58	4	D 6
Polo Pl	65	6	K 5
Pond Pl	58	4	D 6
Pontiac Pl	55	3	F10
Ponton Av	61	7	J 6
Popham Av	53	4	C 8
Poplar Av	65	7	M 7
Poplar St	61	7	H 6
Post Rd	71	5	B 4
Powell Av		7	J 7
1-2139	72	7	J 7
2140-OUT	62	7	J 7
Powers Av	54	3	F11
Pratt Av	66	6	G 2
Prentiss Av	65	7	M 6
Prospect Av		3	F10
1-831	55	3	F10
833-1429 & 832-1434	59	3	F 9
1431-1499 & 1436-1498	56	4	F 8
1500-2299	57	4	F 7
2300-OUT	58	4	F 7
Prospect Pl	57	4	D 8
Provost Av	66	6	H 2
Pugsley Av		7	J 7
1-999	73	7	J 8
1000-1269	72	7	H 7
1270-OUT	62	7	H 7
Purdy St	62	7	H 7
Puritan Av	61	7	K 6
Putnam Av W	63	5	C 5
Putnam Pl	67	5	E 4

Q

STREET NAME AND HOUSE NUMBERS	ZONE NO.	MAP NO.	MAP GRID
Quarry Rd	57	4	E 7
Quimby Av	73	7	J 8
Quincy Av	65	7	K 6
Quincy Av	65	7	L 7

R

STREET NAME AND HOUSE NUMBERS	ZONE NO.	MAP NO.	MAP GRID
Radcliff Av		4	G 6
1-2199	62	4	G 6
2200-OUT	69	6	G 5
Radio Dr	65	6	K 5
Rae St	55	3	E10
Randall Av		3	G10
1-1599	74	3	G10
1600-2499	73	7	J 8
2500-OUT	65	7	L 7
Randolph Pl	65	6	K 5
Rawlins Av	65	7	K 6
Raymond Av	61	7	J 6
Red Oak Dr	62	7	H 7
Reed Pl	65	6	K 5
Reeds Mill La	75	6	H 3
Reeds Mill La *(at intersection of Boston Rd and Steenwick Av)	75	6	H 3
Regina Pl	66	6	H 2
Reiss Pl	67	4	F 6
Research Av	65	6	K 5
Reservoir Av	68	4	C 6
Reservoir Oval E	67	5	E 5
Reservoir Oval W	67	5	E 5
Reservoir Pl	67	5	E 4
Rev James A Polite Av (Dawson to Bristow)	59	3	F 9
Revere Av	65	7	K 6
Review Pl	63	5	C 5
Reville St	64	6	M 4
Reynold St	64	6	M 4
Reynolds Av	65	7	M 6
Rhinelander Av		4	G 6
1-1023	62	4	G 6
1024-OUT	61	7	H 6
Richardson Av		5	E 2
1-4399	66	5	E 2
4400-OUT	70	5	E 2
Richman Plz	53	4	C 8
Rider Av	51	3	E11
Ridge Pl	64	6	J 2
Risse St	68	5	D 5
Ritter Pl	59	3	F 9
River Av		3	D10

STREET NAME AND HOUSE NUMBERS	ZONE NO.	MAP NO.	MAP GRID
1-870	51	3	D10
871-OUT	52	3	D 9
River Rd	63	5	A 5
Rivercrest Rd	71	5	A 4
Riverdale Av		5	A 4
… 1-3899	63	5	B 5
… 3900-OUT	71	5	A 4
Roberts Av	61	6	J 5
Roberts Av	61	7	J 6
Robertson Pl	65	6	K 5
Robertson St	70	5	E 2
Robinson Av	65	7	L 7
Rochambeau Av	67	5	D 4
Rochambeau Av	67	5	E 5
Rochelle St	64	6	M 4
Rockwood St	52	4	D 8
Rodman Pl	60	4	F 8
Roebling Av	61	7	J 6
Rogers Pl	59	3	F 9
Rohr Pl	65	7	K 7
Rombouts Av		6	G 2
… 1-3599	75	6	H 3
… 3600-OUT	66	6	G 2
Roosevelt Av	65	7	L 7
Roosevelt Pl	64	6	K 2
Ropes Av	75	6	H 2
Rosedale Av		7	H 8
… 1-999	73	7	H 8
… 1000-1419	72	7	H 8
… 1420-OUT	60	4	G 7
Roselle St	61	7	H 6
Rosewood St	67	5	F 5
Rowe St	61	7	J 6
Rowland St	61	7	J 6
Ruppert Pl	51	3	D10
Ryawa Av	74	3	H10
Ryer Av		4	D 7
… 1-2299	57	4	D 7
… 2300-OUT	58	4	D 7

S

STREET NAME AND HOUSE NUMBERS	ZONE NO.	MAP NO.	MAP GRID
Sacket Av		7	H 6
… 1-1023	62	7	H 6
… 1024-OUT	61	7	H 6
Sagamore St	62	4	G 6
St. Ann's Av		3	F11
… 1-439	54	3	F11
… 440-740	55	3	E10
… 741-OUT	56	3	E10
St. Ann's Pl	54	3	F11
St. George's Cres	58	5	D 5
St. Lawrence Av		7	H 8
… 1-999	73	7	J 9
… 1000-1419	72	7	H 8
… 1420-OUT	60	7	G 7
St. Mary's St	54	3	F11
St. Ouen St	70	5	E 2
St. Paul Av	61	6	J 5
St. Paul's Pl	56	4	E 8
St. Peter's Av	61	7	H 6
St. Raymond's Av		7	H 7
… 1-2399	62	7	H 7
… 2400-OUT	61	7	J 6
St. Theresa Av	61	6	J 5
Sampson Av	65	7	L 7
Sampson Av	65	7	M 6
Sands Pl	61	6	J 5
Santo Donato Pl	61	6	J 5
Saxon Av	63	5	D 5
Scenic Pl	63	4	A 6
Schieffelin Av	66	6	G 3
Schieffelin Pl	66	6	G 3
Schley Av	65	7	L 7
Schofield St	64	6	M 4
Schorr Pl	69	6	H 4
Schurz Av	65	7	L 8
Schurz Av (Marina Dr (Calhoun Av to Hollywood))	65	7	M 7
Schuyler Pl	61	6	J 5
Schuyler Ter	65	7	N 7
Scott Pl	65	7	L 6
Screvin Av	73	7	J 8
Seabury Av		7	J 6
… 1-1300	62	7	J 7
… 1301-OUT	61	7	J 6
Seabury Pl	60	4	F 8
Secor Av	66	6	G 2
Seddon St	61	7	H 6
Sedgwick Av		5	C 5
… 1-1499	52	3	C 9
… 1500-2199	53	4	C 8
… 2200-3099	68	4	C 6
… 3100-OUT	63	5	C 5
Selwyn Av	57	4	D 8
Seminole Av	61	6	H 5
Seminole St	61	6	H 5
Seneca Av	74	3	G 9
Senger Pl	65	7	K 7
Seton Av	66	5	F 2
Seward Av	73	7	H 9
Sexton Pl	69	6	G 4
Seymour Av	69	6	G 4
Shakespeare Av	52	3	D 9
Sheridan Av		3	D 9
… 1-939	51	3	D10
… 940-1449	56	3	D 9
… 1450-OUT	57	4	D 8
Sheridan Expwy	59	3	G 9
Sherman Av		3	D10
… 802-940	51	3	D10
… 941-OUT	56	3	D 9
Shore Dr	65	7	L 6
Shore Rd (now Pelham Bridge Rd)	64	6	J 3
Shrady Pl	63	5	C 5
Siegfried Pl	65	6	K 5
Sigma Pl	71	5	A 3
Silver St	61	7	H 6
Silverman Pl	57	4	D 8
Simpson St	59	3	F 9
Sommer Pl	65	7	K 6
Soundview Av		7	H 8
… 1-999	73	7	K 9
… 1000-OUT	72	7	H 8
Soundview Dr	65	7	M 6
Soundview Ter	65	7	N 7
South Botanical Sq	58	4	E 6
South Brother Island	54	3	G11
South Oak Dr	67	5	F 5
Southern Blvd		3	F11
… 1-419	54	3	F11
… 420-799	55	3	F10
… 800-1459	59	3	F10
… 1460-2399	60	4	F 8
… 2400-OUT	58	4	F 6
Spencer Av	71	5	B 3
Spencer Dr	65	6	K 5
Spencer Pl (now Anthony J Griffin Pl)	51	3	D11
Spencer Ter *(off Spencer Av)	71	5	B 3
Split Rock Rd	64	6	H 2
Spofford Av	74	3	G10
Stadium Av	65	6	K 5
Starling Av	62	7	H 7
Stearns St	62	7	H 7
Stebbins Av	59	4	F 8
Stedman Pl	69	6	G 5
Steenwick Av	75	6	H 3
Stell Pl	69	6	G 5
Stephens Av	73	7	K 9
Steuben Av	67	5	D 5
Stevens Av	65	7	M 6
Stevenson Pl	63	5	C 5
Stickball Blvd	73	7	J 8
Stickney Pl	69	5	F 4
Stillwell Av		6	H 5
… 1-1699	61	6	H 5
… 1700-1999	69	6	H 5
… 2000-OUT	75	6	J 4
Story Av	73	3	G 9
Strang Av	66	6	G 2
Stratford Av	72	4	G 8
Strong St	68	4	D 6
Suburban Pl	60	4	F 8
Sullivan Pl	65	7	L 6
Summit Av	52	3	C10
Summit Pl	63	5	C 5
Sunset Blvd	73	7	K 9
Sunset Plz	65	7	M 7
Sunset Tr	65	7	M 7
Sutherland St	64	6	L 3
Swinton Av	65	7	K 6
Sycamore Av	71	5	A 4
Sycamore Dr	62	7	H 7
Sylvan Av	71	5	B 4

T

STREET NAME AND HOUSE NUMBERS	ZONE NO.	MAP NO.	MAP GRID
Taylor Av		4	G 7
… 1-999	73	7	H 8
… 1000-1359	72	7	H 8
… 1360-OUT	60	4	G 7
Teller Av		3	E 9
… 1-955 & 2-932	51	3	E10
… 957-1449 & 934-1448	56	3	E 9
… 1450-OUT	57	4	D 8
Tenbroeck Av		6	G 4
… 1-2199	61	6	H 5
… 2200-OUT	69	6	G 4
Tenny Pl	53	4	C 8
Terrace St	64	6	L 3
Terrace View Av	63	4	B 6
Teumissin Pl	63	4	B 6
Theriot Av		7	H 8
… 1-999	73	7	H 8
… 1000-1359	72	7	H 8
… 1360-OUT	60	7	H 7
Third Av		4	E 8
… 2400-2738 (even)	54	3	E11
… 2401-2773 (odd)	51	3	E11
… 2740-3040 (even)	55	3	E10
… 2775-3045 (odd)	55	3	E10
… 3042-3246 (even)	51	3	E10
… 3047-3249 (odd)	51	3	E10
… 3248-3798 & 3251-3799	56	3	E 9
… 3800-4422 & 3801-4529	57	4	E 8
… 4424-OUT & 4531-OUT	58	4	E 7
Throgmorton Av	65	7	K 6
Throgs Neck Blvd	65	7	L 6
Throgs Neck Expwy	65	7	L 6
Throop Av	69	6	G 4
Thwaites Pl	67	4	F 6
Tibbett Av		5	B 4
… 1-3999	63	5	B 5
… 4000-OUT	71	5	B 4
Tiebout Av		4	D 7
… 1-2299	57	4	D 7
… 2300-OUT	58	4	D 7
Tiemann Av	69	6	G 4
Tier St	64	6	M 4
Tierney Pl	65	7	N 7
Tiffany St		3	F 9
… 1-849	74	3	G10
… 850-OUT	59	3	F 9
Tilden St		5	F 4
… 1-899	67	5	F 4
… 900-OUT	69	5	F 4
Tillotson Av		6	G 4
… 1-1999	69	6	G 4
… 2000-OUT	75	6	H 4
Tim Hendrick Pl	63	5	C 5
Timpson Pl	55	3	F10
Tinton Av		3	F 9
… 1-743	55	3	F10
… 744-OUT	56	3	F 9
Tomlinson Av	61	7	H 6
Topping Av	57	4	E 8
Torry Av	73	7	K 8
Townsend Av		4	D 8
… 1-1649	52	4	D 8
… 1650-OUT	53	4	D 8
Trafalgar Pl	60	4	F 8
Tratman Av	61	7	J 6
Tremont Av E		4	D 8
… 1-199	53	4	D 8
… 200-759	57	4	E 7
… 760-1879	60	4	G 7
… 1880-2399	62	7	H 7
… 2400-3400	61	7	H 6
… 3401-OUT	65	7	L 6
Tremont Av W	53	4	C 8
Trinity Av		3	F10
… 1-731 & 2-738	55	3	F10
… 733-OUT & 740-OUT	56	3	F10
Truxton St	74	3	G10
Tryon Av	67	5	E 4
Tudor Pl	52	3	D 9
Tulfan Ter	63	5	B 5
Turnbull Av	73	7	J 8
Turneur Av	73	7	K 8
Tyndall Av	71	5	B 3

U

STREET NAME AND HOUSE NUMBERS	ZONE NO.	MAP NO.	MAP GRID
Undercliff Av		4	C 8
… 1-1499	52	4	C 8
… 1500-OUT	53	4	C 8
Underhill Av		7	J 8
… 1-999	73	7	J 8
… 1000-OUT	72	7	H 8
Union Av		3	F 9
… 1-790	55	3	F10
… 791-OUT	59	3	F 9
Union Pl	52	3	C 9
Unionport Rd	62	4	G 6
Unionport Rd	62	7	H 7
University Av (Now Dr Martin Luther King Jr Blvd)	53	3	C 9
Unknown Soldier Plz	53	4	C 8

V

STREET NAME AND HOUSE NUMBERS	ZONE NO.	MAP NO.	MAP GRID
Valentine Av		4	D 6
… 1-2299	57	4	D 7
… 2300-OUT	58	4	D 6
Valhalla Pl	65	6	K 5
Valles Av	71	5	B 4
Van Buren St	60	4	G 7
Van Corlear Pl	63	4	B 6
Van Cortlandt Av E		5	D 5
… 1-149	68	5	D 5
… 150-199	58	5	D 5
… 200-OUT	67	5	E 5
Van Cortlandt Av W	63	5	C 5
Van Cortlandt Park E	70	5	D 3
Van Cortlandt Park S	63	5	C 5
Van Hoesen Av	61	6	H 5
Van Nest Av		4	G 7
… 1-646	60	4	G 7
… 647-1023	62	7	H 6
… 1024-OUT	61	7	H 6
Vance St	69	6	J 4
Varian Av	75	6	H 3
Verveelen Pl	63	4	C 6
Victor St	62	4	G 7
Viele Av	74	3	H10
Villa Av	68	5	D 5
Vilmont Rd *(near College of Mount Saint Vincent)	71	5	A 3
Vincent Av	65	7	L 6
Vineyard Pl	60	4	F 8
Vireo Av	70	5	E 2
Virgil Pl	73	7	J 8
Virginia Av		7	H 7
… 1-1299	72	7	H 7
… 1300-OUT	62	7	H 7
Vreeland Av	61	7	J 6
Vyse Av		4	F 8
… 1-1459	59	4	F 8
… 1460-OUT	60	4	F 8

W

STREET NAME AND HOUSE NUMBERS	ZONE NO.	MAP NO.	MAP GRID
Wade Sq	57	4	E 7
Waldo Av		5	B 4
… 1-3899	63	5	B 5
… 3900-OUT	71	5	B 4
Wales Av		3	F11
… 1-415	54	3	F11
… 416-OUT	55	3	F11
Wallace Av		5	F 5
… 1-2199	62	4	G 6
… 2200-3299	67	5	F 5
Walnut Av (Rose Feiss Blvd)	54	3	F11
Walton Av		4	D 7
… 1-890	51	3	D11
… 891-1649	52	3	D 9
… 1650-2293	53	4	D 7
… 2294-OUT	68	4	D 7
Ward Av	72	4	G 8
Waring Av		5	F 5
… 1-899	67	5	G 5
… 900-OUT	69	5	G 5
Washington Av		4	E 7
… 1-929	51	3	E10
… 931-1505 & 930-1510	56	3	E 9
… 1507-2289 1512 & 2288	57	4	E 8
… 2290-OUT	58	4	E 7
Waterbury Av		7	J 7
… 1-2599	62	7	J 7
… 2600-3099	61	7	K 6
… 3100-OUT	65	7	K 6
Waterloo Pl	60	4	F 8
Waters Pl	61	7	J 6
Watson Av		4	G 8
… 1-2199	72	4	G 8
… 2200-OUT	62	7	J 7
Watt Av	65	6	K 5
Wayne Av	67	5	E 4
Webb Av	68	4	C 6
Webster Av		4	E 6
… 1-1505	56	3	E 9
… 1506-2285	57	4	E 7
… 2287-3025 & 2286-3010	58	4	E 6
… 3027-3899 & 3012-3898	67	5	E 5
… 3900-OUT	70	5	E 3
Weeks Av	57	4	D 8
Weiher Ct	56	3	E 9
Wellman Av	61	7	J 6
Wenner Pl	65	7	K 7
West Av	62	7	H 7
West Botanical Sq	58	4	E 6
West Burnside Av	53	4	C 7
West Clarke Pl	52	3	D 9
West Farms Rd		3	F 9
… 1-1381	59	3	F 9
… 1382-OUT	60	4	G 8
West Fordham Rd	68	4	C 7
West Gun Hill Rd	67	5	D 4
West Kingsbridge Rd		4	C 6
… 1-148	68	4	C 6
… 149-OUT	63	4	C 6
West Mosholu Pkwy N (all odd numbers)	67	5	D 5
West Mosholu Pkwy S (all even numbers)	68	5	D 5
West Mount Eden Av	52	4	D 8
West Tremont Av	53	4	C 8
West 161st St	52	3	C10
West 162nd St	52	3	C10
West 163rd St	52	3	C10
West 164th St	52	3	C 9
West 165th St	52	3	C 9
West 166th St	52	3	C 9
West 167th St	52	3	C 9
West 168th St	52	3	C 9
West 169th St	52	3	C 9
West 170th St	52	3	C 9
West 171st St	52	3	C 9
West 172nd St	52	4	C 8
West 173rd St	52	4	C 8
West 174th St	53	4	C 8
West 175th St	53	4	C 8
West 176th St	53	4	C 8
West 177th St	53	4	D 8
West 178th St	53	4	C 8
West 179th St	53	4	C 7
West 180th St	53	4	C 7
West 181st St	53	4	D 7
West 182nd St	53	4	D 7
West 183rd St	53	4	C 7
West 184th St	68	4	D 7
West 188th St	68	4	D 6
West 190th St	68	4	D 6
West 192nd St	68	4	D 6
West 193rd St	63	4	C 6
West 195th St	68	4	D 6
West 197th St	68	4	C 6
West 205th St	68	5	D 5
West 225th St	63	5	C 6
West 227th St	63	4	B 6
West 228th St	63	4	C 6
West 229th St	63	4	C 6
West 230th St	63	4	B 6
West 231st St	63	5	B 5
West 232nd St	63	5	B 5
West 233rd St	63	5	C 5
West 234th St	63	5	B 5
West 235th St	63	5	B 5
West 236th St	63	5	B 5
West 237th St	63	5	B 5
West 237th St	63	5	C 5
West 238th St	63	5	B 5
West 238th St	63	5	C 5
West 239th St	63	5	B 5
West 239th St	63	5	C 5
West 240th St		5	B 5
… 1-499	63	5	B 5
… 500-OUT	71	5	B 5
West 242nd St	71	5	B 5
West 244th St	71	5	B 4
West 245th St	71	5	B 4
West 246th St	71	5	B 4
West 247th St	71	5	A 4
West 248th St	71	5	A 4
West 249th St	71	5	A 4
West 250th St	71	5	B 4
West 251st St	71	5	B 4
West 252nd St	71	5	A 4
West 252nd St	71	5	B 4
West 253rd St	71	5	B 4
West 254th St	71	5	A 4
West 255th St	71	5	B 4
West 256th St	71	5	A 4
West 256th St	71	5	B 3
West 259th St	71	5	A 3
West 260th St	71	5	A 3
West 261st St	71	5	A 3
West 262nd St	71	5	A 3
West 263rd St	71	5	A 3
Westchester Av		3	E10
… 1-839	55	3	E10
… 841-1399 & 840-1326	59	3	F 9
… 1401-1899 & 1328-1898	72	4	G 8
… 1900-2379	62	7	H 7
… 2380-OUT	61	7	J 6
Westchester Sq	61	7	J 6
Westervelt Av	69	6	H 4
Whalen St	71	5	B 3
Wheeler Av		4	G 8
… 1-999	73	3	G 9
… 1000-OUT	72	4	G 8
White Plains Rd		5	E 3
… 1-999	73	7	J 8
… 1000-1299	72	7	H 8
… 1300-2199	62	4	G 6
… 2200-3899	67	5	F 5
… 3900-4399	66	5	E 3
… 4400-OUT	70	5	E 2
Whitehall Pl	66	5	F 2
Whitlock Av	59	3	G 9
Whittemore Av	65	7	K 6
Whittier St	74	3	G 9
Wickham Av		5	F 2
… 1-3499	69	6	G 3
… 3500-OUT	66	5	F 2
Wilcox Av	65	7	L 6
Wilder Av		5	F 2
… 1-4799	66	5	F 2
… 4800-OUT	70	5	F 2
Wilkinson Av	61	6	H 5
Wilkinson Av	61	6	J 5
Willett Av	67	5	E 4
William Av	64	6	M 4
William Pl	61	7	J 6
Williamsbridge Rd		5	G 5
… 1-2199	61	7	H 6
… 2200-2899	69	5	G 5
… 2900-OUT	67	5	F 5
Williamsbridge Sq	67	5	F 4
Willis Av		3	E11
… 1-439	54	3	E11
… 440-OUT	55	3	E11
Willow Av	54	3	F11
Willow La	61	6	J 5
Wilson Av		6	G 4
… 1-2199	61	6	H 5
… 2200-OUT	69	6	G 4
Windham Pl	63	4	C 6
Windward La	64	6	M 4
Winter St	64	6	M 4
Wissman Av	65	7	M 6
Wood Av		7	H 7
… 1-1879	60	7	H 7
… 1880-OUT	62	7	H 7
Wood Rd	62	7	H 7
Woodhull Av	69	6	H 4
Woodmansten Pl	62	4	G 6
Woodrow Wilson Sq	73	7	J 9
Woodycrest Av	52	3	C 9
Worthen St	74	3	G10
Wright Av	69	6	H 3
Wyatt St	60	4	G 7
Wythe Pl	52	3	D 9

Y

STREET NAME AND HOUSE NUMBERS	ZONE NO.	MAP NO.	MAP GRID
Yates Av		6	G 5
… 1-2199	61	7	H 6
… 2200-OUT	69	6	G 5
Young Av	69	6	G 4
Yznaga Pl	65	7	K 8

Z

STREET NAME AND HOUSE NUMBERS	ZONE NO.	MAP NO.	MAP GRID
Zerega Av		7	J 7
… 1-999	73	7	K 7
… 1000-OUT	62	7	J 7
Zulette Av	61	7	J 6

NUMBERED STREETS

STREET NAME AND HOUSE NUMBERS	ZONE NO.	MAP NO.	MAP GRID
1st Av	65	7	M 6
2nd Av	65	7	M 6
3rd Av	65	7	M 6
4th Av	65	7	M 6
5th Av	65	7	M 6
7th Av	65	7	M 6
9th Av	65	7	M 6
11th Av	65	7	M 6
229th Dr N	66	5	F 3
229th Dr S	66	5	G 3

NOTE: To obtain ZIP code for Queens; Long Island City add 1110 before postal zone numbers; Jamaica add 114 before postal zone numbers; Flushing add 113 before postal zone numbers; Far Rockaway add 116 before postal zone numbers; Floral Park add 1100 before postal zone numbers.

A

Street Name and House Numbers	Zone No.	Map No.	Map Grid
Abbott Rd	59	10	M 7
Aberdeen Rd		13	M11
180-00 - 187-99	32	13	M11
188-00 - OUT	23	13	M11
Abigail Adams Av	32	13	M11
Abingdon Rd	15	12	K12
Acme Ter	93	16	K17
Adair St	13	15	N13
Adams Ct			
*(off Beach 39th St)	91	16	N18
Adelaide Rd	33	15	M13
Adirondack Blvd	94	17	J 19
Admiral Av	79	11	G12
Aguilar Av	67	12	L 11
Alameda Av	62	10	O 9
Albany Ct			
*(off Beach 109th St)	94	18	K19
Albert Rd	17	14	K14
Albion Av	73	11	H10
Alderton St	74	11	H11
Alecia Av	13	15	N14
Alice Ct			
*(off St. Marks Av)	94	18	K19
Alison St	62	10	O 9
Allen St			
*(off Beach 88th St)	93	18	L 18
Allendale St	35	12	L 12
Almeda Av		18	L 18
51-00 - 53-99	91	18	L 18
54-00 - OUT	92	18	L 18
Almeda Ct			
*(off Beach 107th St)	94	18	K19
Almont Rd	91	16	O17
Alonzo Rd	91	16	O17
Alston Pl	63	10	N 8
Alstyne Av		11	H10
94-00 - 95-99	73	12	J 10
96-00 - OUT	68	12	J 10
Alwick Rd	20	14	L 14
Amber St		14	J 14
105-00 - 109-99	17	14	J 14
133-00 - 156-99	14	14	J 14
Amboy La	28	13	O11
Amboy Pl	29	13	O11
Amelia Rd	34	15	N13
Amory Ct	85	11	G12
Amstel Blvd	92	18	L 18
Anchor Dr	91	16	N17
Anderson Rd	34	15	N13
Andrews Av	78	11	G11
Ankener Av	73	11	H10
Ann Ct			
*(off Beach 49th St)	91	18	M18
Annandale La	62	10	O 8
Annapolis St	91	16	O17
Anthony Ct *(off Seagirt Av near Beach 7th St)	91	16	O18
Apex Pl	75	12	J 10
Arcade Av	12	13	M12
Arcadia Wk	97	17	G20
Arch St	11	11	E10
Archer Av		13	M12
139-00 - 149-99	35	13	L 12
150-00 - OUT	33	13	M12
Archway Pl	75	12	J 11
Ardsley Rd	63	10	N 8
Arion Rd	17	14	J 14
Arleigh Rd	63	10	N 8
Arlene Ct			
*(off Beach 116th St)	94	18	K19
Arlington Ter		14	L 13
145-00 - 147-99	35	14	L 13
150-00 - 155-99	33	15	M13
Arnold Av	78	11	G11
Arnold Ct			
*(off Beach 28th St)	91	16	N18
Arthur St	13	15	N14
Arverne Blvd	92	18	M18
Ascan Av	75	12	K12
Ash Av	55	9	K 9
Ashby Av	58	10	M 9
Ashford St	27	13	O11
Aske Pl	73	11	H10
Aske St	73	11	H10
Aspen Pl	32	13	M11
Asquith Cres	74	12	J 11
Astor Ct			
*(off Beach 107th St)	94	18	K19
Astoria Blvd		8	F 8
1-01 - 32-99	2	8	F 8
33-01 - 38-99 (odd)	3	8	G 9
33-02 - 48-98 (even)	3	8	G 9
40-01 - 47-99	5	8	G 9
49-00 - 85-99	70	8	G 9
86-00 - 112-98	69	8	H 9
Astoria Blvd N	5	8	F 9
Astoria Blvd S	3	8	F 9
Astoria Pk S	2	8	F 8
Astoria Sq	2	8	F 8
Atlantic Av		14	J 13
74-00 - 107-98 (even)	21	14	J 13
74-01 - 99-99 (odd)	21	14	J 13
100-01 - 135-99 (odd)	18	14	K13
108-00 - 135-98 (even)	19	14	K13
Atlantic Ct			
*(off Beach 107th St)	94	18	K19
Atlantic Wk	97	17	G20
Aubrey Av	85	12	J 12
Auburndale La	58	9	L 9
Audley St		12	K12
100 - 119	15	12	K12
124 - 199	18	12	K12
116-00 - 117-99	18	12	K12
119-00 - 121-99	15	12	K12
Auer's Pier			
*(off Beach 95th St)	93	18	L 18
Augusta Ct	34	15	M13
Augustina Av	91	16	O17
Austell Pl	1	11	E10
Austin St		11	H11
61-00 - 66-99	74	12	J 11
67-00 - 79-99	75	12	K11
80-00 - 85-99	15	12	K12
Ava Pl	32	13	M11
Avery Av	55	9	K 9
Avon Rd		13	M11
84-00 - 87-99	32	13	M11
182-00 - 187-99	32	13	M11
188-00 - OUT	23	13	M11
Avon St	32	13	M11
Aztec Pl	91	16	N18

B

Street Name and House Numbers	Zone No.	Map No.	Map Grid
Babbage St	18	12	K12
Babylon Av	12	13	N12
Bagley Av	58	10	M 9
Bailey Ct	91	16	N17
Baisley Blvd		15	M14
131-00 - 180-99	34	15	M14
181-00 - 188-99	12	15	N13
Baker's Ct *(off Beach 101st St near RR)	94	18	L 19
Baldwin Av	75	12	J 11
Balsam Ct *(off Sage St)	91	16	O17
Barbadoes Dr	92	18	L 18
Barclay Av	55	9	K 9
Bardwell Av	29	13	O12
Barnett Av	4	11	F10
Barnwell Av	73	11	H10
Barrington St	32	13	M11
Barron St	34	15	M13
Barrows Ct	62	10	O 9
Barton Av	54	9	L 9
Bascom Av	36	15	M14
Bates Rd	62	10	O 8
Bath Wk	97	17	F20
Battery Rd	91	16	N17
Baxter Av	73	11	H10
Bay Club Dr	60	10	M 8
Bay Ct			
*(off Beach 101st St)	94	18	L 19
Bay Ct	91	16	N17
Bay Park Pl	91	16	N17
Bay St	63	10	N 8
Bay Ter	97	17	F20
Bay 24th St	91	16	N17
Bay 25th St	91	16	N17
Bay 27th St	91	16	N17
Bay 28th St	91	16	N17
Bay 30th St	91	16	N18
Bay 31st St	91	16	N18
Bay 32nd Pl	91	16	N17
Bay 32nd St	91	16	N18
Bayfield Av	92	18	M18
Bayport Pl	91	16	O17
Bayside Av		9	K 8
118-00 - 157-99	54	9	K 8
158-00 - 199-99	58	9	L 8
Bayside Av	97	17	G20
Bayside Dock			
*(off Beach 94th St)	93	18	L 18
Bayside Dr	97	17	G20
Bayside La	58	9	L 8
Bayside St	59	10	M 7
Bayside St	97	17	G20
Bayside Wk	97	17	G20
Bayswater Av	91	16	N17
Bayswater Ct	91	16	N17
Bayview Av	63	10	N 8
Bayview Wk	97	18	L 19
Bayway Wk	97	17	F20
Beach Channel Dr		18	K19
1 - 53-99	91	16	N18
54-00 - 77-99	92	16	O17
78-00 - 97-99	93	16	L 18
98-00 - OUT	94	16	K19
Beach 3rd St	91	16	O18
Beach 4th St	91	16	O18
Beach 5th St	91	16	O18
Beach 6th St	91	16	O18
Beach 7th St	91	16	O18
Beach 8th St	91	16	O18
Beach 9th St	91	16	O18
Beach 11th St	91	16	O18
Beach 12th St	91	16	O17
Beach 13th St	91	16	O18
Beach 14th St	91	16	O18
Beach 15th St	91	16	O18
Beach 16th St	91	16	O18
Beach 17th St	91	16	O18
Beach 18th St	91	16	O17
Beach 19th St	91	16	O18
Beach 20th St	91	16	O18
Beach 21st St	91	16	O18
Beach 22nd St	91	16	N18
Beach 24th St	91	16	N18
Beach 25th St	91	16	N18
Beach 26th St	91	16	N18
Beach 27th St	91	16	N18
Beach 28th St	91	16	N18
Beach 29th St	91	16	N18
Beach 30th St	91	16	N18
Beach 31st St	91	16	N18
Beach 32nd St	91	16	N18
Beach 33rd St	91	16	N18
Beach 34th St	91	16	N18
Beach 35th St	91	16	N18
Beach 36th St	91	16	N18
Beach 37th St	91	16	N18
Beach 38th St	91	16	N18
Beach 39th St	91	16	N18
Beach 40th St	91	16	N18
Beach 41st Pl	91	16	N18
Beach 41st St	91	16	N18
Beach 42nd St	91	16	N18
Beach 43rd St	91	16	N18
Beach 44th St	91	16	N18
Beach 45th St	91	16	N18
Beach 46th Pl	91	16	N18
Beach 46th St	91	16	N18
Beach 46th Way	91	16	N18
Beach 47th St	91	16	N18
Beach 47th Way	91	18	N18
Beach 48th St	91	16	N18
Beach 48th Way	91	18	N18
Beach 49th St	91	18	M18
Beach 50th St	91	18	M18
Beach 51st St	91	18	M18
Beach 52nd St	91	18	M18
Beach 53rd St	91	18	M18
Beach 54th St	92	18	M18
Beach 56th Pl	92	18	M18
Beach 56th St	92	18	M18
Beach 57th St	92	18	M18
Beach 58th St	92	18	M18
Beach 59th St	92	18	M18
Beach 60th St	92	18	M18
Beach 61st St	92	18	M18
Beach 62nd St	92	18	M18
Beach 63rd St	92	18	M18
Beach 64th St	92	18	M18
Beach 65th St	92	18	M18
Beach 66th St	92	18	M18
Beach 67th St	92	18	M18
Beach 68th St	92	18	M18
Beach 69th St	92	18	M18
Beach 70th St	92	18	M18
Beach 71st St	92	18	M18
Beach 72nd St	92	18	L 18
Beach 73rd St	92	18	L 18
Beach 74th St	92	18	L 18
Beach 75th St	92	18	L 18
Beach 76th St	92	18	L 18
Beach 77th St	92	18	L 18
Beach 79th St	93	18	L 18
Beach 80th St	93	18	L 18
Beach 81st St	93	18	L 18
Beach 82nd St	93	18	L 18
Beach 83rd St	93	18	L 18
Beach 84th St	93	18	L 18
Beach 85th St	93	18	L 18
Beach 86th St	93	18	L 18
Beach 87th St	93	18	L 18
Beach 88th St	93	18	L 18
Beach 89th St	93	18	L 18
Beach 90th St	93	18	L 18
Beach 91st St	93	18	L 18
Beach 92nd St	93	18	L 18
Beach 93rd St	93	18	L 19
Beach 94th St	93	18	L 19
Beach 95th St	93	18	L 19
Beach 96th St	93	18	L 18
Beach 97th St	93	18	L 19
Beach 98th St	94	18	L 19
Beach 99th St	94	18	L 19
Beach 100th St	94	18	L 19
Beach 101st St	94	18	L 19
Beach 102nd La	94	18	K19
Beach 102nd St	94	18	L 19
Beach 104th St	94	18	K19
Beach 105th St	94	18	K19
Beach 106th La	94	18	K19
Beach 106th St	94	18	K19
Beach 108th St	94	18	K19
Beach 109th St	94	18	K19
Beach 110th St	94	18	K19
Beach 111th St	94	18	K19
Beach 112th St	94	18	K19
Beach 113th St	94	18	K19
Beach 114th St	94	18	K19
Beach 115th St	94	18	K19
Beach 116th St	94	18	K19
Beach 117th St	94	18	K19
Beach 118th St	94	18	K19
Beach 119th St	94	18	K19
Beach 120th St	94	18	K19
Beach 121st St	94	17	K19
Beach 122nd St	94	17	K19
Beach 123rd St	94	17	K19
Beach 124th St	94	17	K19
Beach 125th St	94	17	K19
Beach 126th St	94	17	J 19
Beach 127th St	94	17	J 19
Beach 128th St	94	17	J 19
Beach 129th St	94	17	J 19
Beach 130th St	94	17	J 19
Beach 131st St	94	17	J 19
Beach 132nd St	94	17	J 19
Beach 133rd St	94	17	J 19
Beach 134th St	94	17	J 19
Beach 135th St	94	17	J 19
Beach 136th St	94	17	J 19
Beach 137th St	94	17	J 19
Beach 138th St	94	17	J 19
Beach 139th St	94	17	J 19
Beach 140th St	94	17	J 19
Beach 141st St	94	17	J 19
Beach 142nd St	94	17	J 19
Beach 143rd St	94	17	J 19
Beach 144th St	94	17	J 19
Beach 145th St	94	17	J 19
Beach 146th St	94	17	J 19
Beach 147th St	94	17	J 19
Beach 148th St	94	17	J 19
Beach 149th St	94	17	J 19
Beach 169th St	94	17	H20
Beach 193rd St	97	17	G20
Beach 201st St	97	17	G20
Beach 204th St	97	17	G20
Beach 207th St	97	17	G20
Beach 208th St	97	17	G20
Beach 209th St	97	17	G20
Beach 210th St	97	17	G20
Beach 213th St	97	17	F 20
Beach 214th St	97	17	F 20
Beach 215th St	97	17	F 20
Beach 216th St	97	17	F 20
Beach 217th St	97	17	F 20
Beach 219th St	97	17	F 20
Beach 220th St	97	17	F 20
Beach 221st St	97	17	F 20
Beach 222nd St	97	17	F 20
Beacon Pl	91	16	N17
Beatrice Ct	91	16	N17
Beaver Rd	33	12	L 12
Beck Rd	91	16	O17
Bedell St		15	M13
112-00 - 113-99	33	15	M13
114-00 - 136-99	34	15	N13
137-00 - OUT	13	15	N14
Bedford Av	97	17	G20
Beech Av	55	9	K 9
Beech Cir	56	9	J 8
Beech Ct	56	9	J 8
Beechknoll Av	62	10	O 9
Beechknoll Pl	75	12	K11
Belknap St	13	15	N13
Bell Blvd		10	M 8
12-00 - 31-99	60	13	M 8
32-00 - 47-99	61	13	M 9
48-00 - 79-99	64	13	N10
80-00 - 85-99	27	13	N10
Bellaire Pl	29	13	N11
Belmont Av	17	14	J 14
Belt Pkwy		14	J 15
Benham St	73	11	H10
Benida Ct *(off Jarvis Ct near Beach 9th St)		16	O18
Bennett Ct	34	15	N13
Bennett St		15	N13
132-00 - 136-99	34	15	N13
137-00 - OUT	13	15	N14
Bentley Rd	22	15	O15
Benton St	13	15	N13
Bergen Rd	30	14	L 14
Berkely Ct			
*(off Beach 50th St)	91	18	M18
Berkey Av	70	8	G 9
Berkley Ct			
*(off Beach 56th Pl)	92	18	M18
Bernal Colony			
*(off Beach 46th St)	91	16	N18
Bernard Ct			
*(off Beach 55th St)	92	18	M18
Berrian Blvd	5	8	G 8
Berrian St	69	8	H 8
Bert Rd	93	16	L 17
Bessemer St	18	12	K12
Bessemund Av	91	16	N18
Betty Ct			
*(off Beach 109th St)	94	18	K19
Beverley Rd	15	12	K12
Beverley Rd	63	10	N 8
Beverly Ct			
*(off Brookhaven Av)	91	16	N18
Billings St	27	13	O11
Birdsall Av	91	16	O17
Birmington Pkwy	64	10	N 9
Blake Av		14	J 14
75-00 - 77-99	14	14	J 14
78-00 - OUT	17	14	J 14
Bleecker St	85	11	G12
Blossom Av	55	9	K 9
Boardwalk		18	M18
1-00 - 53-99	91	18	N18
54-00 - 77-99	92	18	M18
78-00 - 97-99	93	18	L 19
98-00 - OUT	94	18	K19
Boelsen Cres	74	12	J 11
Boker Ct	56	9	J 8
Bolton Rd	91	16	O17
Bonnie La	60	10	M 8
Boody St	77	8	G 9
Booth Memorial Av		12	K10
132-00 - 157-99	55	12	K10
158-00 - OUT	65	12	L 10
Booth St		11	H11
60-00 - 60-99	73	11	H11
61-00 - 66-99	74	12	J 11
67-00 - 68-99	75	12	J 11
Borage Pl	75	12	K11
Borden Av		11	E10
2-01 - 38-99	1	11	F10
44-00 - 68-99	78	11	F10
Borkel Pl	28	13	O11
Borough Pl	77	8	G 9
Boss St	17	14	K13
Boulevard St	57	9	K 7
Boundary Rd	59	10	M 7
Bourton St	74	11	H11
Bow St	75	12	J 11
Bowden Av	61	10	M 9
Bowne St		9	K 9
36-00 - 40-99	54	9	K 9
41-00 - 52-99	55	9	K 9
Boyce Av	61	10	M 9
Braddock Av		13	O11
220-00 - 220-99	27	13	O11
221-01 - 221-99	27	13	O11
221-00 - 235-99 (odd)	28	13	O11
222-01 - 235-99 (even)	28	13	O11
236-00 - OUT	26	13	O11
Bradley Av	1	11	E10
Brant Wk	97	17	G20
Brattle Av	62	10	O 9
Braus Ct *(off 69th St)	92	18	M18
Breezy Point Blvd	97	17	F20
Brefney Ct *(off Beach 108th & 109th Sts)	94	18	K19
Brevoort St	15	12	K12
Brewster Ct			
*(off Beach 109th St)	94	18	K19
Brian Cres	60	10	M 8
Briar Pl	91	16	N18
Bridge Plz N	1	11	E10
Bridge Plz S	1	8	E 9
Bridgeton St	14	14	K14
Bridgewater Av			
(Floral Park)	4	10	P 9
Brinkerhoff Av	12	13	N12
Brisbin St	35	12	L 12
Bristol Av	17	14	K14
Britton Av	73	11	H10
Broacher Rd	34	15	N13
Broadway		8	F 9
8-01 - 36-99	6	8	F 9
37-01 - 48-99	3	8	F 9
49-00 - 69-99	77	8	G 9
70-00 - 73-99	72	11	G10
74-00 - OUT	73	11	H10
Broadway Ct			
*(off Sage St)	91	16	O17
Brookhaven Av	91	16	N18
Brooklyn-Queens Expwy	77	11	F10
Brookside St	63	10	O 8
Brookville Blvd	22	15	O14
Brown Pl	78	11	G11
Brown's Blvd	97	17	H20
Browvale La	62	10	O 8
Brunswick Av	91	16	O17
Budd Pl	54	9	K 9
Buell St	69	9	J 9
Bunnecke Ct	85	11	G12
Burchell Av	92	18	L 18
Burchell Pl *(off Rockaway Beach Blvd near Beach 102nd St)	94	18	L 19
Burchell Rd	92	18	M18
Burden Cres	35	12	L 12
Burdette Pl	32	12	L 12
Burling St	55	9	K 9
Burns St		12	J 11
6 - 898	75	12	K11
66-00 - 66-99	74	12	J 11
67-00 - 78-99	75	12	J 11
Burrough Pl	77	11	G10
Burton St	57	9	L 8
Butler Av	85	11	G12
Butler St	69	9	J 9
Bye St	75	12	K11
Byrd St	55	9	K 9
Byron St	34	15	M14

C

Street Name and House Numbers	Zone No.	Map No.	Map Grid
Cabot Rd	85	14	G13
Caffrey Av	91	16	O18
Calamus Av		11	G10
69-00 - 73-99	77	11	G10
74 - OUT	73	11	H10
Calamus Cir	73	11	H10
Caldwell Av		11	G11
68-00 - 73-99	78	11	G11
74-00 - 81-99	73	11	H11
82-00 - 82-99	79	11	H11
Calloway St	68	12	J 10
Calsing St			
*(off Beach 107th St)	94	18	K19
Cambria Av	62	10	O 9
Cambridge Rd	32	13	M11
Camden Av	12	13	N12
Camp Rd	91	16	N18
Caney La	22	15	O14
Caney Rd	22	15	P14
Capstan Ct	56	9	J 7
Cargo Plz	30	15	M15
Cargo Service Rd	30	14	L15
Carleton Pl	54	9	K 9
Carlton St	74	11	H11
Carolina Rd	62	10	O 9
Carpenter Av	23	13	N12
Carson St	13	15	N14
Case St	73	11	H10

STREET NAME AND HOUSE NUMBERS	ZONE NO.	MAP NO.	MAP GRID
Castlewood St (Floral Park)	4	13	P10
Catalpa Av	85	11	G12
Catherine Ct *(off Beach 104th St)	94	18	K19
Cedar La	63	10	N 8
Cedarcroft Rd	32	13	M12
Cedarhill Rd	91	16	O18
Cedarlawn Av *(off Reads La)	91	16	O17
Cedric Rd	20	14	L 14
Celtic Av	77	11	F 10
Center Cargo Rd	30	15	M15
Center Cargo Rd	63	10	N 8
Center Dr	57	9	K 7
Center Dr	57	9	K 7
Center St	97	17	H20
Centerville St	17	14	K14
Central Av	85	11	H12
Central Av	91	16	O17
Centre St	85	11	G12
Champlain Rd	93	16	K17
Chandler Ct *(near 165th Av & 104th St)	14	14	K15
Chandler St	91	16	N17
Channel Rd	93	16	L 17
Channing Rd	91	16	O17
Chapel Rd	59	10	M 7
Chapel Wk	97	17	G20
Chapin Ct	32	12	L 11
Chapin Pkwy	32	12	L 11
Charlecote Ridge	32	13	M11
Charlotte St	85	11	F 12
Charter Rd	35	12	L 11
Chelsea St	32	13	M11
Cheney St	34	15	N14
Cherry Av	55	9	K 9
Cherry St	63	10	N 8
Chester Wk	97	17	G20
Chevy Chase St	32	13	M11
Chicot Ct	17	14	K13
Christie Av	68	12	J 10
Church Av	97	17	H20
Church Rd	93	16	L 17
Cinder Rd *(off Rockaway Point Blvd)	97	17	G20
Circle Dr	59	10	M 7
Circle Rd	63	10	N 8
Claran Ct	78	11	G11
Claremont Ter	73	11	H10
Claude St	33	15	M13
Clearview Expwy		10	M 8
14-00 - 31-99	60	10	M 8
32-00 - 47-99	61	10	M 9
48-00 - OUT	64	10	M 9
Clinton Av	78	11	G11
Clinton Pl	32	12	L 12
Clinton Ter	32	12	L 12
Clinton Wk	97	17	F 20
Clintonville St	57	9	L 7
Clio St	23	13	N11
Clover Hill Dr	23	13	N11
Clover Hill Rd	23	13	N11
Clover Pl	23	13	N11
Clover Pl	85	14	G13
Cloverdale Blvd	64	10	N 9
Clyde St		12	J 11
66-00 - 66-99	74	12	J 11
67-00 - 68-99	75	12	J 11
Coast Guard Ct *(off Beach 58th St)	92	18	M18
Codwise Pl	73	11	H10
Cody Av	85	14	G13
Cohancy St		14	K14
150-00 - 150-99	17	14	K14
155-00 - 155-99	14	14	K14
Cold Spring Rd	91	16	N17
Colden St	55	9	K 9
Coleman Sq	14	14	K14
Coles La *(off Beach 9th St)	91	16	O18
Colfax St		13	O12
109-00 - 113-99	29	13	O12
114-00 - OUT	11	13	O12
College Pl	56	9	J 7
College Point Blvd		9	J 8
1 - 24-99	56	9	J 8
25-00 - 40-99	54	9	J 9
41-00 - 60-00	55	9	K 9
Collier Av	91	16	N18
Collins Pl	54	9	K 9
Colonial Av	75	12	J 10
Colonial Ct *(off Beach 107th St)	94	18	K19
Columbus Sq	2	8	F 9
Commissary Rd	30	14	L 15
Commonwealth Blvd		10	O 9
63-00 - 73-99	62	10	O 9
74-01 - 90-98	26	13	P10
Como Av	23	13	N11
Compass Rd	30	15	M15
Conch Rd	91	16	N18
Concord St	62	10	O 8
Congressman Rosenthal Av	54	9	K 9
Constance Ct *(off Beach 101st St)	94	18	K19
Continental Av	75	12	J 12
Cook Av	79	11	H12
Coolidge Av		12	L 11
135-00 - 149-99	35	12	L 11
150-00 - OUT	32	12	L 11
Coolidge Ct *(off Beach 39th St)	91	16	N18
Coombs St	13	15	N14
Cooper Av		11	H12
15-00 - 89-31	85	11	G12
89-34 - 89-98	74	12	J 12
Cooper Ter	85	11	H12
Corbett Rd	61	10	N 9
Cornaga Av	91	16	N18
Cornaga Ct *(off Reads La)	91	16	O17
Cornelia St	85	11	G12
Cornell La *(north from Northern Blvd east of Marathon Pkwy)	63	10	O 9
Cornish Av	73	11	H10
Corona Av		11	H10
84-00 - 95-99	73	12	J 10
96-00 - 112-99	68	12	J 10
Coronado Ct *(off Seagirt Av near Beach 6th St)	91	16	O18
Corporal Kennedy St		10	M 8
1-00 - 31-99	60	10	M 8
32-00 - 47-99	61	10	M 9
Corporal Stone St		10	N 9
1-00 - 31-99	60	10	N 9
32-00 - 47-99	61	10	N 9
Corsline St	73	11	H10
Costa Av	92	18	L 18
Couch Pl	69	9	J 9
Court Sq	1	11	E10
Courtney Av	58	10	M 9
Courtney La	97	17	G20
Cove Ct	56	9	J 7
Covert St	85	19	F 13
Cowles Ct	79	11	H11
Craft Av	22	15	O15
Crandall Av	34	15	N14
Crane St	1	11	E10
Cranford St	75	12	K11
Cranston St	34	15	M14
Crawford Ct *(off Beach 19th St near Cornaga Av)	91	16	O18
Creekside Av	97	17	G20
Crescent St (25th St)		11	E10
20-01 - 23-99	5	8	F 8
24-01 - 30-99	2	8	F 8
31-01 - 36-99	6	8	F 9
37-01 - 44-99	1	8	E 9
Creskill Pl	35	12	L 12
Crest Rd *(in Wavecrest Gdns)	91	16	N18
Crocheron Av		9	L 9
161-00 - 199-99	58	9	L 9
200-00 - 223-99	61	10	M 9
Crommelin St	55	9	K 9
Cromwell Cres	74	12	J 11
Cronston Av	94	17	J 19
Cross Bay Blvd		14	K13
103-00 - 151-99	17	16	K16
152-00 - 165-99	14	16	L 17
Cross Bay Pkwy	93	18	L 18
Cross Bay Veterans Memorial Bridge (Broad Channel)	93	18	L 18
Cross Island Pkwy		10	M 8
10-01 - 12-99	57	9	K 7
80-00 - 88-19	26	13	O10
99-00 - 119-98	29	13	O11
114-00 - 119-98	11	15	O13
148-00 - 199-99	57	9	L 8
200-00 - OUT	60	10	M 8
Croydon Rd	32	13	M11
Crugers Rd	92	18	L 18
Cryders La	57	9	L 8
Cullman Av	62	10	O 9
Culloden Pl	16	14	J 13
Curley Ct *(off Beach 102nd St near Beach Channel Dr)	94	16	K18
Curtis St	69	8	H 9
Curzon Rd	18	12	K12
Cuthbert Rd	15	12	K12
Cynthia Ct *(off Beach 101st St near RR)	94	18	L 19
Cypress Av	85	11	F 12
Cypress Hills St	85	11	G12

D

STREET NAME AND HOUSE NUMBERS	ZONE NO.	MAP NO.	MAP GRID
Dahlia Av	55	9	K 9
Daisy Pl	26	10	O 9
Dalny Rd	32	13	M11
Dana Ct	79	11	H11
Dane Pl	75	12	J 11
Daniels St	35	12	L 11
Darren Dr	60	10	M 8
Dartmouth St		12	J 11
1-188	75	12	J 11
66-00 - 66-99	74	12	J 11
67-00 - 70-65	75	12	J 11
Dashby Ct *(off Beach 79th St)	93	18	L 18
Davenport Av		13	O11
220-00 - 235-99	28	13	O11
236-00 - 237-99	26	13	O11
Davenport St	14	14	K15
David Ct *(off Beach 55th St)	92	18	M18
Davies Rd	91	16	O18
Davis Ct *(off Beach 88th St)	93	18	L 18
Davis Ct	1	11	E10
Davis St	1	11	E10
Deauville Wk	97	17	F 20
Decatur St	85	11	G12
De Costa Av	92	18	L 18
Deepdale Av	62	10	O 9
Deepdale Pl	62	10	O 9
Deepdene Pl	75	12	K11
Deerfield Rd	91	16	N18
Defoe St	13	15	N13
De Kalb Av	85	11	F 12
Delaney Ct *(off St. Marks Av near Beach 104th St)	94	18	K19
Delaware Av	55	9	L 9
Delevan St	29	13	O12
Delmore Ct *(off Beach 43rd St)	91	16	N17
Delong St		9	K 9
40-00 - 40-99	54	9	K 9
41-00 - 41-99	55	9	K 9
Demerest Rd (Broad Channel)	93	18	L 18
Denis St	34	15	N13
Denman St	73	11	H10
De Orio Ct *(off St. Marks Av)	94	18	K19
Depew Av	63	10	O 8
Depot Rd		9	L 9
156-00 - 157-99	54	9	L 9
158-00 - OUT	58	9	L 9
Desarc Rd	17	14	J 14
DeSota Pl *(off Beach 92nd St)	93	18	L 18
DeSota Rd	93	18	L 18
Devon Wk	97	17	G20
Devonshire Rd	32	13	M11
Dexter Ct	21	14	H13
Diamond St	21	12	J 12
Diane Pl	60	10	M 8
Dickens St	91	16	N17
Dieterle Cres	74	12	J 11
Digby Pl	16	14	J 13
Dillon St	33	15	M13
Dinsmore Av	91	16	O17
Ditmars Blvd		8	F 8
18-01 - 48-99	5	8	G 8
49-00 - 84-99	70	8	G 9
85-00 - 112-99	69	8	H 8
Division St	22	16	O16
Dix Av	91	16	N17
Dix Pl *(off Beach Channel Dr near Mott Av)	91	16	N17
Donald Ct *(off New Haven Av near Beach 15th St)	91	16	O18
Doncaster Pl	32	13	M11
Dongan Av	73	11	H10
Doran Av	85	12	J 12
Dorian Ct	91	16	O18
Doris La	97	17	G20
Dorman Ct *(off Beach 88th St)	93	18	L 18
Dormans Rd	12	13	N12
Dorothy Ct *(off Rockaway Beach Blvd near Beach 106th St)	94	18	K19
Dorothy Pl	2	8	F 8
Douglas Av	33	13	M12
Douglas Rd	63	10	N 8
Douglaston Pkwy		10	N 9
25-00 - 44-99	63	10	O 9
45-00 - 72-99	62	10	O 9
Downing St	54	9	K 9
Drew St	16	14	J 13
Dry Harbor Rd	79	11	H11
Duane Rd	59	10	M 7
Dumfries Pl	32	13	M11
Dumont Av		14	J 14
75-00 - 78-99	14	14	J 14
83-01 - 87-99	17	14	J 14
Dunbar St	91	16	N17
Dune St *(off Seagirt Blvd at Beach 25th St)	91	16	N18
Dunkirk St		13	M12
104-00 - 115-99	12	15	N13
187-00 - 188-99	12	15	N13
Dunlop Av	12	13	N12
Dunton Av	23	13	N11
Dunton St	23	13	N11
Dutch Kills St	1	11	E10
Dwight Av	91	16	N18

E

STREET NAME AND HOUSE NUMBERS	ZONE NO.	MAP NO.	MAP GRID
East Dock St	22	16	O16
East Dr	63	10	N 8
East Gate Plz	13	15	N14
East Hampton Blvd	64	10	N 9
East Hangar Rd	30	14	L 15
East Loop	59	10	M 7
East Main Dr	21	12	J 12
East Williston Av (Floral Park)	1	13	P10
East 1st Rd	93	16	L 17
East 3rd Rd	93	16	L 17
East 4th Rd	93	16	L 17
East 6th Rd	93	16	L 17
East 7th Rd	93	16	L 17
East 8th Rd	93	16	L 17
East 9th Rd	93	16	L 17
East 10th Rd	93	16	L 17
East 12th Rd	93	16	L 17
East 14th Rd	93	18	L 18
East 16th Rd	93	16	L 18
East 18th Rd	93	16	L 18
East 20th Rd	93	18	L 18
Eckford Av	17	14	K14
Edgemere Av		18	M18
1-00 - 53-99	91	16	N18
54-00 - OUT	92	18	M18
Edgemere Ct *(off Beach 50th St)	91	18	M18
Edgemere Rd	91	16	N18
Edgemere Ter *(off Beach 33rd St)	91	16	N18
Edgerton Blvd	32	13	M11
Edgerton Rd	32	13	M11
Edgewood Av	13	15	N14
Edgewood St	22	15	O15
Edmore Av		13	O11
221-00 - 235-99	28	13	O11
236-00 - OUT	26	13	O11
Edsall Av	85	11	H12
Edward Ct *(off Beach 98th St)	94	18	L 18
Effington Av	58	10	L 9
Eggert Pl	91	16	N17
Egmont Pl	91	16	N17
Elbertson St	73	11	H10
Elder Av	55	9	K 9
Eldert La	21	14	J 13
Eldert St	85	14	G13
Eldsea Ct *(off Rockaway Beach Blvd near Beach 106th St)	94	18	K19
Eleanor Ct *(off Beach 98th St & Beach 109th St)	94	18	K19
Eliot Av		11	G11
60-00 - 61-07	78	11	G11
61-08 - 84-99	79	11	G11
85-00 - 89-00	74	11	H11
Elizabeth Av		18	L 18
200 - 299	91	18	M18
6800 - 7299	92	18	M18
Elizabeth Rd	92	18	M18
Elk Dr	91	16	N18
Elkmont Av	26	13	P10
Elks Rd	73	11	H10
Ellwell Cres	74	12	J 11
Elm Av	55	9	L 9
Elmhurst Av		11	H10
84-00 - 89-99	73	11	H10
90-00 - 91-99	72	11	H10
Elmira Av	12	13	N12
Elvia Ct *(off Beach 15th St)	91	16	O18
Elvira Av	91	16	O18
Emerald St		14	J 14
94-00 - 102-99	16	14	J 14
103-00 - 107-99	17	14	J 14
133-00 - OUT	14	14	J 14
Emily Rd	60	10	M 8
Empire Av	91	16	O17
Enfield Pl	64	10	N 9
Enid Ct *(off Beach 101st St)	94	18	L 19
Enright Rd	91	16	N17
Epsom Course		13	N11
198-00 - 200-99	23	13	N11
201 - OUT	27	13	N11
Ericsson St	69	8	H 9
Essex Wk	97	17	G20
Estates Dr	60	10	M 8
Estates La	60	10	M 8
Estelle Ct *(off Beach 58th St)	92	18	M18
Eton St	32	13	M11
Evans Rd	33	12	L 12
Eveleth Rd	34	15	N13
Everdell Av	91	16	O18
Everdell Pl	91	16	N17
Everitt Pl	12	15	N13
Everton St	74	11	H11
Exeter St	75	12	J 11

F

STREET NAME AND HOUSE NUMBERS	ZONE NO.	MAP NO.	MAP GRID
Faber Ter	91	16	N17
Failing St *(off Beach 69th St)	92	18	M18
Fairbury Av		13	O11
221-00 - 235-99	28	13	O11
236-00 - OUT	26	13	O11
Fairchild Av	58	13	L 10
Fairfield Pl	14	14	J 14
Fairview Av	85	11	G12
Fairway Cl	75	12	K11
Falcon Av	91	16	N18
Fan Rose Ct *(off Beach 55th St)	92	18	M18
Far Rockaway Blvd	91	16	N18
Farmers Blvd		13	N12
99-00 - 103-99	23	13	N12
104-00 - 120-99	12	13	N12
121-00 - 122-26	13	15	N13
122-44 - 147-99	34	15	N13
Farrington St	54	9	K 9
Fay Ct *(off Beach 40th St)	91	16	N18
Federal Cir	30	14	L 15
Felio Ct *(off Beach 52nd St)	91	18	M18
Fern Pl	33	13	M12
Ferndale Av	35	14	L 13
Fernside Pl	91	16	N18
Finnard Av	93	18	L 18
Finns Ct *(off Beach 102nd St)	94	18	K19
Firwood Pl	12	13	N12
Fitchett St	74	11	H11
Fleet Ct	79	11	H11
Fleet St		12	J 11
65-00 - 70-99	75	12	J 11
85-00 - 86-99	74	12	J 11
Floral Ct *(off Beach 108th St)	94	18	K19
Florence Ct *(off Beach 49th St)	91	18	M18
Florence Ct *(off Beach 55th St)	92	18	M18
Flushing Av		11	F 11
17-00 - 19-99	85	11	F 12
51-00 - 64-99	78	11	F 11
Foam Pl	91	16	O17
Foch Blvd		14	L 13
126-00 - 135-99	20	14	L 13
137-00 - 149-99	36	14	L 13
150-00 - 171-99	34	15	M13
186-00 - OUT	12	15	N13
Fonda Av	12	13	N12
Foothill Av	23	13	N11
Forbell St		14	J 13
1 - 50	16	14	J 13
94-00 - 95-99	16	14	J 13
Forest Av	85	11	G12
Forest Pkwy	21	12	J 12
Forest Rd	63	10	N 8
Forley St	73	11	H10
Fowler Av	55	9	K 9
Frame Pl	55	9	K 9
Fran Wayne Ct *(off Beach 51st St)	91	18	M18
Frances Ct *(off Beach 56th St)	92	18	M18
Francis Lewis Blvd		9	L 8
1-00 - 24-99	57	9	L 8
25-00 - 36-99	58	9	L 9
37-00 - 47-99	61	9	M 9
48-00 - 79-99	64	13	M10
80-00 - 89-99	27	13	N11
90-00 - 94-99	28	13	N11
95-00 - 113-99	29	13	N12
114-00 - 120-99	11	13	O12
121-01 - 138-55	13	15	O13
138-57 - 147-99	22	15	O14
217-01 - 226-99	11	15	O13
227-00 - 232-99	13	15	O14
233 - OUT	22	15	O14
Franklin Av	55	9	K 9
Franklin Ct *(off Beach 39th St)	91	16	N18
Frankton St	22	15	P14
Frederick Ct *(off Reads La)	91	16	O17
Freedom Dr	18	12	J 12
Fremont St	85	11	G12
Fresh Meadow La		12	L 10
46-00 - 47-99	58	12	L 10
48-00 - 69-98	65	12	L 10
Fresh Pond Rd		11	G11
55-00 - 60-99	78	11	G11
61-00 - 62-29	79	11	G11
62-30 - OUT	85	11	G12
Friendly Ct *(off Beach 56th St)	92	18	M18
Frisco Av	91	16	O18
Fuller Pl	55	9	K 9
Fulton Wk	97	17	G20
Furmanville Av	79	11	H11

G

STREET NAME AND HOUSE NUMBERS	ZONE NO.	MAP NO.	MAP GRID
Galasso Pl	78	11	F 11
Gale Av	1	11	F 10
Galway Av	12	13	N12
Garbe Ct *(off Beach 51st St)	91	18	M18
Garden Ct *(off Beach 56th St)	92	18	M18
Garden Ct *(off Beach 9th St)	91	16	O17
Garden Ter *(off Beach 56th St)	92	18	M18
Garfield Av	77	11	G10
Garland Dr	64	10	N 9
Garland Ter	64	10	N 9
Garrett St	34	15	N14
Gaskell Rd	62	10	O 9
Gates Av	85	11	G12
Gateway Blvd	91	16	O18
General R W Berry Dr	59	10	M 7
George Ct *(off Beach 50th St)	91	18	M18
George St	85	11	G12
Georgia Rd	55	9	L 9
Georgian Ct *(off Beach 109th St)	94	18	K19
Geranium Av	55	9	K 9
Gerard Ct *(off Beach 57th St)	92	18	K19
Gerard Ct	94	18	M18
Gerard Pl	75	12	J 11
Gettysburg St	26	13	O11
Gilmore St	69	8	H 9
Gipson St	91	16	N17
Gladwin Av	65	12	L 10
Gladys Ct *(off Beach 55th St)	92	18	M18
Glassboro Av	35	14	L 13
Gleane St	73	11	H10
Glenmore Av	17	14	J 13

STREET NAME AND HOUSE NUMBERS	ZONE NO.	MAP NO.	MAP GRID
Glenn Av	32	12	L12
Glenwood St		10	O8
25-00 - 44-99	63	10	O8
45-00 - 48-99	62	10	O8
Goethals Av	32	12	L11
Gold Rd	17	14	J14
Goldington Ct	79	12	H11
Goldsmith St	73	11	H10
Goodward Rd	75	12	K11
Gorsline St	73	11	H10
Gotham Rd	20	14	L14
Gotham Wk	97	17	F20
Gothic Dr	32	12	L11
Gouverneur Av	92	18	L18
Grace Ct	32	12	L12
Grace Ct *(off Beach 107th St)	94	16	K18
Graham Ct	54	9	J8
Graham Pl	97	17	G20
Granada Pl	91	16	N17
Grand Av		11	G11
45-00 - 73-99	78	11	G11
74-00 - OUT	73	11	H10
Grand Central Pkwy		8	H8
61-00 - 78-99 (St)	75	12	J10
80-00 - 80-99 (St)	70	8	M11
90-00 - 90-98	69	8	H9
80-05 - 81-10 (Av)	35	12	L11
135-00 - 149-99	35	12	L11
150-00 - 187-99	32	12	L11
200-00 - 228-99	27	13	N11
229-00 - 229-98 (even)	27	13	N11
229-00 - 231-99 (odd)	64	13	N11
244-00 - 252-98 (even)	26	13	O10
244-01 - 265-95-(odd)	62	13	O10
Grandview Av	85	11	G12
Grandview Ter *(off Caffrey Av near Mott Av)	91	16	O17
Granger St	68	12	J10
Grannatt Pl	34	15	M14
Grassmere Ter	91	16	N18
Gravett Rd	67	12	K10
Gray St	79	11	H11
Grayson St	13	15	N13
Greene Av	85	11	F12
Greenpoint Av		11	E10
30-01 - 38-99	1	11	E10
39-01 - 47-99	4	11	F10
Greenway N	75	12	K11
Greenway S	75	12	K11
Greenway Ter	75	12	K11
Grenfell St	15	12	K12
Grosvenor La	18	12	K12
Grosvenor Rd	18	12	K12
Grosvenor St	63	10	N8
Groton St	75	12	J11
Grove Ct *(off Seagirt Av)	91	16	O18
Grove St	85	11	G12
Grover Ct *(off Beach 39th St)	91	16	N18
Guilford St	75	12	J12
Guinzburg Rd	33	12	L12
Gull Ct	93	18	L18
Guy R Brewer Blvd		13	M12
92-00 - 113-99	33	15	N14
114-00 - OUT	34	15	N15

H

STREET NAME AND HOUSE NUMBERS	ZONE NO.	MAP NO.	MAP GRID
Haddon St	32	13	M11
Hague Pl	34	15	M14
Haight St	55	9	K9
Hamilton Pl	78	11	G11
Hampton St	73	11	H10
Hancock St	85	19	F13
Hand Rd	62	10	O8
Hanford St	62	10	O9
Hannibal St	12	13	N12
Hanover Ct *(off St. Marks Av near Beach 105th St)	94	18	K19
Hantz Rd	91	16	N18
Harbour Ct	91	16	N17
Haring St	74	11	H11
Harmon St	85	11	F12
Harmony Rd	97	17	H20
Harold Ct *(off Beach 52nd St)	91	18	M18
Harper St	68	9	J9
Harriet Ct *(off Beach 56th St)	92	18	M18
Harris St	91	16	O17
Harrison Ct *(off Beach 39th St)	91	18	M18
Harrow St	75	12	J11
Harry Van Ardsley Av (see Jewel Av)			
Hart St	85	11	F12
Hartland Av	64	13	N10
Hartman La *(off Cornaga Av)	91	16	N18
Haspel St	73	11	H10
Hassock St	91	16	O17
Hawthorne Av	55	9	L9
Hawtree Creek Rd	20	14	L13
Hawtree St		14	K14
103-00 - 104-99	17	14	K14
133-00 - 135-98	17	14	K14
Haywood Rd	23	13	N11
Hazen St	70	8	G9
Healy Av	91	16	N17
Helen Ct *(off Beach 26th St)	91	16	N18
Hempstead Av	29	13	O11
Henderson Av	23	13	M12
Hendrickson Pl	33	13	M12
Henley Rd	32	13	M11
Henry Av	77	11	G10
Henry Rd	91	16	O18
Herrick Av	75	12	J12
Hessler Av	92	18	M18
Hewlett St		10	P9
56-00 - 60-99	62	10	P9
271-00 - OUT (New Hyde Park)	40	10	P9
Heyson Rd	91	16	O18
Hiawatha Av	23	13	N11
Hicks Dr	77	11	G10
Hicksville Rd	91	16	O18
Higgins La	54	9	L8
Higgins St	54	9	K9
Highland Av	32	12	L12
Highland Ct	91	16	N18
Highland Pl	97	17	G20
Hilburn Av	12	13	N12
Hillcrest Av	63	10	N8
Hillcrest Wk	97	17	G20
Hillmeyer Av	92	18	L18
Hillside Av		12	K12
117-00 - 136-99	18	12	K12
137-00 - 149-99	35	12	L12
150-00 - 187-99	32	12	L12
188-00 - 205-99	23	13	N11
206-00 - 235-99	27	13	N11
236-00 - 253-99	26	13	O10
254-00 - 267-99 (Floral Park)	4	13	P10
268-00 - OUT (even) (Floral Park)	1	13	P10
268-01 - OUT (odd) (New Hyde Park)	40	13	P10
Hillside Av	97	17	H20
Hillyer St	73	11	H10
Himrod St	85	11	F12
Hobart St	77	8	G9
Hoffman Dr	73	11	H10
Holder Pl	75	12	K11
Holland Av	93	18	L18
Hollis Av		13	N12
99-00 - 192-99	23	13	N12
193-00 - 205-99	12	13	N12
206-00 - 218-99	29	13	O12
Hollis Court Blvd		13	M10
46-00 - 47-99	58	10	M9
48-01 - 58-99	65	13	M10
80-01 - 89-99	27	13	N11
90-00 - 94-99	28	13	N11
188-00 - 192-99	58	13	M10
Hollis Hills Ter	64	13	N10
Holly Av	55	9	K9
Hollyhurst Ct *(off Beach 101st St near RR)	94	18	L18
Hollywood Av		9	L9
0 - 148-00	63	10	N8
149-00 - 149-99	55	9	L9
200 - 399	63	10	N8
Hollywood Ct *(off McBride St)	91	16	N17
Hollywood Ct *(off Beach 29th St)	91	16	N18
Home Lawn St	32	13	M11
Homenhurst Ct *(off Beach 107th St)	94	18	K19
Honeywell St	1	11	F10
Hook Creek Blvd	22	15	P15
Hoover Av		12	K11
135-00 - 149-99	35	12	K11
150-00 - OUT	32	12	L11
Horace Harding Blvd *(service road for Long Island Expwy)		12	J10
Horatio Pkwy	64	10	N9
Hortense Ct *(off Beach 40th St)	91	16	N18
Horton Av	91	16	O17
Hough Pl *(off Beach 45th St North of Beach Channel Dr)	91	16	N18
Hovendon Rd	32	13	M11
Hoxie Dr	64	10	N9
Hoyt Av N	2	8	F8
Hoyt Av S	2	8	F8
Hudson Wk	97	17	F20
Hull Av	78	11	G11
Humphreys St	69	8	H9
Hungry Harbor Rd	22	15	P15
Hunter St	1	11	E10
Hunters Point Av		11	E10
29-01 - 38-99	1	11	E10
39-01 - 39-99	4	11	F10
Hurley Ct	91	16	O18
Huron St	14	14	K14
Huxley St	22	15	O15

I

STREET NAME AND HOUSE NUMBERS	ZONE NO.	MAP NO.	MAP GRID
Ida Ct *(off Beach 101st St near Beach Channel Dr)	94	18	L19
Ide Ct	91	16	N17
Ilion Av	12	13	N12
Indiana Av	85	11	H12
Ingram St	75	12	J11
Interborough Pkwy	85	14	G13
Interstate Hwy 278		8	F8
		8	G9
Interstate Hwy 295		10	M7
		13	N10
Interstate Hwy 495		11	E10
		11	F11
		12	K10
		10	N9
Interstate Hwy 678		9	K8
		12	K11
		14	L13
Inwood St		14	L13
104-00 - 113-99	35	15	L13
114-00 - 133-99	36	15	M13
Iowa Rd	62	10	O8
Ireland St	73	11	H10
Irene Ct *(off St. Marks Av near Beach 108th St)	94	18	K19
Irving Av	85	11	F12
Irving Ct *(off Beach 49th St)	91	18	M18
Irving Wk	97	17	F20
Irwin Pl	34	15	N13
Ithaca St	73	11	H10
Ives Ct *(off Dickens Av)	91	16	N17
Ivy Close	75	12	K11

J

STREET NAME AND HOUSE NUMBERS	ZONE NO.	MAP NO.	MAP GRID
Jack Ct *(off Beach 56th St)	92	18	M18
Jackie Robinson Pkwy	85	14	G13
Jackson Av	1	11	E10
Jackson Mill Rd	69	8	H9
Jacobus St	73	11	H10
Jaegers La *(off Albert Rd)	17	14	K14
Jamaica Av		14	J13
74-00 - 98-99	21	14	J13
100-00 - 135-99	18	12	K12
137-00 - 149-99	35	12	L12
150-00 - 180-99	32	12	L12
181-00 - 205-99	23	13	M12
206-00 - 235-99	28	13	N11
237-01 - OUT	26	13	P11
Jamaica Wk	97	17	F20
James Ct	34	15	M13
Janet La	97	17	G20
Janet Pl	54	9	K9
Jarman Rd	59	10	M7
Jarvis Ct	91	16	O18
Jasmine Av	55	9	L9
Java Pl	93	18	L18
Jay Av	78	11	G11
Jefferson Av	85	19	F13
Jefferson Ct *(off Beach 40th St)	91	16	N18
Jessie Ct *(off Beach 49th St)	91	16	N18
Jessie Ct	63	10	O8
Jewel Av		12	K11
67-00 - 113-99	75	12	K11
128-00 - 157-99	67	12	K11
158-00 - OUT	65	12	L10
Jones Ct *(off Beach 81st St)	93	18	L18
Jordan Av	12	13	N12
Jordan Ct	60	10	M8
Jordan Dr	60	10	M8
Jordan St	58	10	M8
Judell Ct *(off Beach 55th St)	92	18	M18
Judge St	73	11	H10
Jullius Rd	56	9	J7
Junction Blvd		8	H9
33-00 - 34-99	72	8	H9
35-00 - 48-99	68	8	H9
49-00 - 60-99	73	11	H10
Juniper Av	55	9	K9
Juniper Blvd N	79	11	H11
Juniper Blvd S	79	11	H11
Juniper Valley Rd	79	11	H11
Juno St	75	12	J11
Justice Av	73	11	H10

K

STREET NAME AND HOUSE NUMBERS	ZONE NO.	MAP NO.	MAP GRID
Kalmia Av	55	12	K10
Kathy Ct *(off Beach 56th St)	92	18	M18
Kearney St	69	8	H9
Keel Ct	56	9	J7
Keeseville Av	12	13	N12
Kelp Rd	92	18	M18
Kendrick Pl	32	13	M11
Kenilworth Dr	64	10	N9
Kenmore Rd	63	10	N8
Keno Av	23	13	N11
Kent St	32	13	M11
Kessel St	75	12	J11
Ketch Ct	56	9	J7
Ketcham Pl	73	11	H10
Ketcham St	73	11	H10
Kew Forest La	75	12	K11
Kew Gardens Rd		12	K11
9-00 - 130-99	15	12	K11
131-00 - 136-99	18	12	L12
Kildare Rd	32	13	M11
Kildare Wk	97	17	F20
Killarney St	14	14	K14
King Rd	54	9	K9
Kingsbury Av	64	13	N10
Kingston Pl	32	13	M11
Kissena Blvd		9	K9
41-00 - 60-99	55	9	K9
61-00 - OUT	67	12	L10
Kneeland Av	73	11	H10
Knollwood Av	63	10	N8
Kramer Ct *(off Beach 54th St)	92	18	M18
Kramer Ct *(off Beach 70th St)	92	18	M18
Krayer Ct *(off Beach 54th St)	92	18	M18
Kruger Rd	32	13	M11

L

STREET NAME AND HOUSE NUMBERS	ZONE NO.	MAP NO.	MAP GRID
La Rue Av	68	12	J10
Laburnum Av		12	K10
137-00 - 157-99	55	9	L9
158-00 - OUT	58	9	L9
Lafayette Ct *(off Beach 51st St)	91	18	M18
Lafayette St	17	14	K14
Lahn St	14	14	K14
Lake Av	34	15	M13
Lakeview Blvd	34	15	M13
Lakeview La	34	15	M13
Lakeview St	13	15	N14
Lakewood Av	35	14	L13
Lamont Av	73	11	H10
Lanark Rd	93	16	L17
Lander St	35	12	L11
Lanett Av	91	16	O18
Langdale St (New Hyde Park)	40	10	P9
Langston Av	4	10	P9
Lansing Av	13	15	O14
Larkin Av	92	18	M18
Larkin Ct *(off Beach 65th St)	92	18	M18
Larue Av	68	12	J10
Lasan Ct *(off Beach 105th St)	94	18	K19
Latham La	34	15	N14
Latimer Pl	54	9	K9
Laurel Av	68	12	J10
Laurel Hill Blvd		11	G10
34-00 - 35-00	78	11	F11
44-60 - 69-99	77	11	G10
Laurelton Pkwy		15	O14
120-00 - 120-99	11	15	P13
121-00 - OUT	22	15	O14
Law Rd	79	11	H11
Lawrence St		12	K10
57-00 - 60-99	55	12	K10
61-00 - OUT	67	12	K10
Lax Av	56	9	J7
Layton St	73	11	H10
Leavitt St	54	9	K9
Lee Ct	57	9	K8
Lee Rd	59	10	M7
Leeds Rd	62	10	O9
Lefferts Blvd		12	K12
80-00 - 85-99	15	12	K12
86-00 - 91-99	18	12	K12
94-00 - 107-99	19	14	K13
109-00 - 150-99	20	14	L13
155-00 - OUT	14	14	K14
Leggett Pl	57	9	L7
Leith Pl	62	10	O9
Leith Rd	62	10	O9
Leslie Rd	34	15	N13
Lester Ct *(off Beach 40th St)	91	16	N18
Leverich St	72	11	G10
Lewis Av	68	12	J10
Lewiston Av	12	13	N12
Lewmay Rd	91	16	N18
Liberty Av		14	L13
74-00 - 107-99	17	14	J13
108-00 - 135-99	19	14	K13
137-00 - 149-99	35	12	L12
150-00 - 180-99	33	12	M12
181-00 - OUT	12	13	M12
Liberty La	97	17	G20
Lincoln Ct *(off Beach 56th Pl)	92	18	M18
Lincoln St	20	14	L14
Lincoln Wk	97	17	G20
Linden Blvd		14	K14
75-00 - 79-89	14	14	J14
79-00 - 107-99	17	14	K14
108-00 - 135-99	20	14	K13
137-00 - 149-99	36	15	L13
150-00 - 180-99	34	15	N13
181-00 - 205-99	12	15	N13
206-00 - 235-99	11	15	O13
Linden Pl	54	9	K8
Linden Spring Ct *(off Beach 56th St)	92	18	M18
Linden St	85	11	G12
Lineaus Pl	54	9	K9
Lithonia Av	65	12	L10
Little Bay Rd	59	10	M7
Little Neck Blvd	60	10	M8
Little Neck Pkwy		10	O8
24-00 - 44-99	63	10	O8
45-00 - 63-99	62	10	O8
69-00 - 83-99 (Floral Park)	4	10	P10
84-00 - 88-99 (Floral Park)	1	13	P10
Liverpool St	35	12	L12
Lloyd Rd	35	14	L13
Locke Av	57	9	L8
Long Island Expwy		11	E10
1-00 - 41-99	1	12	J10
58-00 - 73-99	78	11	G11
74-00 - 82-99	73	11	H10
92-00 - 101-99	74	12	J10
102-00 - 113-99	75	12	J11
130-00 - 157-99	67	12	K10
158-00 - 199-99	65	12	L10
200-00 - 239-99	64	10	N9
248-00 - 260-99	62	10	O9
Long St	34	15	M13
Loop Rd	30	15	M15
Loretta Rd	91	16	N18
Lori Dr	60	10	M8
Loubet St	75	12	J11
Louise Ct *(off Beach 50th St)	91	18	M18
Lovingham Pl	12	15	N13
Lowe Ct	35	12	L12
Lucas St		15	N13
120-00 - 120-99	12	15	N13
121-00 - 125-99	13	15	N13
Ludlum Av	12	13	N12
Luke Pl	64	10	N9
Luther Rd	85	11	H12
Lutheran Av	79	11	H11
Lux Rd	35	14	L13
Lyman St	27	13	O11
Lynch Ct *(off Beach 105th St)	94	18	K19

M

STREET NAME AND HOUSE NUMBERS	ZONE NO.	MAP NO.	MAP GRID
MacIntosh Pl	77	11	G10
MacNish St	73	11	H10
Madison St	85	11	G12
Mador Ct *(off Cornaga Av)	91	16	O17
Mae Ct *(off Beach 109th St)	94	18	K19
Magnolia Pl	55	9	K9
Main Av	2	8	F8
Main St		9	K9
36-00 - 40-99	54	9	K9
41-00 - 60-99	55	9	K9
61-00 - 79-99	67	12	K10
80-00 - OUT	35	12	L11
Malba Dr	57	9	K7
Mangin Av	12	13	N12
Manilla St	73	11	H10
Manor Rd	63	10	N8
Manor Rd	27	13	O10
Manse St	75	12	J11
Manton St	35	12	L12
Manville La	97	17	G20
Maple Av	55	9	K9
Marathon Pkwy		10	O9
34-00 - 44-99	63	10	O9
45-00 - 66-99	62	10	O9
Marengo St	23	13	N11
Margaret Pl	85	12	J12
Marie Ct *(off Beach 101st St near RR)	94	18	K19
Marie Jean Ct *(off Beach 56th St)	92	18	M18
Marietta Ct *(off St. Marks Av near Beach 105th St)	94	18	K19
Marine Terminal Rd	71	8	H9
Marinette St	63	10	N8
Marion Ct *(off Beach 56th Pl)	92	18	M18
Marion Wk	97	17	F20
Marissa St	13	15	N14
Market St	97	17	G20
Markwood Pl	75	12	K12
Marne Pl	33	15	M13
Mars Pl	34	15	N13
Marsden St	34	15	M13
Marsells Ct *(off Beach 98th St)	94	18	L19
Marshall Av	97	17	G20
Martense Av	68	12	J10
Marvin Ct *(off Beach 28th St)	91	18	M18
Marvin Ct	92	16	N18
Mary Morris Ct *(off Beach 98th St)	94	18	L19
Maryland Rd	62	10	O9
Maspeth Av	78	11	F11
Mathewson Ct	34	15	N13
Mathias Av	33	15	M13
Maurice Av		11	G11
52-00 - 64-99	78	11	G11
65-00 - 73-99	77	11	G10
74-00 - OUT	73	12	H10
May Ct *(off St. Marks Ave near Beach 107th St)	94	18	K19
Mayda Rd	22	15	O14
Mayfair Rd	18	12	K12
Mayfield Rd	32	13	M11
Mayville St	12	13	N12
Mazeau St	78	11	G11
McBride St	91	16	N17
McIntosh St	69	8	H9
McKin Av	61	10	M9
McLaughlin Av	23	13	M11
Meehan Av	91	16	O18
Mekin Av	61	10	M9
Melbourne Av	67	12	K10
Melissa Ct	60	10	M8
Melrose La	63	10	N8
Melvina Pl	78	11	G11
Memorial Cir	94	18	K19
Memorial Dr	18	12	K12
Memphis Av	22	15	O14
Menahan St	85	11	G12
Mentone Av		15	O14
225-00 - 232-99	13	15	O14
233-00 - 236-99	22	15	O14

STREET NAME AND HOUSE NUMBERS	ZONE NO.	MAP NO.	MAP GRID
Spiller Rd	59	10	M 7
Sprague Pl			
*(off Beach 88th St)	93	18	L 18
Springer Ct			
*(off Beach 58th St)	92	18	M18
Springfield Blvd		13	N10
41-00 - 47-99	61	10	N 9
48-00 - 79-99	64	13	N10
80-00 - 89-99	27	13	O10
90-00 - 94-99	28	13	O11
95-00 - 113-99	29	13	O12
114-00 - 120-99	11	13	O12
121-00 - 152-99	13	15	N14
Springfield La	13	15	N15
Spritz Rd	17	14	K14
Spruce St	68	12	J 10
Stafford Av	75	12	J 11
Standish Pl	75	12	K11
Stanhope St	85	11	F12
Stanley Ct			
*(off Beach 40th St)	91	16	N18
Stanton Ct *(off St. Marks Av near Beach 106th St)	94	18	K19
Stark Ct			
*(off Beach 55th St)	92	18	M18
Starr Av	1	11	E10
Starr St	85	11	F12
State Hwy 24		18	P12
State Hwy 25		11	H10
		13	N11
		13	O11
		13	P11
State Hwy 25A		11	E10
		8	H 9
		9	L 9
State Hwy 25B		13	P10
State Hwy 27		14	K14
		14	L 14
		15	N14
State Hwy 27A		14	J 15
State Rd	95	17	G20
Station Rd		9	L 9
157-00 - 158-99	55	9	L 9
159-01 - 196-99	58	9	L 9
Station Sq	75	12	J 11
Steeplechase Ct			
*(off Beach 100th St near RR)	94	18	L 19
Steinway Pl	5	8	G 8
Steinway St		8	F 9
18-00 - 23-99	5	8	G 8
24-00 - 32-99	3	8	F 9
34-00 - 36-99	1	8	F 9
Stephen St	85	11	G12
Stewart Rd		13	N10
217-01 - 217-99	64	13	N10
218-01 - OUT	27	13	N10
Stier Pl	85	11	G12
Stockholm St	85	11	F12
Story Av	59	10	M 7
Story Rd	92	18	M18
Stratford St	75	12	K12
Strong Av	68	12	J 10
Stronghurst Av	27	13	O10
Suffolk Dr	12	15	N13
Suffolk Wk	97	17	F20
Sullivan Rd	12	15	N13
Summer St	75	12	K11
Summerfield St	85	11	G12
Summit Ct	55	9	K 9
Summit Pl	57	9	K 7
Sunbury St	34	15	N13
Sunnyside St	91	16	N17
Sunrise Hwy	22	15	O14
Surf Ct			
*(off Beach 107th St)	94	18	K19
Surf Rd	91	16	N18
Surrey Pl	32	13	M11
Susan Ct *(off Beach 106th St & 109th St)	94	18	K19
Sutphin Blvd		12	L 12
87-00 - 113-99	35	12	L 12
114-00 - 125-99	36	15	M13
Sutro St	23	13	N11
Sutter Av		14	J 14
77-00 - 107-99	17	14	J 14
108-00 - 135-99	20	14	L 14
137-00 - 149-99	36	15	M14
Sutton Pl	65	12	L 11
Suydam St	85	11	F12
Swan Rd	92	18	M18
Sybilla St	75	12	J 12
Sylvester La	59	10	M 7
Syringa Pl	55	9	K 9

T

STREET NAME AND HOUSE NUMBERS	ZONE NO.	MAP NO.	MAP GRID
Tahoe St	17	14	K14
Talbot St	15	12	K12
Teal Dr	91	16	N18
Tennis Pl	75	12	J 13
Theater Rd	59	10	M 7
Thebes Av	62	10	O 9
Theresa Ct			
*(off Beach 51st St)	91	16	N18
Theresa Pl	75	12	J 12
Thetford La	97	17	G20
Thompson Pl			
*(off Cedar Grove Cem)	67	12	K10
Thomson Av	1	11	E10
Thornhill Av	62	10	O 9
Thornton Pl		12	J 11
66-00 - 66-99	74	12	J 11
67-00 - 67-99	75	12	J 11
Thursby Av	92	18	M18
Thurston St		15	N14
136-00 - 136-99	34	15	N14
137-00 - OUT	13	15	N14
Tilden Wk *(off State St)	97	17	H20
Tioga Dr	12	15	N13
Tioga Wk	97	17	F20
Tonsor St	85	11	G12
Totten Av	59	10	M 7
Totten St	57	10	M 7
Traffic Av	85	11	G12
Trappe Pl	33	13	M12
Triborough Plz	2	8	F 8
Trimble Rd	77	11	G10
Trist Pl	91	16	N17
Troon Rd	32	13	M11
Trotting Course La		12	J 12
69-00 - 70-99	74	12	J 12
73-01 - OUT	85	12	J 12
Troutman St	85	11	F12
Troutville Rd	34	15	N13
Tryon Pl	32	13	M11
Tuckerton St	33	12	L 12
Tudor Rd	32	13	M11
Turin Dr	12	15	N13
Turpin Ct			
*(off Beach 99th St)	94	18	L 19
Tyler Av	77	11	G10

U

STREET NAME AND HOUSE NUMBERS	ZONE NO.	MAP NO.	MAP GRID
Underhill Av		13	M10
164-00 - 194-99	65	13	M10
200-00 - OUT	64	13	N10
Underhill Rd	59	10	M 7
Underwood Rd	75	12	K11
Union Hall St	33	27	M12
Union St		9	K 9
25-00 - 40-99	54	9	K 9
41-00 - 47-99	55	9	K 9
Union Tpk		12	J 12
1-00 - 96-00	85	12	J 12
103-01 - 119-99 (odd)	75	12	J 12
117-00 - 119-98 (even)	15	12	K11
135-01 - 138-99 (odd)	67	12	L 11
135-02 - 135-98 (even)	35	12	L 11
141-00 - 157-99	67	12	L 11
158-00 - 199-99	66	13	M11
200-00 - 230-99	64	13	N10
231-00 - 237-99	27	13	O10
242-00 - 252-99	26	13	O10
253-00 - 264-99 (Floral Park)	4	13	P10
265-00 - 268-98 (even) (Floral Park)	4	13	P10
265-01 - 268-99 (odd) (New Hyde Park)	40	10	P 9
269-00 - OUT (New Hyde Park)	40	10	P 9
Upland Rd	62	10	O 8
Upshaw Rd	75	12	K12
Ursina Rd	34	15	N13
Ursula Pl	75	12	J 12
Utica Wk	97	17	F20
Utopia Pkwy		10	M 8
1-00 - 24-99	57	10	M 8
25-00 - 47-99	58	10	M 9
48-00 - 72-99	65	13	M10
73-00 - 79-99	66	13	M11
80-00 - 82-99	32	13	M11

V

STREET NAME AND HOUSE NUMBERS	ZONE NO.	MAP NO.	MAP GRID
Valentine Pl	85	11	H12
Van Brunt Rd	93	18	L 18
Van Cleef St	68	12	J 10
Van Dam St	1	11	F10
Van Doren St	68	12	J 10
Van Horn St	73	11	H10
Van Kleeck St	73	11	H10
Van Loon St	73	11	H10
Van Sicklen St	19	14	L 13
Van Wyck Expwy		9	K 9
84-01 - 113-99 (odd)	35	12	L 12
85-02 - 93-98(even)	18	12	L 12
94-02 - 107-98(even)	19	14	L 13
109-02 - 135-98(even)	20	14	L 13
114-01 - 135-99 (odd)	36	14	L 14
140-01 - 140-99	30	15	L 14
Van Zandt Av	62	10	O 9
Vanderveer St		13	N11
88-00 - 89-99	27	13	N11
90-00 - 94-99	28	13	O11
Vaux Rd	77	11	G10
Vermont Av	7	14	G13
Vernon Blvd		8	E 9
29-00 - 30-99	2	8	E 9
31-00 - 36-99	6	8	E 9
37-00 - OUT	1	8	E 9
Victor Ct			
*(off Beach 55th St)	92	18	M18
Victoria Dr	34	15	N13
Victoria Rd	34	15	N13
Vietor Av	73	11	H10
Village Rd		12	L 11
144-00 - 149-99	35	12	L 11
150-00 - OUT	32	12	L 11
Virginia St	91	16	O17
Vleigh Pl	67	12	L 11

W

STREET NAME AND HOUSE NUMBERS	ZONE NO.	MAP NO.	MAP GRID
Wainwright Ct	94	18	K19
Walden Av	62	10	O 8
Waldron St	68	12	J 10
Walnut St	75	12	J 12
Walter Reed Rd	59	10	M 7
Waltham St	35	12	L 12
Walton Rd	93	16	L 17
Wareham Pl	32	13	M11
Warren St		8	H 9
37-00 - 37-99	72	8	H 9
40-00 - 41-99	73	11	H10
Warwick Av	63	10	N 8
Warwick Cres	32	13	M12
Washington Ct			
*(off Beach 56th St)	92	18	M18
Water Edge Dr	60	10	M 8
Waterloo Pl	91	16	N17
Waterloo Rd	91	16	N17
Waterview Pl			
*(off Bayswater Av)	91	16	N17
Waterview St	91	16	N17
Watjean Ct	91	16	N18
Watson Pl	33	13	M12
Wavecrest La *(off Beach 21st & 22nd Sts)	91	16	N18
Weaver Av	59	10	M 7
Webe Pl	57	9	L 8
Weeks La		10	M 9
47-00 - 47-99	61	10	M 9
48-00 - 51-99	65	10	M 9
196-00 - 196-99	65	10	M 9
Weimar St	73	11	H10
Weirfield St	85	19	F13
Weller Av	22	15	O14
Weller La	22	15	O15
Welling Ct	2	8	F 8
Wendover Rd	75	12	K12
West Alley Rd	64	10	O 9
West Dr	63	10	N 8
West End Dr	62	10	O 8
West End Dr	21	12	H12
West Hangar Rd	30	14	L15
West Main Dr	21	12	J 12
West Market St	97	17	G20
West Rd	93	16	L 17
West St	1	11	E10
Westaway Rd	59	10	M 7
Westbourne Av	91	16	N17
Westbourne Blvd			
*(off Mott Av)	91	16	N17
Westgate St	13	15	N14
Westmoreland Pl	63	10	N 8
Westmoreland St	63	10	O 8
Westside Av	68	12	J 10
Wetherole St		12	H11
60-00 - 60-99	73	12	H11
61-00 - 66-99	74	12	J 11
Wexford Ter		13	M11
175-00 - 187-99	32	13	M11
188-00 - OUT	23	13	M11
Wheatley St	91	16	O17
Whistler Av	59	10	M 7
White Oak Ct	70	8	G 9
White St *(off Elk Ct Near Beach 22nd St)	91	16	O18
Whitehall Ter	27	13	N11
Whitehouse Ct			
*(off Beach 110th St)	94	18	K19
Whitelaw St	17	14	K14
Whitestone Expwy		9	K 8
6-00 - 23-99	57	9	K 8
26-00 - 31-99	54	9	K 9
133-00 - 133-98	57	9	K 9
Whitney Av	73	11	H10
Whitson St	75	12	K12
Wicklow Pl	32	13	M11
Wilder Ct			
*(off Beach 98th St)	94	18	L 19
Willets Point Blvd		9	L 8
126-00 - 128-99	68	9	J 9
143-00 - 199-99	57	9	L 8
200-00 - OUT	60	10	M 8
Willets St	59	10	M 7
William Ct	91	16	O18
Williamson Av	13	15	N13
Willoughby Av	85	11	F12
Willow St	63	10	N 8
Winchester Blvd		13	O10
80-00 - 88-99	27	13	O10
90-00 - 92-99	28	13	O11
Winter St	75	12	K11
Witthoff St	29	13	O12
Wood St	12	13	N12
Woodbine St	85	11	G12
Woodhaven Blvd		11	H11
60-00 - 60-99	73	11	H11
61-00 - 70-99	74	12	J 11
71-00 - 83-51	85	12	J 12
83-52 - 93-99	21	12	J 12
94-00 - 102-99	16	14	J 13
103-00 - OUT	17	14	K13
Woodhaven Ct	16	14	J 13
Woodhull Av	23	13	N12
Woodrow Ct			
*(off Beach 56th St)	92	18	M18
Woodside Av		11	G10
33-02 - 37-98 (even)	1	8	G 9
37-01 - 38-99 (odd)	77	11	G10
38-02 - 38-98 (even)	4	11	F10
39-00 - 73-99	77	11	G10
74-00 - OUT	73	11	H10
Woodside Ct *(off St Marks Av Near Beach 107th St)	94	18	K19
Woodward Av	85	11	F12
Wren Pl	33	13	M12
Wyckoff Av	85	11	G12

X

STREET NAME AND HOUSE NUMBERS	ZONE NO.	MAP NO.	MAP GRID
Xenia St	68	12	J 10

Y

STREET NAME AND HOUSE NUMBERS	ZONE NO.	MAP NO.	MAP GRID
Yates Rd	33	15	L 13
Yellowstone Blvd		12	J 11
61-00 - 73-99	75	12	J 11
74-00 - 75-99	74	12	J 11

Z

STREET NAME AND HOUSE NUMBERS	ZONE NO.	MAP NO.	MAP GRID
Zion St	62	10	O 9
Zoller Rd	34	15	N13

NUMBERED STREETS

STREET NAME AND HOUSE NUMBERS	ZONE NO.	MAP NO.	MAP GRID
1st Rd	93	16	K17
1st St	2	8	E 8
1st St	14	14	K15
2nd Av	57	9	K 7
2nd Rd	93	16	K17
2nd St		8	E 8
25-00 - 29-99	2	8	E 8
50-00 - 56-99	1	11	D10
3rd Av	57	9	K 7
3rd Rd	93	16	L 17
3rd St	2	8	E 8
4th Av	57	9	K 7
4th Av	97	17	F20
4th Rd	93	16	L 17
4th St	2	8	F 8
5th Av		9	J 7
115-00 - 126-99	56	9	J 7
144-00 - 149-99	57	9	K 7
5th Av	97	17	F20
5th Rd	93	16	L 17
5th St	1	11	D10
6th Av		9	J 7
119-00 - 129-99	56	9	J 7
145-00 - 150-99	57	9	K 7
6th Rd	57	9	L 7
7th Av		9	J 7
119-00 - 130-99	56	9	J 7
145-00 - 161-99	57	9	K 7
7th Av	97	17	G20
8th Av		9	J 7
117-00 - 121-99	56	9	J 7
145-00 - 150-99	57	9	K 7
8th Av	97	17	G20
8th Rd	57	9	L 7
8th Rd	93	16	L 17
8th St	2	8	F 8
9th Av		9	J 7
115-00 - 129-99	56	9	J 7
138-00 - 138-99	57	9	K 7
145-00 - 166-99	57	9	K 7
9th Av	97	17	G20
9th Rd	56	9	J 8
9th Rd	93	16	L 17
9th St		8	E 9
25-01 - 26-99	2	8	F 8
33-01 - 36-99	6	8	E 9
37-01 - 44-99	1	8	E 9
10th Av		9	J 8
115-00 - 126-99	56	9	J 8
138-00 - 138-99	57	9	K 8
145-00 - 160-99	57	9	K 7
10th Av	97	8	G20
10th Rd	93	16	K17
10th St		8	E 9
33-01 - 36-99	6	8	E 9
37-01 - 44-99	1	8	E 9
11th Av		9	J 8
121-00 - 130-99	56	9	J 8
138-00 - 160-99	57	9	L 7
11th Rd	93	16	K17
11th St		8	E 9
32-00 - 36-99	6	8	E 9
37-00 - 53-99	1	11	E10
12th Av		9	J 8
117-00 - 121-99	56	9	J 8
147-00 - 168-99	57	9	L 7
12th Av	97	17	G20
12th Rd	57	9	L 7
12th Rd	93	16	L 17
12th St		8	E 9
25-00 - 30-99	2	8	F 8
31-00 - 36-99	6	8	E 9
37-00 - 43-99	1	11	E10
13th Av		9	J 8
122-00 - 125-99	56	9	J 8
138-00 - 162-99	57	9	K 8
13th Rd	57	9	K 8
13th Rd	93	16	K17
13th St		8	E 9
33-01 - 36-99	6	8	E 9
37-01 - 43-99	1	11	E10
14th Av		9	J 8
109-00 - 137-99	56	9	J 8
138-00 - 168-99	57	9	K 8
208-00 - 214-99	60	10	M 8
14th Pl		8	F 8
25-01 - 26-99	2	8	F 8
32-01 - 32-99	6	8	F 9
14th Rd		9	J 8
110-00 - 132-99	56	9	J 8
149-00 - 167-99	57	9	L 8
14th Rd	93	16	K18
14th St		8	E 9
25-00 - 30-99	2	8	F 8
31-00 - 36-99	6	8	E 9
37-00 - 37-99	1	8	E 9
15th Av		9	J 8
109-00 - 131-99	56	9	J 8
138-00 - 167-99	57	9	K 8
208-00 - 214-99	60	10	M 8
15th Dr		9	K 8
147-00 - 166-99	57	9	L 8
208-00 - only	60	10	M 8
215-00 - only	60	10	M 8
15th Rd		9	K 8
144-00 - 149-99	57	9	L 8
200-00 - 216-99	60	10	M 8
15th Rd	93	16	L 18
16th Av		9	L 8
157-00 - 199-99	57	9	L 8
200-00 - 214-99	60	10	K 8
16th Rd	57	9	L 8
16th Rd	93	16	L 18
17th Av		9	K 8
145-00 - 199-99	57	9	L 8
200-00 - 216-99	60	10	M 8
17th Rd	57	9	L 8
17th Rd	93	16	L 18
18th Av		9	J 8
119-00 - 130-99	56	9	J 8
145-00 - 168-99	57	9	L 8
209-00 - 214-99	60	10	M 8
18th Rd	93	16	K18
18th St		8	F 8
20-01 - 20-99	5	8	F 8
25-01 - 27-99	2	8	F 8
19th Av		8	G 8
35-01 - 48-99	5	8	G 8
49-00 - 80-99	70	8	G 8
138-00 - 199-99	57	9	K 8
200-00 - OUT	60	10	M 8
19th Dr	70	8	G 8
19th Rd	70	8	G 8
19th Rd	93	16	L 18
19th St		8	F 8
20-00 - 23-99	5	8	F 8
24-00 - 24-99	2	8	F 8
20th Av		8	F 8
18-00 - 48-99	5	8	G 8
49-00 - 84-99	70	8	G 8
109-00 - 130-99	56	9	J 8
143-00 - 169-99	57	9	L 8
20th Rd		8	F 8
18-00 - 45-99	5	8	G 8
146-00 - 166-99	57	9	L 8
20th Rd	93	16	L 18
20th St	5	8	F 8
21st Av		8	F 8
18-00 - 48-99	5	8	F 8
49-00 - 84-99	70	8	G 8
122-00 - 123-99	56	9	J 8
143-00 - 199-99	57	9	K 8
200-00 - OUT	60	10	M 8
21st Dr	5	8	F 8
21st Rd		8	F 8
18-00 - 21-99	5	8	F 8
143-00 - 143-99	57	9	K 8
160-00 - 169-99	57	9	L 8
21st St		8	E 9
20-01 - 23-99	5	8	F 8
24-01 - 30-99	2	8	F 8
31-01 - 36-99	6	8	F 9
37-01 - 51-99	1	8	E 9
22nd Av		9	J 8
118-00 - 128-99	56	9	J 8
138-00 - 199-99	57	9	L 8
200-00 - 223-99	60	10	M 8
22nd Dr		8	F 8
19-00 - 21-99	5	8	F 8
98-00 - 98-99	69	8	H 8
22nd Rd		8	F 8
19-00 - 21-99	5	8	F 8
143-00 - 144-99	57	9	K 8
22nd St		8	E 9
25-01 - 26-99	2	8	F 8
36-01 - 36-99	6	8	E 9
37-01 - 43-99	1	8	E 9
23rd Av		8	F 8
19-01 - 46-99	5	8	F 8
85-00 - 101-99	69	9	H 9
119-00 - 130-99	56	9	J 8
138-00 - 199-99	57	9	K 8
200-00 - 223-99	60	10	M 8
23rd Dr	5	8	F 8
23rd Rd		8	F 8
19-00 - 42-99	5	8	F 8
102-00 - 102-99	69	8	H 9
207-00 - 217-99	60	10	M 8
23rd St		8	F 8
20-01 - 23-99	5	8	F 8
24-01 - 30-99	2	8	F 8
31-01 - 36-99	6	8	F 9
37-01 - 51-99	1	11	E10
23rd Ter	5	8	F 8
24th Av		8	F 8
19-01 - 32-99	2	8	F 8
33-01 - 38-99	3	8	F 8
77-00 - 84-99	70	8	G 9
85-00 - 102-99	69	9	H 9
145-00 - 199-99	57	9	K 8
200-00 - 215-99	60	10	M 8
24th Dr	2	8	F 8

STREET NAME AND HOUSE NUMBERS	ZONE NO.	MAP NO.	MAP GRID
24th Rd		8	F 8
19-00 - 31-99	2	8	F 8
90-00 - 102-99	69	9	H 9
149-00 - 199-99	57	9	L 8
200-00 - OUT	60	10	M 8
24th St		11	E10
20-01 - 23-99	5	8	F 8
24-01 - 24-99	2	8	F 8
34-01 - 36-99	6	8	F 9
37-01 - 43-99	1	11	E 9
24th Ter	2	8	F 8
25th Av		8	F 9
40-01 - 48-99	3	8	G 9
49-00 only	77	8	G 9
71-00 - 84-99	70	8	G 9
85-00 - 102-99	69	9	H 9
120-00 - 129-99	56	9	J 8
141-00 - 199-99	57	9	K 8
25th Dr		9	K 8
118-00 - 157-99	54	9	L 8
158-00 - 199-99	58	9	L 8
25th Rd		8	F 8
18-01 - 26-99	2	8	F 8
118-00 - 146-99	54	9	J 8
25th St (Crescent St)		11	E10
20-01 - 23-99	5	8	F 8
24-01 - 30-99	2	8	F 8
31-01 - 36-99	6	8	F 9
49-01 - 51-99	1	11	E10
26th Av		8	E 8
1-00 - 18-99	2	8	F 8
118-00 - 157-99	54	9	J 8
158-00 - 199-99	58	9	L 8
200-00 - 223-99	60	10	M 8
26th Rd		8	F 8
18-00 - 21-99	2	8	F 8
97-00 - 97-99	69	8	H 9
26th St		8	F 8
20-01 - 23-99	5	8	F 8
24-01 - 24-99	2	8	F 8
27th Av		8	E 8
1-01 - 18-99	2	8	F 8
60-00 - 60-99	77	8	G 9
99-00 - 107-99	69	8	H 9
118-00 - 157-99	54	9	K 8
158-00 - 199-99	58	10	M 8
200-00 - 217-99	60	10	M 8
27th Rd	2	8	F 8
27th St		11	E10
20-00 - 23-99	5	8	F 8
24-00 - 27-99	2	8	F 9
37-00 - 51-99	1	11	E10
28th Av		8	F 8
11-01 - 32-99	2	8	F 8
33-01 - 48-99	3	8	F 9
49-00 - 69-99	77	8	G 9
118-00 - 157-99	54	9	J 8
158-00 - 199-99	58	9	L 8
200-00 - 217-99	60	10	M 8
28th Rd		8	F 9
31-01 - 31-99	2	8	F 8
138-00 - 141-99	54	9	K 8
209-00 - 216-99	60	10	N 8
28th St		11	E10
20-01 - 23-99	5	8	F 8
24-01 - 26-99	2	8	F 8
33-01 - 36-99	6	8	F 9
37-01 - 46-99	1	11	E10
29th Av		8	E 9
12-01 - 23-99	2	8	F 8
102-00 - 107-99	69	9	J 9
118-00 - 157-99	54	9	K 8
158-00 - 199-99	58	9	L 8
200-00 - 217-99	60	10	M 8
29th Rd	54	9	K 8
29th St		8	F 8
20-00 - 23-99	5	8	F 8
24-00 - 30-99	2	8	F 9
31-00 - 36-99	6	8	F 9
37-00 - 53-99	1	11	E10
30th Av		8	F 9
11-01 - 32-99	2	8	F 8
33-01 - 48-99	3	8	F 9
49-00 - 69-99	77	8	G 9
70-00 - 84-99	70	8	G 9
85-00 - 95-99	69	8	H 9
119-00 - 120-99	54	9	J 8
198-00 - 198-99	58	10	M 9
208-00 - 209-99	60	10	M 8
30th Dr	2	8	F 9
30th Pl	1	11	E10
30th Rd		8	F 8
8-00 - 25-99	2	8	F 9
44-00 - 46-99	3	8	F 9
30th St		11	E10
26-00 - 30-99	2	8	F 9
31-00 - 36-99	6	8	F 9
37-00 - 52-99	1	11	E10
31st Av		8	E 9
8-01 - 36-99	6	8	F 9
37-01 - 48-99	3	8	F 9
49-01 - 69-99	77	8	G 9
70-00 - 84-99	70	8	G 9
85-00 - 107-99	69	8	H 9
120-00 - 130-99	54	9	J 9
31st Dr		8	E 9
11-01 - 23-99	6	8	E 9
108-00 - 108-99	69	9	J 9
134-00 - OUT	54	9	K 9
31st Pl	1	11	E10
31st Rd		8	F 9
14-01 - 23-99	6	8	F 9
118-00 - 157-99	54	9	K 9
216-00 - 217-99	60	10	N 8
31st St		11	E10
20-00 - 23-99	5	8	F 8
24-00 - 30-99	2	8	F 9
31-00 - 36-99	6	8	F 9
37-00 - 49-99	1	11	E10
32nd Av		8	G 9
51-00 - 69-99	77	8	G 9
70-00 - 84-99	70	8	G 9
85-00 - 109-99	69	9	H 9
130-00 - 157-99	54	9	K 9
158-00 - 199-99	58	9	L 9
200-00 - 217-99	61	10	M 8
32nd Rd		10	M 8
198-00 - 199-99	58	10	M 9
214-00 - 214-99	61	10	M 8
32nd St		8	F 8
20-00 - 23-99	5	8	F 8
24-00 - 30-99	2	8	F 9
31-00 - 36-99	6	8	F 9
37-00 - 39-99	1	8	F 9
33rd Av		8	E 9
11-01 - 28-99	6	8	F 9
130-00 - 157-99	54	9	K 9
158-00 - 199-99	58	9	L 9
200-00 - 215-99	61	10	M 8
33rd Rd		8	E 9
9-01 - 23-99	6	8	F 9
131-00 - 157-99	54	9	L 9
200-00 - 223-99	61	10	M 8
33rd St		8	F 8
20-00 - 23-99	5	8	F 8
24-00 - 30-99	2	8	F 9
31-00 - 36-99	6	8	F 9
37-00 - 48-99	1	11	F10
34th Av		8	E 9
8-01 - 36-99	6	8	F 9
37-01 - 46-99	1	8	F 9
58-00 - 69-99	77	8	G 9
70-00 - 95-99	72	8	H 9
96-00 - 127-99	68	9	J 9
131-00 - 157-99	54	9	K 9
158-00 - 199-99	58	10	M 9
200-00 - 223-99	61	10	M 9
250-00 - 254-99	63	10	O 8
34th Rd		8	H 9
70-00 - 95-99	72	8	H 9
131-00 - 157-99	54	9	K 9
200-00 - 223-99	61	10	M 9
34th St		11	E10
25-00 - 30-99	3	8	F 9
31-00 - 36-99	6	8	F 9
37-00 - OUT	1	11	F10
35th Av		8	E 9
7-01 - 36-99	6	8	E 9
37-01 - 43-99	1	8	F 9
54-00 - 69-99	77	11	G10
70-00 - 92-99	72	9	H 9
96-00 - 127-99	68	9	J 9
131-00 - 157-99	54	9	K 9
159-00 - 199-99	58	9	L 9
200-00 - 223-99	61	10	M 9
35th Rd	72	11	G10
35th St		11	E10
20-00 - 23-99	5	8	F 8
24-00 - 30-99	3	8	F 9
31-00 - 36-99	6	8	F 9
37-00 - OUT	1	11	F10
36th Av		8	E 9
7-01 - 36-99	6	8	F 9
37-01 - 41-99	1	8	F 9
108-00 - 127-99	68	9	J 9
200-00 - 223-99	61	10	M 9
36th Rd	54	9	K 9
36th St		8	F 8
19-00 - 23-99	5	8	G 8
24-00 - 30-99	3	8	F 9
31-00 - 36-99	6	8	F 9
37-00 - 48-99	1	11	F10
37th Av		8	E 9
8-01 - 52-99	1	11	F10
53-00 - 69-99	77	11	G10
70-00 - 95-99	72	11	H10
96-00 - 127-99	68	9	J 9
131-00 - 157-99	54	9	K 9
158-00 - 199-99	58	10	M 9
200-00 - 223-99	61	10	N 9
224-00 - OUT Ex 1-399	63	10	O 8
37th Dr	68	9	J 9
37th Rd		11	G10
53-00 - 69-99	77	11	G10
70-00 - 95-99	72	11	G10
96-00 - 127-99	68	9	J 9
37th St		8	F 9
19-00 - 23-99	5	8	G 8
24-00 - 32-99	3	8	F 9
34-00 - OUT	1	11	F10
38th Av		8	E 9
8-01 - 52-99	1	8	E 9
54-00 - 69-99	77	11	G10
96-00 - 127-99	68	9	J 9
131-00 - 157-99	54	9	K 9
200-00 - 223-99	61	10	M 9
224-00 - OUT E 1-399	63	10	O 8
38th Dr	63	10	N 8
38th Rd	63	10	N 8
38th St		8	F 9
18-00 - 23-99	5	8	G 8
24-00 - 32-99	3	8	F 9
34-00 - OUT	1	11	F10
39th Av		8	E 9
21-01 - 32-99	1	8	E 9
44-02 - 48-98 (even)	4	11	F10
44-01 - 52-99 (odd)	4	11	F10
49-00 - 52-98 (even)	77	11	F10
53-00 - 69-99	77	11	G10
96-00 - 127-99	68	9	J 9
131-00 - 157-99	54	9	K 9
158-00 - 199-99	58	10	M 9
200-00 - 223-99	61	10	N 9
224-00 - OUT	63	10	N 8
39th Dr	77	11	F10
39th Pl	4	11	F10
39th Rd		11	F10
52-00 - 52-99	77	11	F10
223-00 - 233-99	63	10	O 8
39th St		11	F10
36-00 - 40-99	1	11	F10
41-00 - OUT	4	11	F10
40th Av		8	E 9
8-00 - 30-99	1	8	E 9
213-00 - 220-99	61	10	N 9
233-00 - 236-99	63	10	N 8
247-00 - OUT	63	10	O 8
40th Dr	73	11	H10
40th Rd		11	E10
29-00 - 29-99	1	11	E10
94-00 - 95-99	73	11	H10
96-00 - 127-99	68	11	H10
131-00 - 135-99	54	9	K 9
40th St	4	11	F10
41st Av		8	E 9
10-01 - 30-99	1	11	E10
52-00 - 73-99	77	11	G10
74-00 - 95-99	73	11	H10
96-00 - 127-99	68	9	J 9
131-00 - 149-99	55	9	K 9
150-00 - 157-99	54	9	L 9
158-00 - 199-99	58	9	L 9
200-00 - 223-99	61	10	M 9
224-00 - OUT	63	10	O 8
41st Dr		11	G10
58-00 - 58-99	77	11	G10
250-00 - 260-99	63	10	O 8
41st Rd		8	E 9
10-00 - 11-99	1	8	E 9
94-00 - 95-99	73	11	H10
131-00 - 157-99	55	9	K 9
222-00 - 222-99	61	10	N 9
250-00 - 260-99	63	10	O 8
41st St		8	G 8
19-00 - 23-99	5	8	G 8
24-00 - 32-99	3	8	F 9
34-00 - 36-99	1	8	F 9
41-00 - OUT	4	11	F10
42nd Av (Sanford Ave)		11	H10
94-00 - 95-99	73	11	H10
96-00 - 127-99	68	12	J 10
131-00 - 157-99	55	9	K 9
158-00 - 199-99	58	10	M 9
200-00 - 223-99	61	10	N 9
234-00 - 260-99	63	10	O 8
42nd Pl	1	8	F 9
42nd Rd		11	E10
23-00 - 28-99	1	11	E10
196-00 - 196-99	58	10	M 9
42nd St		8	G 8
18-00 - 23-99	5	8	G 8
24-00 - 32-99	3	8	F 9
34-00 - 35-99	1	8	F 9
41-00 - 50-99	4	11	F10
43rd Av		11	E10
7-01 - 38-99	1	11	E10
39-01 - 48-99	4	11	F10
49-00 - 73-99	77	11	G10
74-00 - 95-99	73	11	H10
96-00 - 127-99	68	12	J 10
131-00 - 157-99	55	9	L 9
158-00 - 199-99	58	9	L 9
200-00 - 223-99	61	10	M 9
224-00 - 260-99	63	10	O 9
43rd Rd		11	E10
8-00 - 11-99	1	11	E10
158-00 - 199-99	58	10	M 9
43rd St		8	G 8
18-01 - 23-99	5	8	G 8
24-01 - 32-99	3	8	F 9
34-01 - 38-99	1	8	F 9
39-01 - 47-17 (odd)	4	11	F10
39-02 - 47-24 (even)	4	11	F10
47-25 - 50-99	77	11	F10
52-00 - 55-99	78	11	F11
44th Av		11	E10
8-01 - 22-99	1	11	E10
58-00 - 73-99	77	11	G10
74-00 - 95-99	73	11	H10
96-00 - 127-99	68	12	J 10
158-00 - 199-99	58	10	M 9
200-00 - 223-99	61	10	M 9
224-00 - 260-99	63	10	O 9
44th Dr	1	11	E10
44th Rd	1	11	E10
44th St		8	F 9
24-01 - 32-99	3	8	F 9
34-01 - 34-99	1	8	F 9
39-01 - 45-99	4	11	F10
47-00 - 51-09	77	11	F10
51-10 - 54-99	78	11	F11
45th Av		11	E10
5-00 - 23-99	1	11	E10
69-00 - 73-99	77	11	G10
74-00 - 95-99	73	11	H10
96-00 - 127-99	68	12	J 10
131-00 - 157-99	55	9	L 9
158-00 - 199-99	58	9	L 9
200-00 - 223-99	61	10	M 9
45th Dr		10	M 9
158-00 - 199-99	58	10	M 9
200-00 - 223-99	61	10	M 9
45th Rd		11	E10
10-01 - 23-99	1	11	E10
158-00 - 199-99	58	10	M 9
200-00 - 223-99	61	10	M 9
45th St		8	F 9
18-00 - 23-99	5	8	G 8
24-00 - 32-99	3	8	G 9
34-00 - 34-99	1	8	F 9
39-01 - 45-45 (odd)	4	11	F10
39-02 - 45-50 (even)	4	11	F10
45-51 - 51-99	77	11	F10
46th Av		11	E10
5-00 - 21-99	1	11	E10
74-00 - 95-99	73	11	H10
96-00 - 127-99	68	12	J 10
131-00 - 157-99	55	9	L 9
158-00 - 199-99	58	10	M 9
200-00 - 223-99	61	10	N 9
46th Rd		11	E10
4-01 - 21-99	1	11	E10
189-00 - 199-99	58	10	M 9
200-00 - 223-99	61	10	N 9
46th St		8	G 8
18-00 - 23-99	5	8	G 8
24-00 - 32-99	3	8	G 9
34-00 - 34-99	1	8	F 9
39-01 - 45-27 (odd)	4	11	F10
39-02 - 45-32 (even)	4	11	F10
45-35 - 51-99	77	11	F10
52-00 - 56-99	78	11	F11
47th Av		11	E10
4-00 - 38-99	1	11	F10
39-00 - 43-99	4	11	F10
44-00 - 73-99	77	11	G10
74-00 - 95-99	73	11	H10
96-00 - 127-99	68	12	J 10
131-00 - 157-99	55	9	L 9
158-00 - 199-99	58	10	M 9
200-00 - 223-99	61	10	M 9
47th Rd		11	E10
4-00 - 11-99	1	11	E10
217-00 - 218-99	61	10	N 9
47th St		8	F 9
18-01 - 23-99	5	8	G 8
24-01 - 32-99	3	8	G 9
39-01 - 45-11 (odd)	4	11	F10
39-02 - 45-16 (even)	4	11	F10
45-17 - 51-99	77	11	F10
55-00 - 58-99	78	11	F11
48th Av		11	D10
4-00 - 38-99	1	11	E10
39-00 - 41-99	4	11	F10
42-00 - 73-99	77	11	F10
74-00 - 95-99	73	11	H10
96-00 - 127-99	68	12	J 10
158-00 - 199-99	65	10	M 9
200-00 - 233-99	64	10	N 9
48th St		8	F 9
18-01 - 22-99	5	8	G 8
23-01 - 32-99	3	8	G 9
34-01 - 36-99	1	11	F 9
37-01 - 43-99	4	11	F10
45-00 - 51-99	77	11	F10
52-00 - 57-99	78	11	F11
49th Av		11	E10
10-01 - 27-99	1	11	E10
66-00 - 73-99	77	11	G10
74-00 - 95-99	73	11	H10
96-00 - 127-99	68	12	J 10
158-00 - 199-99	65	10	M 9
200-00 - 233-99	64	10	N 9
49th Rd	64	10	N 9
49th St	78	11	F11
49th St		8	G 9
18-01 - 22-99	5	8	G 8
23-01 - 30-99 (odd)	3	8	G 9
23-02 - 32-98 (even)	3	8	G 9
31-01 - 31-99 (odd)	77	8	G 9
32-01 - 32-99 (odd)	3	8	F 9
39-01 - 43-99	4	11	F10
45-00 - 50-99	77	11	F10
57-00 - 58-99	78	11	F11
50th Av		11	E10
2-00 - 27-99	1	11	E10
39-00 - 41-99	4	11	F10
42-00 - 73-99	77	11	F10
74-00 - 95-99	73	11	H10
96-00 - 127-99	68	12	J 10
158-00 - 199-99	65	13	M10
200-00 - 23-99	64	10	N 9
50th St		8	G 9
24-00 - 37-99	77	8	G 9
38-01 - 38-99	4	11	F10
39-00 - 45-99	77	11	F10
53-00 - 54-99	78	11	F11
51st Av		11	D10
2-01 - 27-99	1	11	E10
43-00 - 73-99	77	11	G10
74-00 - 95-99	73	11	H10
96-00 - 109-99	68	12	J 10
196-00 - 198-99	65	13	M10
200-00 - 233-99	64	10	N 9
240-00 - 251-99	62	10	O 9
51st Dr	77	11	G10
51st Rd	77	11	F10
51st St	77	11	F10
52nd Av		11	G10
42-00 - 44-99	78	11	F10
58-00 - 59-99	77	11	G10
60-99 - 73-99	78	11	G10
74-00 - 95-99	73	11	H10
96-00 - 127-99	68	12	J 10
240-00 - 254-99	62	10	O 9
52nd Ct	78	11	G11
52nd Dr	78	11	G10
52nd Rd		11	G10
66-00 - 73-99	78	11	G10
254-00 - 254-99	62	10	O 8
52nd St		11	F10
38-01 - 38-99	4	11	F10
39-00 - 43-99	77	11	F10
53rd Av		11	E10
10-01 - 11-99	1	11	E10
42-00 - 46-99	78	11	F11
60-00 - 73-99	78	11	G11
74-00 - 95-99	73	11	H10
96-00 - 127-99	68	12	J 10
158-00 - 199-99	65	13	M10
200-00 - 233-99	64	10	N 9
240-00 - 254-99	62	10	O 9
53rd Dr	78	11	G11
53rd Pl	77	8	G 9
53rd Rd		11	G11
66-00 - 73-99	78	11	G11
254-00 - 254-99	62	10	O 9
53rd St		11	F10
38-01 - 38-99 (odd)	77	11	F10
39-00 - 43-99	77	11	F10
52-00 - 60-99	78	11	F11
54th Av		11	D10
1-01 - 5-99	1	11	E10
42-00 - 73-99	78	11	F11
74-00 - 95-99	73	11	G11
96-00 - 127-94	68	12	J 10
200-00 - 233-99	64	10	N 9
242-00 - 260-00	62	10	O 9
54th Dr	78	11	F11
54th Pl	78	11	F11
54th Rd	78	11	F11
54th St		11	G10
30-00 - 43-99	77	11	G10
58-00 - 60-99	78	11	F11
55th Av		11	D10
1-00 - 2-99	1	11	D10
42-00 - 73-99	78	11	F11
74-00 - 95-99	73	11	H10
96-00 - 127-99	68	12	J 10
55th Dr	78	11	F11
55th Rd		11	F11
43-00 - 73-99	78	11	F11
74-00 - 95-99	73	11	H10
55th St		11	G10
31-00 - 43-99	77	11	G10
58-00 - 61-99	78	11	F11
56th Av		11	G11
1-01 - 1-99	1	11	D10
43-00 - 73-99	78	11	G11
74-00 - 95-99	73	11	H10
96-00 - 127-99	68	12	J 10
131-00 - 157-99	55	12	K10
158-00 - 199-99	65	13	M10
200-00 - 231-99	64	10	N 9
56th Dr	78	11	F11
56th Pl	77	8	G 9
56th Rd		11	F11
42-00 - 73-99	78	11	F11
131-00 - 157-00	55	12	K10
223-00 - 226-99	64	10	N 9
56th St		11	F11
31-00 - 43-99	77	8	G 9
58-00 - 62-99	78	11	F11
56th Ter	78	11	F11
57th Av		11	F11
56-00 - 73-99	78	11	F11
74-00 - 95-99	73	12	H10
96-00 - 127-99	68	12	J 10
132-00 - 134-00	55	12	K10
223-00 - 231-99	64	10	N 9
243-00 - 263-99	62	10	O 9
57th Dr		11	G11
57-00 - 73-99	78	11	G11
244-00 - 246-99	62	10	O 9
57th Pl	78	11	F11
57th Rd		11	G11
56-00 - 73-99	78	11	G11
74-00 - 95-99	73	11	H11
130-00 - 138-00	55	12	K10
223-00 - 230-99	64	10	N 9
57th St		11	F11
32-00 - 43-99	77	8	G 9
58-00 - 61-99	78	11	F11
58th Av		11	G11
46-00 - 73-99	78	11	G11
74-00 - 95-99	73	11	H11
96-00 - 127-99	68	12	J 10
132-00 - 134-00	55	12	K10
158-00 - 199-99	65	13	M10
200-00 - 233-99	64	10	N 9
58th Dr	78	11	G11
58th La	77	11	G10
58th Pl		11	G10
48-00 - 53-99	77	11	G10
54-00 - 58-99	78	11	G11
58th Rd		11	G11
58-00 - 73-99	78	11	G11
74-00 - 95-99	73	11	H11
130-00 - 157-99	55	12	K10
230-00 - 230-99	64	10	N 9
58th St		11	F11
30-00 - 53-99	77	8	G 9
54-00 - 58-99	78	11	F11
59th Av		11	G11
48-00 - 73-99	78	11	G11

STREET NAME AND HOUSE NUMBERS	ZONE NO.	MAP NO.	MAP GRID
74-00 - 95-99	73	11	H10
96-00 - 127-99	68	12	J 10
130-00 - 157-00	55	12	K10
158-00 - 199-99	65	12	L 10
221-00 - 228-99	64	10	N 9
262-00 - 262-98	62	10	O 9
59th Dr	78	11	G11
59th Pl		11	G10
47-00 - 53-99	77	11	G10
54-00 - 60-99	78	11	G11
59th Rd	78	11	G11
59th St		11	G10
33-00 - 53-99	77	11	G10
56-00 - 60-99	78	11	G11
60th Av		11	G11
59-00 - 73-99	78	11	G11
74-00 - 95-99	73	11	H11
96-00 - 127-99	68	12	J 10
130-00 - 153-00	55	12	K10
243-00 - 264-99	62	10	O 9
60th Ct	78	11	G11
60th Dr		11	G11
60-00 - 73-99	78	11	G11
83-00 - 86-99	73	11	H11
60th La		11	G11
58-00 - 62-99	78	11	G11
63-00 - 79-99	85	11	G12
60th Pl		8	G 9
33-00 - 33-99	77	8	G 9
53-00 - 62-08	78	11	G11
62-47 - 76-99	85	11	G12
60th Rd		11	G11
59-00 - 73-99	78	11	G11
74-00 - 95-99	73	11	H11
262-00 - 264-99	62	10	P 9
60th St		8	G 9
30-00 - 50-99	77	11	G10
52-00 - 62-20	78	11	G11
62-30 - 79-99	85	11	G12
61st Av	62	11	G11
61st Dr	79	11	H11
61st Rd		11	G11
61-00 - 84-99	79	11	H11
85-00 - 85-99	74	11	H11
131-00 - 157-99	67	12	K10
61st St		8	G 9
31-00 - 51-99	77	11	G10
52-00 - 60-99	78	11	G11
62-00 - 79-99	85	11	G12
62nd Av		11	G11
56-00 - 60-99	78	11	G12
61-00 - 84-99	79	11	H11
85-00 - 99-99	74	11	H11
100-00 - 112-99	75	12	J 10
131-00 - 157-99	67	12	K10
245-00 - 259-99	62	10	O 9
62nd Dr		11	H11
69-00 - 84-99	79	11	H11
85-00 - 99-99	74	11	H11
100-00 - 112-99	75	12	J 10
62nd Rd		11	G12
61-00 - 84-99	79	11	G12
85-00 - 99-99	74	11	H11
100-00 - 112-99	75	12	J 10
131-00 - 157-99	67	12	K10
62nd St		8	G 9
32-00 - 51-99	77	8	G 9
52-00 - 60-99	78	11	G11
61-00 - 61-99	79	11	G12
67-00 - 80-99	85	11	G12
63rd Av		11	H11
69-00 - 84-99	79	11	H11
85-00 - 99-99	74	12	J 10
102-00 - 112-99	75	12	J 10
131-00 - 157-99	67	12	K10
245-00 - 255-99	62	10	O 9
63rd Dr		12	J 11
85-00 - 99-99	74	12	J 11
102-00 - 112-99	75	12	J 10
63rd Pl	78	11	G11
63rd Rd		11	H11
61-00 - 84-99	79	11	H11
85-00 - 99-99	74	12	J 10
102-00 - 112-99	75	12	J 10
131-00 - 157-99	67	12	K10
63rd St		11	G10
35-00 - 51-99	77	11	G10
52-00 - 60-99	78	11	G11
61-00 - 61-99	79	11	G11
64th Av		12	J 11
97-00 - 99-99	74	12	J 11
102-00 - 112-99	75	12	J 10
131-00 - 157-99 330	67	12	K10
158-00 - 199-99	65	13	M10
200-00 - 233-99	64	13	N10
249-00 - 249-99	62	10	O 9
64th Cir	65	13	M10
64th La	79	11	G12
64th Pl	85	11	G12
64th Rd		11	H11
61-00 - 84-99	79	11	H11
85-00 - 99-99	74	12	J 11
102-00 - 112-99	75	12	J 10
136-00 - 137-99	67	12	K10
64th St		8	G 9
34-00 - 51-99	77	8	G 9
52-00 - 59-99	78	11	G11
61-00 - 62-99	79	11	G12
66-00 - 80-99	85	11	G12
65th Av		12	J 11
85-00 - 99-99	74	12	J 11
102-00 - 112-99	75	12	J 10
131-00 - 157-99	67	12	L 10

STREET NAME AND HOUSE NUMBERS	ZONE NO.	MAP NO.	MAP GRID
158-00 - 199-99	65	12	L 10
200-00 - 233-99	64	13	N10
234-00 - OUT	62	10	O 9
65th Cres	65	13	M10
65th Dr		11	H11
69-00 - 84-99	79	11	H11
85-00 - 99-99	74	12	J 11
65th La	79	11	G12
65th Pl		11	G10
39-00 - 51-99	77	11	G10
52-00 - 59-99	78	11	G11
64-00 - 64-99	79	11	G12
67-00 - 72-99	85	11	G12
65th Rd		12	J 11
35-00 - 99-99	74	12	J 11
61-00 - 84-99	75	12	J 11
65th St		11	G10
34-00 - 51-99	77	11	G10
52-00 - 59-99	78	11	G11
61-00 - 64-99	79	11	G12
67-00 - 80-99	85	11	G12
66th Av		12	J 11
85-00 - 99-99	74	12	J 11
102-00 - 112-99	75	12	J 11
234 - OUT	62	10	O 9
66th Dr	79	11	H12
66th Pl	85	11	H12
66th Rd		11	H11
61-00 - 84-99	79	11	H11
85-00 - 99-99	74	12	J 11
102-00 - 112-99	75	12	J 11
66th St		11	G10
41-00 - 51-99	77	11	G10
52-00 - 60-99	78	11	G11
69-00 - 72-99	85	11	H12
67th Av		11	G12
59-00 - 60-99	85	11	G12
85-00 - 101-99	74	12	J 11
102-00 - 112-99	75	12	J 11
158-00 - 199-99	65	13	M10
200-00 - 233-99	64	13	N10
234-00 - 240-99	62	10	O 9
67th Dr		11	H12
69-00 - 84-99	79	11	H12
85-00 - 85-99	74	12	J 11
100-00 - 112-99	75	12	J 11
67th Pl	85	11	H12
67th Rd		11	H12
73-00 - 84-99	79	11	H12
85-00 - 85-99	74	12	J 11
99-00 - 112-99	75	12	J 11
67th St		11	G10
40-00 - 51-99	77	11	G10
52-00 - 60-99	78	11	G11
61-00 - 61-99	79	11	G11
69-00 - 72-99	85	11	H12
68th Av		11	G12
59-00 - 72-99	85	11	G12
73-00 - 84-99	79	11	H12
85-00 - 85-99	74	12	J 11
89-00 - 112-99	75	12	J 11
131-00 - 157-99	67	12	K10
158-00 - 199-99	65	12	L 10
216-00 - 220-99	64	13	N10
240-01 - 240-83	62	10	O 9
68th Dr		12	J 11
103-00 - 112-99	75	12	J 11
135-00 - 157-99	67	12	K10
68th Pl	85	11	H12
68th Rd		11	G12
59-00 - 72-99	85	11	G12
73-00 - 84-99	79	11	H12
85-00 - 85-99	74	12	J 11
103-00 - 112-99	75	12	J 11
131-00 - 157-99	67	12	K10
68th St		8	G 9
30-00 - 51-99	77	8	G 9
52-00 - 60-99	78	11	G11
61-00 - 61-99	79	11	G11
69-00 - 72-99	85	11	H12
69th Av		11	G12
58-00 - 72-99	85	11	G12
73-00 - 79-00	79	11	H12
87-00 - 112-99	75	12	J 11
131-00 - 157-99	67	12	K10
158-00 - 199-99	65	12	L 10
200-00 - 233-99	64	13	N10
234-00 - 259-99	62	10	O 9
260-00 - OUT			
(Floral Park)	4	10	P 9
69th Dr	79	11	H12
69th La		11	G11
54-00 - 60-99	78	11	G11
61-00 - 62-99	79	11	H11
69th Pl		11	G10
50-00 - 51-99	77	11	G10
52-00 - 60-99	78	11	G11
61-00 - 64-99	79	11	H11
69-00 - 76-99	85	11	H12
69th Rd		11	H12
73-00 - 79-99	79	11	H12
86-00 - 112-99	75	12	J 12
131-00 - 157-99	67	12	K10
69th St		8	G 9
30-00 - 51-99	77	11	G10
52-00 - 60-99	78	11	G11
61-00 - 66-99	79	11	H11
69-00 - 73-99	85	11	H12
70th Av		11	G12
58-00 - 73-49	85	11	H12
73-50 - 84-99	79	11	H12
89-00 - 112-99	75	12	J 11
131-00 - 157-99	67	12	K11

STREET NAME AND HOUSE NUMBERS	ZONE NO.	MAP NO.	MAP GRID
234-00 - 252-99	62	10	O 9
70th Dr	75	12	J 12
70th Rd		12	K11
88-00 - 112-99	75	12	J 12
131-00 - 157-99	67	12	K11
70th St		8	G 9
22-00 - 32-99	70	8	G 9
33-00 - 35-99	72	11	G10
40-00 - 51-99	77	11	G10
52-00 - 60-99	78	11	G11
61-00 - 66-99	79	11	H12
69-00 - 76-99	85	11	H12
71st Av		11	G12
58-00 - 89-99	85	11	G12
74-00 - 74-99	79	11	H12
90-00 - 112-99	75	12	J 11
131-00 - 157-99	67	12	K11
158-00 - 199-99	65	12	L 11
251-00 - 252-99	26	10	O 9
71st Cres	65	13	M10
71st Dr	75	12	J 12
71st Pl	85	11	H12
71st Rd		12	J 12
91-00 - 112-99	75	12	J 12
131-00 - 157-99	67	12	K11
251-00 - 252-99	26	10	O 9
71st St		8	G 9
21-00 - 32-99	70	8	G 9
33-00 - 35-99	72	8	G 9
40-00 - 51-99	77	11	G10
52-00 - 60-99	78	11	G11
61-00 - 66-99	79	11	H11
69-00 - 77-99	85	11	H12
72nd Av		12	J 12
83-00 - 89-99	85	12	J 12
131-00 - 157-99	67	12	K11
158-00 - 199-99	65	12	L 11
243-00 - 244-99	62	10	O 9
251-00 - 252-99	26	10	P 9
72nd Cres	67	12	K11
72nd Dr		12	K11
97-00 - 112-99	75	12	K11
131-00 - 157-99	67	12	K11
72nd La	85	11	H12
72nd Pl		11	G10
50-00 - 51-99	77	11	G10
52-00 - 53-99	78	11	G11
70-00 - 77-99	85	11	H12
72nd Rd		12	K11
96-00 - 113-99	75	12	K11
131-00 - 157-99	67	12	K11
266-00 - OUT			
(Floral Park)	4	10	P 9
72nd St		8	G 9
21-00 - 32-99	70	8	G 9
33-00 - 37-99	72	8	G 9
40-00 - 51-99	77	11	G10
52-00 - 60-99	78	11	G11
61-00 - 64-99	79	11	H11
70-00 - 77-99	85	11	H12
73rd Av		12	J 12
84-00 - 89-99	85	12	J 12
100-00 - 112-99	75	12	K11
131-00 - 157-99	67	12	K11
158-00 - 199-99	66	12	L 11
200-00 - 233-99	64	13	N10
243-00 - 244-99	62	10	O 9
253-00 - OUT			
(Floral Park)	4	10	P 9
73rd Pl		11	G10
50-00 - 50-99	77	11	G10
54-00 - 60-99	78	11	H11
61-00 - 69-99	79	11	H11
70-00 - 78-99	85	11	H12
73rd Rd		12	K11
110-00 - 110-99	75	12	K11
214-00 - 216-99	64	13	N10
253-00 - OUT	4	10	P 9
73rd St		8	G 9
21-00 - 32-99	70	8	G 9
33-00 - 37-99	72	11	G10
40-00 - 51-99	77	11	G10
52-00 - 60-99	78	11	G10
70-00 - 78-99	85	11	H12
73rd Ter	67	12	K11
74th Av		12	J 12
62-00 - 89-99	85	12	J 12
98-00 - 112-99	75	12	J 12
158-00 - 199-99	66	13	M11
200-00 - 233-99	64	13	N10
253-00 - OUT			
(Floral Park)	4	13	P10
74th Pl	21	14	J 13
74th St		8	G 9
20-00 - 32-99	70	8	G 9
33-00 - 37-99	72	11	G10
40-00 - 60-99	73	11	G10
61-00 - 70-99	79	11	H11
71-00 - 78-99	85	11	H12
86-00 - 93-99	21	14	J 13
94-00 - 95-99	16	14	J 13
75th Av		12	J 12
60-00 - 89-99	85	12	J 12
100-00 - 112-99	75	12	K12
131-00 - 157-99	67	12	L 11
158-00 - 199-99	66	12	L 11
200-00 - 233-99	64	13	N10
253-00 - OUT			
(Floral Park)	4	13	P10
75th Pl	79	11	H11
75th Rd		12	K11
101-00 - 112-99			
(Puritan Av)	75	12	K12

STREET NAME AND HOUSE NUMBERS	ZONE NO.	MAP NO.	MAP GRID
131-00 - 157-99	67	12	K11
158-00 - 199-99	66	12	L 11
75th St		8	G 9
19-00 - 32-99	70	8	G 9
33-00 - 37-99	72	8	G 9
40-00 - 60-99	73	11	G10
61-00 - 69-99	79	11	H11
70-00 - 78-99	85	11	H12
84-00 - 93-99	21	14	J 13
94-00 - 102-99	16	14	J 13
103-00 - 131-99	17	14	J 14
132-00 - 154-99	14	14	J 14
76th Av		12	J 12
69-00 - 89-99	85	12	J 12
131-00 - 157-99	67	12	L 11
158-00 - 199-99	66	12	L 11
200-00 - 233-99	64	13	N10
245-00 - 252-99	26	13	O10
253-00 - OUT			
(New Hyde Park)	40	10	P 9
76th Dr	75	12	K11
76th Rd		12	K11
108-00 - 113-99	75	12	K11
131-00 - 157-99	67	12	L 11
158-00 - 199-99	66	12	L 11
200-00 - 233-99	64	13	N10
76th St		8	G 8
19-00 - 32-99	70	8	G 9
33-00 - 37-99	72	8	G 9
40-00 - 60-99	73	11	H10
61-00 - 69-99	79	11	H11
70-00 - 78-99	85	11	H12
85-00 - 93-99	21	14	J 13
94-00 - 102-99	16	14	J 13
103-00 - 132-99	17	14	J 13
133-00 - OUT	14	14	J 14
77th Av		11	H12
72-00 - 89-99	85	11	H12
103-00 - 113-99	75	12	K11
131-00 - 157-99	67	12	K11
158-00 - 199-99	66	12	L 11
200-00 - 233-99	64	13	N10
253-00 - OUT			
(New Hyde Park)	40	10	P 9
77th Cres	26	13	O10
77th Pl		11	H11
58-00 - 60-99	73	11	H11
61-00 - 66-99	79	11	H11
77th Rd		11	H12
79-00 - 79-99	85	11	H12
111-00 - 112-99	75	12	K11
131-00 - 157-99	67	12	L 11
158-00 - 199-99	66	12	L 11
271-00 - OUT			
(New Hyde Park)	40	10	P 9
77th St		8	G 8
19-00 - 32-99	70	8	G 9
33-00 - 37-99	72	8	G 9
40-00 - 60-99	73	11	G10
61-00 - 69-99	79	11	H11
86-00 - 92-99	21	14	J 13
94-00 - 102-99	16	14	J 13
103-00 - 132-99	17	14	J 13
133-00 - 154-99	14	14	J 14
78th Av		11	G12
57-00 - 89-99	85	11	H12
105-00 - 113-99	75	12	K12
131-00 - 157-99	67	12	L 11
158-00 - 199-99	66	12	L 11
265-00 - 268-99			
(Floral Park)	4	10	P 9
269-00 - OUT			
(New Hyde Park)	40	10	P 9
78th Cres	75	12	K11
78th Dr	67	12	K11
78th Rd		11	H12
79-00 - 79-99	85	11	H12
135-00 - 153-99	67	12	L 11
158-00 - 199-99	66	12	L 11
78th St		8	G 8
19-00 - 32-99	70	8	G 9
33-00 - 37-99	72	8	G 9
40-00 - 60-99	73	11	H11
61-00 - 69-99	79	11	H11
77-00 - 78-99	85	11	H12
86-00 - 92-99	21	14	J 13
94-00 - 101-99	16	14	J 13
103-00 - 132-99	17	14	J 13
133-00 - OUT	14	14	J 14
79th Av		11	G12
94-00 - 102-99	85	12	J 12
131-00 - 157-99	67	12	L 11
158-00 - 199-99	66	12	L 11
257-00 - 268-99			
(Floral Park)	4	13	P10
269-01 - OUT			
(New Hyde Park)	40	10	P 9
79th La	85	11	H12
79th Pl		11	H11
65-00 - 66-99	79	11	H11
70-00 - 78-99	85	11	H12
79th St		8	G 8
19-00 - 32-99	70	8	G 9
33-00 - 37-99	72	11	H10
40-06 - 60-99	73	11	H10
61-00 - 69-99	79	11	H11
70-00 - 78-99	85	11	H12
103-00 - 132-99	17	14	J 13
133-00 - OUT	14	14	J 14
80th Av		11	G12
60-00 - 65-99	85	11	G12
251-00 - 252-99	26	13	P10

STREET NAME AND HOUSE NUMBERS	ZONE NO.	MAP NO.	MAP GRID
253-00 - 268-99			
(Floral Park)	4	13	P10
269-01 - OUT			
(New Hyde Park)	40	13	P10
80th Dr	32	13	M11
80th Rd		11	G12
62-00 - 62-99	85	11	G12
101-00 - 157-99	15	12	K12
176-00 - 186-99	32	13	M11
244-00 - 245-99	26	13	O10
80th St		8	G 8
19-00 - 32-99	70	8	G 8
33-00 - 37-99	72	8	H 9
40-00 - 60-99	73	11	H10
61-00 - 69-99	79	11	H11
70-00 - 78-99	85	11	H12
85-00 - 91-99	21	14	J 12
94-00 - 102-99	16	14	J 13
103-00 - 132-99	17	14	J 13
137-00 - 164-99	14	14	J 14
81st Av		12	J 12
87-00 - 88-99	85	12	J 12
104-124	15	12	K12
135-00 - 141-99	35	12	L 11
164-00 - 169-99	32	12	L 11
242-00 - 252-99	26	13	P10
253-00 - 268-99			
(Floral Park)	4	13	P10
269-01 - OUT			
(New Hyde Park)	40	13	P10
81st Rd	85	12	J 12
81st St		8	G 8
19-00 - 32-99	70	8	H 9
33-00 - 37-99	72	8	H 9
40-00 - 60-99	73	11	H10
61-00 - 64-99	79	11	H11
70-00 - 78-99	85	12	J 12
91-00 - 91-99	21	14	J 13
94-00 - 102-99	16	14	J 13
107-00 - 132-99	17	14	J 14
137-00 - OUT	14	14	J 14
82nd Av		12	J 12
88-00 - 99-99	85	12	J 12
101-153	15	12	K12
120-00 - 125-99	15	12	K12
126-02(only)	15	12	K11
135-00 - 138-99	35	12	K11
170-00 - 173-99	32	13	M11
208-00 - 219-99	27	13	N10
242-00 - 252-99	26	13	P10
253-00 - OUT			
(Floral Park)	4	13	P10
82nd Dr		12	K12
100 and 199	18	12	K12
116-00 - 117-99	18	12	K12
122-00 - 122-99	15	12	K12
135-00 - 141-99	35	12	L 11
158-00 - 160-99	32	12	L 11
252-00 - 252-99	26	13	P10
253-00 - 268-99			
(Floral Park)	4	13	P10
82nd Pl	79	11	H11
82nd Rd		12	J 12
89-00 - 90-99	85	12	J 12
99-122	15	12	K12
121-01 - 123-99	15	12	K12
164-00 - 167-99	32	12	L 11
252-00 - 252-99	26	13	P10
253-00 - OUT			
(Floral Park)	4	13	P10
82nd St		8	H 9
19-00 - 32-99	70	8	H 9
33-00 - 37-99	72	8	H 9
40-00 - 60-99	73	11	H10
70-000 - 79-99	85	12	J 12
91-00 - 91-99	21	14	J 13
95-00 - 102-99	16	14	J 13
103-00 - 132-99	17	14	J 14
137-00 - OUT	14	14	J 14
83rd Av		12	J 12
89-00 - 90-99	85	12	J 12
10-190	15	12	K12
118-00 - 123-99	15	12	K12
135-00 - 139-99	35	12	L 11
170-00 - 172-99	32	13	M11
240-00 - 253-99	26	13	P10
254-00 - 268-99			
(Floral Park)	4	13	P10
269-01 - OUT			
(New Hyde Park)	40	13	P10
83rd Dr		12	K12
80-00 - 80-99	15	12	K12
88-00 - 88-99	85	12	J 12
115-00 - 115-99	18	12	K12
83rd Pl		12	H11
58-00 - 60-99	73	12	H11
62-00 - 64-99	79	12	H11
83rd Rd	4	13	P10
83rd St		8	H 9
19-00 - 32-99	70	8	H 9
33-00 - 37-99	72	8	H 9
40-00 - 60-99	73	11	H10
61-00 - 64-99	79	11	H11
70-00 - 78-99	85	12	J 12
94-00 - 102-99	16	14	J 13
103-00 - 133-99	17	14	J 14
149-00- OUT	14	14	J 14
84th Av		12	K12
110-00 - 117-99	18	12	K12
118-00 - 125-99	35	12	L 11
143-00 - 149-99	15	12	K12
150-00 - OUT	32	12	L 11

STREET NAME AND HOUSE NUMBERS	ZONE NO.	MAP NO.	MAP GRID
84th Dr		12	L 12
138-00 - 149-99	35	12	L 12
150-00 - 170-99	32	12	L 11
253-00 - 253-99	26	13	P 10
254-00 - OUT			
(Floral Park)	1	13	P 10
84th Pl		11	H 11
58-00 - 58-99	73	11	H 11
61-00 - 64-99	79	11	H 11
84th Rd		12	K 12
124-00 - 125-99	15	12	K 12
139-00 - 149-99	35	12	L 11
150-00 - 172-99	32	12	L 11
243-00 - 244-99	26	13	P 10
254-00 - OUT			
(Floral Park)	1	13	P 10
84th St		8	H 9
19-00 - 32-99	70	8	H 9
33-00 - 37-99	72	8	H 9
52-00 - 60-99	73	11	H 11
61-00 - 64-99	79	11	H 11
70-00 - 78-99	85	12	J 12
89-00 - 91-99	21	14	J 13
94-00 - 102-99	16	14	J 13
103-00 - 133-99	17	14	J 13
149- OUT	14	14	J 14
85th Av		12	J 12
80-00 - 94-99	21	12	J 12
102-00 - 117-99	18	12	K 12
118-00 - 124-99	15	12	K 12
144-00 - 149-99	35	12	L 12
150-00 - 165-99	32	12	L 12
209-00 - 218-99	27	13	N 11
241-00 - 253-99	26	13	P 10
254-00 - OUT			
(Floral Park)	1	13	P 10
85th Dr		12	J 12
74-00 - 84-99	21	12	J 12
102-00 - 102-99	18	12	J 12
139-00 - 149-99	35	12	L 12
150-00 - OUT	32	12	L 12
85th Rd		12	J 12
76-00 - 94-99	21	12	J 12
101-00 - 102-99	18	12	J 12
141-00 - 149-99	35	12	L 12
188-00 - 193-99	23	13	M 11
241-00 - 253-99	26	13	P 10
85th St		8	H 9
19-00 - 32-99	70	8	H 9
33-00 - 37-99	72	8	H 9
58-00 - 60-99	73	11	H 10
61-00 - 64-99	79	11	H 11
70-00 - 78-99	85	12	J 12
84-00 - 91-99	21	14	J 13
94-00 - 102-99	16	14	J 13
103-00 - 133-99	17	14	J 14
149- OUT	14	14	J 14
86th Av		12	J 12
76-00 - 94-99	21	12	J 12
101-00 - 114-99	18	12	K 12
138-00 - 148-99	35	12	L 12
150-00 - 164-99	32	12	L 12
211-00 - 218-99	27	13	N 11
239-00 - 254-99	26	13	P 10
255-00 - OUT			
(Floral Park)	1	13	P 10
86th Cres	32	12	L 12
86th Dr		12	J 12
91-00 - 93-99	21	12	J 12
209-00 - OUT	27	13	N 11
86th Rd		12	J 12
74-00 - 94-99	21	12	J 12
102-00 - 134-99	18	12	K 12
139-00 - 139-99	35	12	L 12
162-00 - 164-99	32	12	L 12
206-00 - 214-99	27	13	N 11
241-00 - 246-99	26	13	P 10
86th St		8	H 9
19-00 - 32-99	69	8	H 9
33-00 - 37-99	72	8	H 9
58-00 - 60-99	73	11	H 11
70-00 - 78-99	85	12	J 12
84-00 - 91-99	21	12	J 12
94-00 - 102-99	16	14	J 13
103-00 - 133-99	17	14	J 13
155-00 - OUT	14	14	J 14
87th Av		14	J 13
74-00 - 80-99	21	14	J 13
100-00 - 136-99	18	12	K 12
137-00 - 149-99	35	12	L 12
150-00 - 150-99	32	12	L 12
223-00 - 235-99	27	13	O 10
236-00 - 254-99	26	13	O 10
225-00 - OUT			
(Floral Park)	1	13	P 10
87th Dr		12	L 12
139-00 - 139-99	35	12	L 12
175-00 - 187-99	32	13	M 11
188-00 - 188-99	23	13	N 11
247-00 - 254-99	26	13	P 11
255-00 - OUT			
(Floral Park)	1	13	P 11
87th Dr	23	13	M 11
87th Rd		14	J 13
74-00 - 80-99	21	14	J 13
127-00 - 127-99	18	12	K 12
139-00 - 149-99	35	12	L 12
150-00 - 187-99	32	13	M 11
194-00 - 202-99	23	13	N 11
247-00 - 254-99	26	13	P 11
87th St		8	H 9
19-00 - 32-99	69	8	H 9
33-00 - 37-99	72	8	H 9
49-00 - 60-99	73	11	H 10
70-00 - 78-99	85	12	J 12
84-00 - 91-99	21	14	J 13
94-00 - 102-99	16	14	J 13
103-00 - 133-99	17	14	J 14
156-00 - OUT	14	14	K 15
87th Ter (Floral Pk)	1	13	P 11
88th Av		14	J 13
74-00 - 92-99	21	14	J 13
100-00 - 104-99	18	12	K 12
139-00 - 148-99	35	12	L 12
150-00 - 175-99	32	12	L 12
225-00 - 235-99	27	13	O 11
236-00 - 244-99	26	13	P 11
88th Dr	26	13	P 11
88th La	85	12	J 12
88th Pl	85	12	J 12
88th Rd		14	J 13
74-00 - 92-99	21	14	J 13
127-00 - 127-99	18	12	K 12
139-00 - 139-99	35	12	L 12
210-00 - 210-99	27	13	N 11
242-00 - 250-99	26	13	P 11
88th St		8	H 9
19-00 - 32-99	69	8	H 9
33-00 - 37-99	72	8	H 9
46-00 - 60-99	73	11	H 10
70-00 - 81-99	85	12	J 12
84-00 - 91-99	21	14	J 13
94-00 - 102-99	16	14	J 13
103-00 - 132-99	17	14	J 13
149-00 - OUT	14	14	J 14
89th Av		14	J 13
78-00 - 92-99	21	14	J 13
100-00 - 135-99	18	12	K 12
139-00 - 148-99	35	12	L 12
150-00 - 175-99	32	13	M 12
181-00 - 205-99	23	13	N 11
206-00 - 220-99	27	13	O 11
89th Rd		12	L 12
130-00 - 130-99	18	12	L 12
196-00 - 197-99	23	13	N 11
211-00 - OUT	27	13	N 11
89th St		8	H 9
19-00 - 32-99	69	8	H 9
33-00 - 37-99	72	8	H 9
70-00 - 82-99	85	12	J 12
84-00 - 91-99	21	12	J 12
94-00 - 102-99	16	14	J 13
103-00 - 132-99	17	14	J 13
136-00 - OUT	14	14	K 14
90th Av		14	J 13
74-00 - 80-99	21	14	J 13
100-00 - 130-99	18	14	K 13
137-00 - 147-00	35	12	L 12
153-00 - 180-99	32	13	M 12
181-00 - 205-99	23	13	N 11
206-00 - 235-99	28	13	N 11
90th Ct *		13	N 11
90th Pl	69	8	H 9
90th Rd		14	J 13
78-00 - 80-99	21	14	J 13
148-00 - 148-99	35	12	L 12
90th St		8	H 9
19-00 - 32-99	69	8	H 9
33-00 - 37-99	72	8	H 9
46-00 - 60-99	73	11	H 10
84-00 - 91-99	21	14	J 13
95-00 - 102-99	16	14	J 13
103-00 - 132-99	17	14	J 13
150-00 - OUT	14	14	K 14
91st Av		14	J 13
74-00 - 98-99	21	14	J 13
100-00 - 135-99	18	14	K 13
137-00 - 146-99	35	12	L 12
160-00 - 173-99	32	13	M 12
181-00 - 196-99	23	13	N 11
208-00 - 221-99	28	13	O 11
242-00 - 247-99	26	13	P 11
91st Dr	21	14	J 13
91st Pl	73	11	H 10
91st Rd		14	J 13
96-00 - 96-99	21	14	J 13
183-00 - 197-99	23	13	M 12
219-00 - 222-99	28	13	O 11
91st St		8	H 9
19-00 - 32-99	69	8	H 9
33-00 - 37-99	72	8	H 9
48-00 - 60-99	73	11	H 10
84-00 - 91-99	21	12	J 12
95-00 - 102-99	16	14	J 13
103-00 - 107-99	17	14	J 13
155-00 - 164-99	14	14	K 14
92nd Av		14	J 13
92-00 - 96-99	21	14	J 13
100-00 - 130-99	18	14	K 13
212-00 - 235-99	28	13	O 11
92nd Rd		13	M 12
168-00 - 168-99	33	13	M 12
217-00 - 235-99	28	13	O 11
236-00 - 237-99	26	13	O 11
92nd St		8	H 9
19-00 - 32-99	69	8	H 9
33-00 - 37-99	72	8	H 9
47-00 - 60-99	73	11	H 10
87-00 - 93-99	21	14	J 13
94-00 - 102-99	16	14	J 13
103-00 - 107-99	17	14	J 13
155-00 - 164-99	14	14	K 15
93rd Av		14	J 13
74-00 - 96-99	21	14	J 13
100-00 - 113-99	18	14	K 14
150-00 - 180-99	33	13	M 12
181-00 - 199-99	23	13	N 11
206-00 - 224-99	28	13	O 11
237-00 - 242-99	26	13	O 11
93rd Rd		13	O 11
211-00 - 224-99	28	13	N 11
237-00 - 239-99	26	13	O 11
93rd St		8	H 9
19-00 - 32-99	69	8	H 9
33-00 - 37-99	72	8	H 9
47-00 - 60-99	73	11	H 10
94-00 - 102-99	16	14	J 13
103-00 - 107-99	17	14	J 13
129-00 - 131-00	18	12	L 12
94th Av		14	K 13
100-00 - 107-99	16	14	K 13
119-00 - 134-99	18	12	K 12
137-00 - 149-99	35	12	L 12
150-00 - 150-99	33	12	L 12
204-00 - 204-99	23	13	N 11
206-00 - OUT	28	13	O 11
94th Dr	28	13	O 11
94th Pl	17	14	K 14
94th Rd	28	13	N 11
94th St		8	H 8
19-00 - 32-99	69	8	H 9
33-00 - 37-99	72	8	H 9
40-00 - 60-99	73	11	H 10
82-00 - 87-99	21	12	J 12
94-00 - 102-99	16	14	J 13
103-00 - 149-99	17	14	K 14
155-00 - OUT	14	14	K 14
95th Av		14	J 13
73-00 - 107-99	16	14	J 13
108-00 - 134-99	19	14	K 13
137-00 - 149-99	35	12	L 12
220-00 - 226-99	29	13	O 11
238-00 - OUT	26	13	O 11
95th Pl	17	14	K 14
95th St		8	H 9
19-00 - 32-99	69	8	H 9
33-00 - 37-99	72	14	J 13
40-00 - 60-99	73	11	H 10
87-00 - 93-99	21	14	J 13
94-00 - 102-99	16	14	J 13
103-00 - 149-99	17	14	K 13
155-00 - 164-99	14	14	K 14
96th Av	29	13	O 11
96th Pl	17	14	K 14
96th Rd	29	13	O 11
96th St		8	H 9
19-00 - 32-99	69	8	H 9
33-00 - 60-99	68	8	H 9
84-00 - 91-99	21	12	J 12
94-00 - 102-99	16	14	K 13
103-00 - 149-99	17	14	K 13
155-00 - OUT	14	14	K 14
97th Av		14	J 13
74-00 - 107-99	16	14	J 13
108-01 - 135-99	19	14	K 13
137-00 - 149-99	35	12	L 12
218-00 - OUT	29	13	O 11
97th Pl		12	J 10
41-00 - 60-99	68	12	H 10
61-00 - 61-99	74	12	J 10
97th St		8	H 9
19-00 - 32-99	69	8	H 9
33-00 - 60-99	68	8	H 9
61-00 - 61-99	74	12	J 10
87-00 - 91-99	21	14	J 13
94-00 - 102-99	16	14	K 13
103-00 - 149-99	17	18	L 18
155-00 - OUT	14	14	K 14
98th Av	29	13	O 11
98th Pl		12	J 10
47-00 - 60-99	68	12	J 10
61-00 - 66-99	74	12	J 10
98th St		8	H 9
19-00 - 32-99	69	8	H 9
33-00 - 60-99	68	8	H 9
61-00 - 66-99	74	12	J 10
83-00 - 91-99	21	14	J 13
94-00 - 102-99	16	14	K 13
103-00 - 109-99	17	14	K 13
155-00 - 164-99	14	14	K 14
99th Av		14	K 13
95-00 - 97-99	16	14	K 13
190-00 - 205-99	23	13	N 12
206-00 - 222-99	29	13	O 11
99th Pl	17	14	K 14
99th Rd *(off 197th St)	23	13	N 12
99th St		8	H 9
19-00 - 32-99	69	8	H 9
33-00 - 60-99	68	8	H 9
61-00 - 66-99	74	12	J 10
97-00 - 102-99	16	14	K 13
103-00 - 135-99	17	14	K 13
155-00 - 165-99	14	14	K 14
100th Av		13	N 12
192-00 - 205-99	23	13	N 12
206-00 - 222-99	29	13	O 11
100th Dr	29	13	O 11
100th Rd	29	13	O 11
100th St		8	H 9
19-00 - 32-99	69	8	H 9
33-00 - 60-99	68	8	H 9
87-00 - 93-99	18	12	J 12
94-00 - 102-99	16	14	K 13
103-00 - 132-99	17	14	K 13
155-00 - OUT	14	14	K 14
101st Av		14	J 13
74-00 - 107-99	16	14	J 13
108-00 - 135-99	19	14	K 13
137-00 - 145-99	35	12	L 12
218-00 - 223-99	29	13	O 11
101St Rd *(off 105th St)	16	14	K 13
101st St		8	H 9
19-00 - 32-99	69	8	H 9
33-00 - 60-99	68	8	H 9
84-00 - 86-99	18	12	J 12
95-00 - 102-99	16	14	K 13
103-00 - 133-99	17	14	K 13
154-00 - 159-99	14	14	K 14
102nd Av		14	J 13
81-00 - 88-99	16	14	J 13
127-00 - 134-99	19	14	L 13
137-00 - 143-99	35	14	L 13
185-00 - 191-99	23	13	N 12
212-00 - 220-99	29	13	O 11
102nd Rd		14	J 13
81-00 - 90-99	16	14	J 13
127-00 - 127-99	19	14	L 13
102nd St		8	H 9
19-00 - 32-99	69	8	H 9
33-00 - 60-99	68	8	H 9
61-00 - 66-99	74	12	J 10
67-00 - 67-99	75	12	J 11
84-00 - 93-99	18	12	J 12
94-00 - 102-99	16	14	K 13
103-00 - 104-99	17	14	K 13
155-00 - OUT	14	14	K 14
103rd Av		14	K 13
84-00 - 107-99	17	14	K 13
108-00 - 133-99	19	14	K 13
190-00 - 190-99	23	13	N 12
217-00 - 225-99	29	13	O 11
103rd Dr	17	14	K 13
103rd Rd		14	K 13
105-00 - 105-99	17	14	K 13
127-00 - 127-99	19	14	L 13
171-00 - 173-99	33	13	M 12
103rd St		9	J 9
19-00 - 32-99	69	9	J 9
33-00 - 60-99	68	9	J 9
61-00 - 70-99	75	12	J 11
95-00 - 102-99	16	14	K 13
103-00 - OUT	17	14	K 13
104th Av		14	L 13
142-00 - 144-99	35	14	L 13
168-01 - 178-99	33	13	M 12
183-00 - 205-99	12	13	N 12
206-00 - OUT	29	13	O 12
104th Rd		13	M 12
164-00 - 173-99	33	13	M 12
212-00 - OUT	29	13	O 12
104th St		9	J 9
19-00 - 32-99	69	9	J 9
33-00 - 60-99	68	9	J 9
84-00 - 93-99	18	14	K 13
94-00 - 102-99	16	14	K 13
103-00 - 107-99	17	14	K 13
162-00 - 164-99	14	14	K 15
105th Av		14	L 13
134-00 - 135-99	19	14	L 13
143-00 - 148-99	35	12	L 12
168-00 - 177-99	33	13	M 12
187-00 - 192-99	12	13	N 12
218-00 - 225-99	29	13	O 12
105th Pl	17	14	K 13
105th St		9	J 9
19-00 - 32-99	69	9	J 9
33-00 - 60-99	68	9	J 9
61-00 - 70-99	75	12	J 10
84-00 - 86-99	18	12	K 12
94-00 - 102-99	16	14	K 13
103-00 - OUT	17	14	K 13
106th Av		14	J 13
84-00 - 84-99	17	14	J 13
138-00 - 147-99	35	14	L 13
168-00 - 177-99	33	13	M 12
215-00 - 225-99	29	13	O 12
106th Rd	33	13	M 12
106th St		9	J 9
19-00 - 32-99	69	9	J 9
33-00 - 60-99	68	9	J 9
84-00 - 86-99	18	12	K 12
93-00 - 102-99	16	14	K 13
103-00 - OUT	17	14	K 13
107th Av		14	J 13
84-00 - 107-99	17	14	J 13
108-00 - 135-99	19	14	K 13
137-00 - 149-99	35	14	L 13
150-00 - 173-99	33	15	M 12
218-00 - 227-99	29	13	O 12
107th Rd	35	14	L 13
107th St		9	J 9
19-00 - 32-99	69	9	J 9
33-00 - 60-99	68	9	J 9
84-00 - 93-99	18	12	K 12
94-00 - 102-99	16	14	K 13
103-00 - OUT	17	14	K 13
108th Av		14	J 13
84-00 - 95-99	17	14	K 13
150-00 - 175-99	33	15	M 12
220-00 - 228-99	29	13	O 12
108th Dr	33	13	M 12
108th Pl	35	14	L 13
108th Rd	33	13	M 12
108th St		9	J 9
19-00 - 32-99	69	9	J 9
33-00 - 60-99	68	9	J 9
61-00 - 71-99	75	12	J 10
84-00 - 91-99	18	12	K 12
94-00 - 107-99	19	14	K 13
109-00 - 110-99	20	14	K 13
109th Av		14	J 13
84-00 - 107-99	17	14	K 13
108-00 - 135-99	20	14	K 13
137-00 - 149-99	35	15	L 13
150-00 - 176-99	33	13	M 12
188-00 - 205-99	12	13	M 12
206-00 - OUT	29	13	O 12
109th Dr	33	15	M 13
109th Rd		14	L 13
139-00 - 139-99	35	14	L 13
150-00 - 169-99	33	15	M 12
190-00 - 194-99	12	13	N 12
109th St		9	J 9
33-00 - 36-99	68	9	J 9
84-00 - 91-99	18	12	K 12
94-00 - 107-99	19	14	K 13
109-00 - OUT	20	14	K 13
110th Av		15	L 13
77-00 - 92-99	17	14	J 14
143-00 - 149-99	35	15	L 13
150-00 - 180-99	33	15	M 13
194-00 - 205-99	12	13	N 12
208-00 - 223-99	29	13	O 12
110th Rd		15	M 13
147-00 - 147-99	35	15	M 13
150-00 - 169-99	33	15	M 13
190-00 - 194-99	12	13	N 12
216-00 - 217-99	29	13	O 12
110th St		9	J 9
1-00 - 14-99	56	9	J 8
32-00 - 32-99	69	9	J 9
33-00 - 34-99	68	9	J 9
61-00 - 72-99	75	12	J 10
84-00 - 91-99	18	12	K 12
94-00 - 107-99	19	14	K 13
109-00 - OUT	20	14	K 13
111th Av		14	K 13
109-01 - 135-99	20	14	K 13
137-00 - 149-99	35	14	L 13
150-00 - 176-99	33	15	M 13
190-00 - 205-99	12	13	N 12
206-00 - OUT	29	13	O 12
111th Rd		15	M 13
150-00 - 153-99	33	15	M 13
190-00 - 205-99	12	13	N 12
206-00 - 215-99	29	13	O 12
111th St		9	J 8
1-00 - 14-99	56	9	J 8
31-00 - 32-99	69	9	J 9
33-00 - 60-99	68	9	J 9
61-00 - 66-99	75	12	J 10
85-00 - 91-99	18	12	K 12
94-00 - 107-99	19	14	K 13
109-00 - OUT	20	14	K 13
112th Av		15	M 13
148-00 - 148-99	35	15	M 13
150-00 - 179-99	33	13	N 12
190-00 - 205-99	12	13	N 12
206-00 - OUT	29	13	O 12
112th Pl	69	9	J 9
112th Rd		15	M 13
162-00 - 162-99	33	15	M 13
191-00 - 205-99	12	13	N 12
206-00 - 227-99	29	13	O 13
112th St		9	J 8
1-00 - 14-99	56	9	J 8
32-00 - 32-99	69	9	J 9
33-00 - 60-99	68	9	J 9
61-00 - 72-99	75	12	J 10
84-00 - 93-99	18	12	K 12
94-00 - 107-99	19	14	K 13
109-00 - OUT	20	14	K 13
113th Av		15	M 13
150-00 - 173-99	33	15	M 13
181-00 - 205-99	12	13	N 12
206-00 - OUT	29	13	O 12
113th Dr	29	13	O 12
113th Pl	75	12	K 11
113th Rd	12	13	N 12
113th St		9	J 8
1-00 - 14-99	56	9	J 8
34-00 - 34-98	68	9	J 9
61-00 - 78-99	75	12	K 11
84-00 - 91-99	18	12	K 12
94-00 - 107-99	19	14	K 13
109-00 - OUT	20	14	K 13
114th Av		14	K 13
112-00 - 135-99	20	14	L 13
137-00 - 149-99	36	15	M 13
150-00 - 180-99	34	15	M 13
181-00 - 205-99	12	13	N 12
206-00 - 235-99	11	13	O 12
114th Dr		13	N 12
188-00 - 205-99	12	13	O 12
227-00 - 228-99	11	13	O 12
114th Pl	20	14	K 14
114th Rd		15	M 13
150-00 - 180-99	34	15	M 13
181-00 - 205-99	12	13	N 12
216-00 - 229-99	11	13	O 12
114th St		9	J 8
1-00 - 14-99	56	9	J 8
37-00 - 43-99	68	9	J 9
84-00 - 93-99	18	12	K 12
94-00 - 107-99	19	14	K 13
109-00 - 150-99	20	14	K 14
114th Ter	11	13	O 12
115th Av		14	L 13
117-01 - 135-99	20	14	L 13
137-00 - 149-99	36	15	M 13
150-00 - 180-99	34	15	M 13
181-00 - 205-99	12	13	N 12
206-00 - 231-99	11	13	O 12
115th Ct	11	13	O 12

STREET NAME AND HOUSE NUMBERS	ZONE NO.	MAP NO.	MAP GRID
115th Dr		15	M13
150-00 - 155-99	34	15	M13
190-00 - 205-99	12	15	N13
115th Rd		15	M13
150-00 - 159-99	34	15	M13
187-00 - 205-99	12	15	N13
215-00 - 232-99	11	13	O12
115th St		9	J 8
1-00 - 14-99	56	9	J 8
83-00 - 91-99	18	12	K12
94-00 - 107-99	19	14	K13
109-00 - 150-99	20	14	K14
115th Ter	11	13	O12
116th Av		14	L13
122-01 - 135-99	20	15	M13
137-00 - 149-99	36	15	N13
150-00 - 180-99	34	15	O13
181-00 - 205-99	12	15	N13
206-00 - 233-99	11	13	O12
116th Dr	34	15	M13
116th Rd		14	L13
142-00 - 142-99	36	15	M13
150-00 - 155-99	34	15	M13
189-00 - 205-99	12	15	N13
206-00 - 209-99	11	13	O12
116th St		9	J 8
1-00 - 14-99	56	9	J 8
82-00 - 91-99	18	12	K12
94-00 - 107-99	19	14	K13
109-00 - 150-99	20	14	K14
117th Rd		14	L14
132-00 - 132-99	20	14	L14
189-00 - 194-99	12	15	N13
216-00 - 216-99	11	15	O13
117th St		9	J 8
1-00 - 14-99	56	9	J 8
83-00 - 91-99	18	12	K12
94-00 - 107-99	19	14	K13
109-00 - 154-99	20	14	K14
118th Av		15	M13
150-00 - 170-99	34	15	M13
188-00 - 205-99	12	15	N13
216-00 - 235-99	11	15	O13
118th Rd		15	M13
160-00 - 170-99	34	15	M13
186-00 - 191-99	12	15	N13
118th St		9	J 8
1-00 - 14-99	56	9	J 8
83-00 - 85-99	15	12	K12
86-00 - 91-99	18	12	K12
94-00 - 107-99	19	14	K13
109-00 - 150-99	20	14	K14
119th Av		15	M13
143-00 - 149-99	36	15	M13
150-00 - 172-99	34	15	M13
188-00 - 205-99	12	15	N13
216-00 - 236-99	11	15	O13
119th Dr		15	M13
160-00 - 161-99	34	15	M13
187-00 - OUT	12	15	N13
119th Rd		15	M13
142-00 - 142-99	36	15	M13
150-00 - 180-99	34	15	M13
181-00 - 188-99	12	15	N13
119th St		9	J 7
5-00 - 22-00	56	9	J 8
25-00 - 31-99	54	9	J 8
120th Av		14	L14
132-00 - 135-99	20	14	L14
137-00 - 148-99	36	15	L14
150-00 - 180-99	34	15	M13
181-00 - 203-99	12	15	N13
216-00 - 237-99	11	15	O13
120th Rd	12	15	N13
120th St		9	J 8
9-00 - 23-00	56	9	J 8
25-00 - 31-99	54	9	J 8
84-00 - 85-99	15	12	K12
86-00 - 91-99	18	12	K12
94-00 - 107-99	19	14	K13
109-00 - OUT	20	14	L14
121st Av		15	M13
150-00 - 161-99	34	15	M13
186-00 - 201-99	12	15	N13
216-00 - 238-99	11	15	O13
121st St		9	J 7
9-00 - 23-00	56	9	J 8
25-00 - 32-99	54	9	J 8
84-00 - 85-99	15	12	K12
86-00 - 91-99	18	12	K12
94-00 - 107-99	19	14	K13
109-00 - OUT	20	14	L14
122nd Av		15	M13
142-00 - 142-99	36	15	M14
150-00 - 164-99	34	15	M13
186-00 - 201-99	13	15	N13
122nd Pl	20	14	L14
122nd St		9	J 8
5-00 - 23-00	56	9	J 8
25-00 - 32-99	54	9	J 8
82-01 - 85-99	15	12	K12
86-00 - 91-99	18	12	K12
104-00 - 107-99	19	14	L13
109-00 - OUT	20	14	L14
123rd Av		15	M14
140-00 - 147-99	36	15	M14
150-00 - 154-99	34	15	M14
123rd St		9	J 8
5-00 - 23-00	56	9	J 8
25-00 - 32-99	54	9	J 9
84-00 - 85-99	15	12	K12
86-00 - 87-99	18	12	K12
93-00 - 107-99	19	14	K13
109-00 - OUT	20	14	L14
124th Av	34	15	M14
124th Pl	15	12	K12
124th St		9	J 8
5-00 - 23-00	56	9	J 8
25-00 - 32-99	54	9	J 8
84-00 - 85-99	15	12	K12
86-00 - 87-99	18	12	K12
93-00 - 107-99	19	14	K13
109-00 - OUT	20	14	L14
125th Av		15	M14
150-00 - 177-99	34	15	M14
231-00 - 232-99	13	15	O13
125th St		9	J 8
3-00 - 23-00	56	9	J 8
25-00 - 32-99	54	9	J 8
83-00 - 85-99	15	12	K12
86-00 - 87-99	18	12	K12
94-00 - 107-00	19	14	K13
109-00 - 152-99	20	14	L14
126th Av		15	N13
168-00 - 176-99	34	15	N13
231-00 - 232-99	13	15	O13
126th Pl	68	9	J 9
126th St		9	J 8
3-00 - 23-00	56	9	J 8
25-00 - 32-99	54	9	J 8
33-00 - 40-90	68	9	J 9
84-00 - 85-99	15	12	K12
86-00 - 89-99	18	12	K12
94-00 - 107-99	19	14	L13
109-00 - OUT	20	14	L14
127th Av	34	15	N13
127th Pl	68	9	J 9
127th St		9	J 8
3-00 - 23-00	56	9	J 8
25-00 - 32-99	54	9	J 8
33-00 - 35-99	68	9	J 9
84-00 - 85-99	15	12	K12
86-00 - 89-99	18	12	K12
94-00 - 107-99	19	14	L13
109-00 - OUT	20	14	L14
128th Av		15	M14
157-00 - 174-99	34	15	M14
231-00 - 232-99	13	15	O13
233-00 - 240-99	22	15	O13
128th Dr		15	O13
231-00 - 232-99	13	15	O13
240-00 - OUT	22	15	P13
128th Rd		15	O13
231-00 - 232-99	13	15	O13
240-00 - OUT	22	15	P13
128th St		9	J 8
5-00 - 23-00	56	9	J 8
104-00 - 107-99	19	14	L13
109-00 - 152-99	20	14	L14
129th Av		15	M14
142-00 - 146-99	36	15	M14
156-00 - 180-99	34	15	O13
181-00 - 232-99	13	15	O13
233-00 - OUT	22	15	O13
129th Rd	22	15	P13
129th St		9	J 8
5-00 - 23-00	56	9	K 8
84-00 - 85-99	15	12	K12
86-00 - 89-99	18	12	K12
94-00 - 107-99	19	14	L13
118-00 - OUT	20	14	L14
130th Av		14	L14
114-00 - 135-99	20	14	L14
137-00 - 149-99	36	15	M14
158-00 - 180-99	34	15	M14
181-00 - 232-99	13	15	O13
233-00 - 245-99	22	15	O13
130th Dr	13	15	O13
130th Pl		14	L14
133-01 - 135-99	20	14	L14
133-01 - 135-99	30	14	L15
130th Rd		15	N13
178-00 - 180-99	34	15	N13
219-00 - 219-99	13	15	O13
242-00 - 243-99	22	15	O14
130th St		9	K 8
7-00 - 23-00	56	9	K 8
84-00 - 85-99	15	12	K12
86-00 - 91-99	18	12	K12
94-00 - 107-99	19	14	L13
109-00 - OUT	20	14	L14
131st Av		14	L14
130-00 - 135-99	20	14	L14
137-00 - 142-99	36	14	L14
159-00 - 178-99	34	15	N13
216-00 - 232-99	13	15	O13
233-00 - OUT	22	15	O14
131st Rd	22	15	P14
131st St		9	K 8
11-00 - 18-00	56	9	K 8
85-00 - 85-99	15	12	K11
86-00 - 87-99	18	12	K12
94-00 - 107-99	19	14	L13
109-00 - 135-99	20	14	L14
140-00 - out	30	14	L14
132nd Av		14	L14
73-00 - 75-99	14	14	J14
94-00 - 97-99	17	14	K14
137-00 - 137-99	36	15	L14
153-00 - 180-99	34	15	M14
181-00 - 219-99	13	15	N13
241-00 - 243-99	22	15	O14
132nd Rd		15	O13
216-00 - 219-99	13	15	O14
241-00 - 243-99	22	15	P14
132nd St		9	K 8
1-00 - 24-99	56	9	K 8
86-00 - 89-99	18	12	L12
94-00 - 107-99	19	12	L12
109-00 - 135-99	20	14	L14
140-00 - out	30	14	L14
133rd Av		14	J14
75-00 - 78-99	14	14	J14
79-00 - 107-99	17	14	J14
108-00 - 135-99	20	14	K14
137-00 - 149-99	36	15	M14
151-00 - 180-99	34	15	N14
181-00 - 232-99	13	15	O13
233-00 - OUT	22	15	O14
133rd Dr	22	15	P14
133rd Pl	56	9	K 8
133rd Rd		15	N14
176-00 - 180-99	34	15	N14
181-00 - 218-99	13	15	N13
245-00 - OUT	22	15	O14
133rd St		9	K 8
1-00 - 24-99	56	9	K 8
25-00 - 40-99	54	9	K 9
55-01 - 55-99	55	12	K10
87-00 - 89-99	18	12	L12
94-00 - 107-99	19	14	L13
109-00 - 135-99	20	14	L14
140-00 - 140-99	30	14	L14
134th Av		14	K14
94-00 - 97-99	17	14	K14
132-00 - 135-99	20	14	L14
137-00 - 137-99	36	15	L14
151-00 - 179-99	34	15	M14
242-00 - 246-99	22	15	N14
134th Pl	20	14	L14
134th Rd		14	K14
96-00 - 97-99	17	14	K14
165-00 - 165-99	34	15	N14
217-00 - 223-99	13	15	N13
234-00 - OUT	22	15	O14
134th St		12	K10
41-00 - 60-99	55	12	K10
61-00 - 61-99	67	12	K10
80-00 - 82-99	35	12	K11
86-00 - 89-99	18	12	L12
94-00 - 107-99	19	14	L13
109-01 - 135-99	20	15	L14
148-00 - OUT	30	15	L14
135th Av		14	L14
75-00 - 78-99	14	14	J14
83-00 - 98-99	17	14	K14
114-00 - 135-99	20	15	L14
137-00 - 149-99	36	15	M14
150-00 - 180-99	34	15	M14
181-00 - 228-99	13	15	O13
234-00 - 247-99	22	15	O14
135th Dr	17	14	K14
135th Pl	20	14	L14
135th Rd		14	K14
97-00 - 97-99	17	14	K14
246-00 - 247-99	22	15	P14
135th St		12	K10
11-00 - 18-00	56	9	K 8
41-00 - 60-99	55	12	K10
61-00 - 79-99	67	12	K11
80-00 - 82-99	35	12	K11
86-00 - 89-99	18	12	L12
102-00 - 107-99	19	14	L13
109-00 - 135-99	20	14	L14
136th Av		15	M14
93-00 - 96-99	17	14	K14
151-00 - 180-99	34	15	M14
181-00 - 221-99	13	15	N14
234-00 - 247-99	22	15	O14
136th Rd		15	N14
216-00 - 217-99	13	15	N14
244-00 - 247-99	22	15	O14
136th St		9	K 8
11-00 - 18-00	56	9	K 8
41-00 - 60-99	55	12	K10
61-00 - 79-99	67	12	K10
86-00 - 88-99	18	12	L12
137th Av		15	M14
153-00 - 80-99	34	15	N14
181-00 - 232-99	13	15	O14
233-00 - 247-99	22	15	O14
137th Pl	55	9	K 9
137th Rd		15	O14
217-00 - 220-99	13	15	N14
235-00 - 247-99	22	15	O14
137th St		9	K 9
11-00 - 18-00	56	9	K 8
25-00 - 40-99	54	9	K 9
41-00 - 60-99	55	12	K10
61-00 - 79-99	67	12	K11
88-00 - 88-99	35	12	L12
138th Av		15	N14
152-00 - 180-99	34	15	N14
181-00 - 232-99	13	15	N14
233-00 - 244-99	22	15	O14
138th Pl	57	9	K 8
138th Pl	35	12	L12
138th Rd	13	15	N14
138th St		9	K 8
11-00 - 18-00	56	9	K 8
25-00 - 40-99	54	9	K 9
41-00 - 60-99	55	12	K10
61-00 - 79-99	67	12	K11
80-00 - 111-99	35	12	L12
114-00 - 115-99	36	14	L14
139th Av		15	N14
186-00 - 232-99	13	15	O14
233-00 - 253-99	22	15	P14
139th Rd	34	15	N14
139th St		9	K 8
13-00 - 14-00	57	9	K 8
25-00 - 40-99	54	9	K 9
61-00 - 79-99	67	12	K11
81-00 - 111-99	35	12	L12
114-00 - 119-99	36	14	L13
140th Av		15	M14
153-00 - 180-99	34	15	M14
181-00 - 219-99	13	15	N14
241-00 - OUT	22	15	O14
140th St		9	K 8
13-00 - 14-00	57	9	K 8
25-00 - 40-99	54	9	K 9
61-00 - 79-99	67	12	K11
111-00 - 111-99	35	15	L13
114-00 - 135-99	36	15	L14
141st Av		15	N14
180-00 - 180-99	34	15	N14
181-00 - 232-99	13	15	N14
233-00 - 241-99	22	15	O14
141st Pl	67	12	K11
141st Rd	13	15	N14
141st St		9	K 8
13-00 - 14-99	57	9	K 8
25-00 - 40-99	54	12	K10
56-00 - 56-99	55	12	K10
61-00 - 79-99	67	12	K11
82-00 - 111-99	35	12	L11
114-00 - 120-99	36	15	L13
142nd Av		15	N14
167-00 - 179-99	34	15	N14
240-00 - 241-99	22	15	O14
142nd Pl	36	15	M14
142nd Rd	13	15	N14
142nd St		9	K 8
13-00 - 14-99	57	9	K 8
56-00 - 60-99	55	12	K10
103-00 - 111-99	35	12	L11
114-00 - 135-99	36	15	L13
143rd Av		15	N14
179-00 - 180-99	34	15	N14
181-00 - 232-99	13	15	N14
233-00 - 247-99	22	15	O14
143rd Pl	57	9	K 8
143rd Rd		15	N14
170-00 - 180-99	34	15	N14
181-00 - 225-99	13	15	N14
143rd St		9	K 8
13-00 - 23-99	57	9	K 8
29-00 - 33-99	54	9	K 9
84-00 - 111-99	35	15	L12
114-00 - 135-99	36	15	M14
144th Av		15	N14
162-00 - 180-99	34	15	N14
181-00 - 230-99	13	15	N14
240-00 - 243-99	22	15	O14
144th Dr	34	15	M14
144th Pl		9	K 8
13-00 - 14-99	57	9	K 8
90-00 - 91-99	35	12	L12
144th Rd		15	M14
165-00 - 179-99	34	15	M14
184-00 - 184-99	13	15	N14
144th St		9	K 7
15-01 - 23-99	57	9	K 7
85-00 - 111-99	35	12	L12
114-00 - 135-99	36	14	M13
144th Ter	34	15	M14
145th Av		15	M14
155-00 - 180-99	34	15	M14
181-00 - 231-99	13	15	N14
240-00 - 259-99	22	15	O14
145th Dr		15	N14
154-00 - 180-99	34	15	N14
181-00 - 183-99	13	15	N14
145th Pl		9	K 8
1300 - 1500	57	9	K 8
29-00 - 33-99	54	9	K 9
145th Rd		15	M14
157-00 - 180-99	34	15	M14
181-00 - 227-99	13	15	N14
145th St		9	K 8
1-00 - 24-99	57	9	K 9
25-00 - 40-99	54	9	K 9
88-00 - 111-99	35	15	L13
114-00 - 133-99	36	15	M14
146th Av		15	N14
156-00 - 180-99	34	15	N14
181-00 - 231-99	13	15	N14
240-00 - 241-99	22	15	O15
146th Dr	34	15	N14
146th Pl		9	K 8
1300 - 1500	57	9	K 8
61-00 - 61-99	67	12	K10
146th Rd		15	N14
167-00 - 180-99	34	15	N14
181-00 - 183-99	13	15	N14
146th St		9	K 8
1-00 - 24-99	57	9	K 8
25-00 - 40-99	54	9	K 9
41-00 - 60-99	55	12	K10
61-00 - 79-99	67	12	L11
87-00 - 111-99	35	12	L12
114-00 - 133-99	36	15	L13
146th Ter		15	N14
178-00 - 180-99	34	15	N14
181-00 - 183-99	13	15	N14
147th Av		15	N14
150-00 - 180-99	34	15	N14
181-00 - 232-99	13	15	N14
233-00 - 245-99	22	15	O15
147th Dr	22	15	O15
147th Pl		9	K 7
200 - 300	57	9	K 7
25-00 - 40-99	54	9	K 9
92-00 - 97-99	35	12	L12
147th Rd	22	15	O15
147th St		9	K 8
1-00 - 24-99	57	9	K 8
25-00 - 40-99	54	9	K 9
41-00 - 60-99	55	9	K 9
61-00 - 79-99	67	12	K11
110-00 - 111-99	35	15	M13
114-00 - 133-99	36	15	M13
148th Av		15	N14
167-00 - 176-99	34	15	N14
225-00 - 231-99	13	15	N15
253-00 - 257-99	22	15	O15
148th Dr	22	15	N15
148th Pl		12	K10
61-00 - 61-99	67	12	K10
91-00 - 91-99	35	12	L12
148th Rd		15	N15
167-00 - 175-99	34	15	N15
235-00 - 259-99	22	15	O15
148th St		9	K 7
1-00 - 24-99	57	9	K 7
25-00 - 40-99	54	9	K 9
41-00 - 60-99	55	12	K10
61-00 - 79-99	67	12	K10
84-00 - 112-99	35	12	L12
114-00 - 133-99	36	15	M13
149th Av		14	J14
78-00 - 87-99	14	14	J14
94-00 - 107-99	17	14	K14
108-00 - 135-99	20	14	L14
175-00 - 179-99	34	15	N15
182-00 - 232-99	13	15	N15
233-00 - OUT	22	15	O15
149th Dr	22	15	O15
149th Pl		9	K 7
200 - 300	57	9	K 7
25-00 - 40-99	54	9	L 9
41-00 - 60-99	55	9	L 9
149th Rd		15	N15
169-00 - 180-99	34	15	N15
181-00 - 182-99	13	15	N15
236-00 - OUT	22	15	O15
149th St		12	K10
1-00 - 24-99	57	9	K 8
25-00 - 40-99	54	9	L 9
41-00 - 60-99	55	9	L 9
61-00 - 79-99	67	12	L11
85-00 - 95-99	35	12	L12
114-00 - 133-99	36	15	M13
150th Av		14	L14
114-00 - 129-99	20	14	K14
130-00 - 130-99	30	15	M14
175-01 - 179-01	34	15	N15
182-00 - 183-99	13	15	N15
150th Dr	13	15	N15
150th Pl		9	L 7
600 - 16-00	57	9	L 7
25-00 - 40-99	54	9	L 9
150th Rd		14	K14
95-00 - 95-99	17	14	K14
179-00 - 179-99	34	15	N15
182-00 - 183-99	13	15	N15
150th St		9	L 8
200 - 24-00	57	9	L 7
24-00 - 40-99	54	9	L 9
41-00 - 60-99	55	9	L 9
61-00 - 79-99	67	12	K10
80-00 - 107-99	35	12	L11
130-01 - 174-99	36	15	M14
151st Av	14	14	J14
151st Dr	13	15	N15
151st Pl	57	9	L 7
151st St		9	L 7
600 - 799	57	9	L 7
54-00 - 54-99	55	12	L10
84-00 - 88-99	32	12	L12
92-00 - 92-99	33	12	L12
152nd Av	20	14	L14
152nd St		9	L 7
600 - 14-00	57	9	L 7
25-00 - 40-99	54	9	L 9
41-00 - 60-99	55	12	L10
61-00 - 79-99	67	12	L11
84-00 - 88-99	32	12	L11
118-00 - 123-99	34	15	M13
153rd Av	14	14	J14
153rd Ct	34	15	M14
153rd La	34	15	M14
153rd Pl		9	L 8
15-00 - 15-99	57	9	L 8
144-00 - OUT	34	15	M14
153rd St		9	L 9
25-00 - 40-99	54	9	L 9
41-00 - 60-99	55	12	L10
61-00 - 79-99	67	12	L10
87-00 - 90-99	32	12	L12
92-00 - 113-99	33	15	M13
114-00 - 129-99	34	15	M13
153rd Way	34	15	M14
154th Pl		9	L 7
600 - 8-99	57	9	L 7
59-00 - 59-99	55	12	L10
154th St		9	L 8
700 - 24-00	57	9	L 8
25-00 - 40-99	54	9	L 9
41-00 - 60-99	55	9	L 9
61-00 - 79-99	67	12	L11
106-00 - 113-99	33	13	M12
114-00 - 140-99	34	15	M13
155th Av	14	14	J14

STREET NAME AND HOUSE NUMBERS	ZONE NO.	MAP NO.	MAP GRID
155th St		9	L 8
14-00 - 16-00	57	9	L 8
25-00 - 40-99	54	9	L 9
41-00 - 60-99	55	9	L 9
61-00 - 79-99	67	12	L 10
106-00 - 113-99	33	13	M12
114-00 - 147-99	34	15	M13
156th Av	14	14	J 14
156th Ct	54	9	L 8
156th Pl	33	12	L 12
156th St		9	L 8
14-00 - 16-00	57	9	L 8
25-00 - 40-99	54	9	L 9
41-00 - 60-99	55	9	L 9
61-00 - 79-99	67	12	L 10
105-00 - 113-99	33	12	L 12
114-00 - 146-99	34	15	M14
157th Av	14	14	J 14
157th St		9	L 8
7-00 - 24-99	57	9	L 8
24-00 - 40-99	54	9	L 9
41-00 - 60-99	55	9	L 9
61-00 - 79-99	67	12	L 10
95-00 - 113-99	33	12	L 12
114-00 - 146-99	34	15	M13
158th Av	14	14	J 15
158th St		9	L 7
600 - 14-00	57	9	L 8
25-00 - 47-99	58	9	L 9
48-00 - 72-99	65	12	L 10
73-00 - 79-99	66	12	L 11
94-00 - 113-99	33	15	M13
114-00 - 145-99	34	15	M14
159th Av	14	14	J 15
159th Rd	14	14	K15
159th St		9	L 7
600 - 15-00	57	9	L 8
25-00 - 47-99	58	9	L 9
48-00 - 72-99	65	12	L 10
73-00 - 79-99	66	12	L 11
80-00 - 90-99	32	12	L 11
92-00 - 113-99	33	13	M12
114-00 - 145-99	34	13	M13
160th Av	14	14	J 15
160th Dr *(off 102nd St)	14	14	K15
160th Rd *(off 102nd St)	14	14	K15
160th St		9	L 8
6-00 - 24-00	57	9	L 8
25-00 - 47-99	58	9	L 9
48-00 - 72-99	65	12	L 10
73-00 - 79-99	68	12	L 11
80-00 - 90-99	32	12	L 11
92-00 - 113-99	33	13	M12
114-00 - 140-99	34	15	M13
161st Av	14	14	J 15
161st Pl	34	15	M13
161st St		9	L 7
6-00 - 14-00	57	9	L 8
25-00 - 47-99	58	9	L 9
48-00 - 72-99	65	12	L 10
73-00 - 79-99	66	12	L 11
80-00 - 90-99	32	12	L 12
92-00 - 113-99	33	0	0
114-00 - 144-99	34	15	M14
162nd Av	14	14	K15
162nd Rd *(off 102nd St)	14	14	K15
162nd St		9	L 8
7-00 - 14-00	57	9	L 8
25-00 - 47-99	58	9	L 9
48-00 - 72-99	65	12	L 10
73-00 - 79-99	66	12	L 11
80-00 - 89-99	32	12	L 12
92-00 - 113-99	33	13	L 12
114-00 - 144-99	34	15	L 13
163rd Av	14	14	K15
163rd Dr	14	14	K15
163rd Pl	58	9	L 9
163rd Rd *(off 102nd St)	14	14	K15
163rd St		9	L 8
14-00 - 24-99	57	9	L 8
25-00 - 47-99	58	9	L 9
48-00 - 72-99	65	12	L 10
73-00 - 78-99	66	12	L 11
88-00 - 89-99	32	12	L 11
92-00 - 113-99	33	13	L 12
114-00 - OUT	34	15	L 13
164th Av	14	14	K15
164th Dr	14	14	K15
164th Pl		12	L 11
80-00 - 83-99	32	12	L 11
103-00 - 113-99	33	13	M12
164th Rd	14	14	K15
164th St		9	L 8
1400	57	9	L 8
25-00 - 47-99	58	9	L 9
48-00 - 72-99	65	13	L 10
73-00 - 78-99	66	12	L 11
79-00 - 89-99	32	12	L 12
103-00 - 110-99	33	13	M12
116-00 - 120-99	34	15	M13
165th Av	14	14	K15
165th Pl	33	13	M12
165th St		9	L 8
1400	57	9	L 8
25-00 - 47-99	58	9	L 9
48-00 - 72-99	65	12	L 10
73-00 - 78-99	66	12	L 11
80-00 - 89-99	32	12	L 11
92-00 - 113-99	33	13	L 12
114-00 - 120-99	34	15	M13
166th Pl	34	15	N14
166th St		9	L 8
7-00 - 24-00	57	9	L 8
25-00 - 47-99	58	9	L 9
48-00 - 72-99	65	12	L 10
73-00 - 78-99	66	12	L 11
80-00 - 91-99	32	12	L 11
92-00 - 113-99	33	13	M12
114-00 - 146-99	34	15	M13
167th St		9	L 9
25-00 - 47-99	58	9	L 9
48-00 - 72-99	65	12	L 10
73-00 - 78-99	66	12	L 11
80-00 - 87-99	32	12	L 12
108-00 - 113-99	33	13	M12
114-00 - 145-99	34	15	M13
168th Pl		12	L 11
83-00 - 89-99	32	12	L 11
92-00 - 103-99	33	13	M12
137-00 - OUT	34	15	N14
168th St		9	L 9
25-00 - 47-99	58	9	L 9
48-00 - 72-99	65	12	L 10
73-00 - 79-99	66	12	L 11
80-00 - 91-99	32	12	L 11
92-00 - 113-99	33	13	M12
114-00 - 142-99	34	15	M13
169th Pl	33	13	M12
169th St		9	L 9
18-00 - 24-00	57	9	L 8
25-00 - 47-99	58	9	L 9
48-00 - 72-99	65	12	L 10
73-00 - 78-99	66	12	L 11
80-00 - 91-99	32	13	M12
103-00 - 113-99	33	13	M12
114-00 - 140-99	34	15	M13
170th Pl	65	12	L 10
170th St		9	L 9
25-00 - 47-99	58	9	L 9
48-00 - 72-99	65	12	L 10
73-00 - 77-99	66	12	L 11
80-00 - 91-99	32	13	M11
92-00 - 113-99	33	13	M12
114-00 - 151-99	34	15	M13
171st Pl		9	L 9
25-00 - 47-99	58	9	L 9
105-00 - 110-99	33	15	M12
171st St		9	L 9
25-00 - 47-99	58	9	L 9
48-00 - 72-99	65	12	L 10
73-00 - 77-99	66	12	L 11
84-00 - 91-99	32	13	M12
103-00 - 113-99	33	13	M12
114-00 - 140-99	34	15	M13
172nd St		9	L 9
25-00 - 47-99	58	9	L 9
48-00 - 72-99	65	12	L 10
73-00 - 77-99	66	12	L 11
82-00 - 91-99	32	13	M11
92-00 - 113-99	33	13	M12
114-00 - 140-99	34	15	M13
173rd St		12	L 11
48-00 - 72-99	65	12	L 10
73-00 - 77-99	66	12	L 11
87-00 - 91-99	32	13	M12
92-00 - 113-99	33	13	M12
114-00 - 140-99	34	15	M14
174th Pl	34	15	N13
174th St		12	L 10
48-00 - 72-99	65	12	L 10
73-00 - 77-99	66	13	M11
108-00 - 111-99	33	13	M12
114-00 - 142-99	34	15	M13
175th Pl		13	M10
49-00 - 56-99	65	13	M10
112-00 - 113-99	33	13	M12
114-00 - 115-99	34	15	M13
175th St		13	M10
48-00 - 72-99	65	13	M10
73-00 - 77-99	66	13	M11
87-00 - 91-99	32	13	M12
92-00 - 113-99	33	13	M12
114-00 - 148-99	34	15	M13
176th Pl	34	15	N13
176th St		13	M11
73-00 - 77-99	66	13	M11
90-00 - 90-99	32	13	M12
92-00 - 113-99	33	13	M12
114-00 - 146-99	34	15	M13
177th Pl	34	15	N13
177th St		13	M11
73-00 - 72-99	66	13	M11
92-00 - 113-99	33	13	M12
114-00 - 151-99	34	15	M13
178th Pl		13	M12
92-00 - 113-99	33	13	M12
114-00 - 145-99	34	15	N13
178th St		13	M10
48-00 - 72-99	65	13	M11
73-00 - 75-99	66	13	M12
83-00 - 91-99	32	13	M13
92-00 - 113-99	33	13	M12
114-00 - 131-99	34	15	M13
179th Pl		13	M12
88-00 - 90-99	32	13	M12
92-00 - 92-99	33	13	M12
131-00 - 131-99	34	15	M13
179th St		13	M10
48-00 - 72-99	65	13	M10
73-00 - 75-99	66	13	M11
88-00 - 90-99	32	13	M12
111-00 - 113-99	33	13	M12
114-00 - 145-99	34	15	N13
180th Pl	33	13	M12
180th St		13	M10
48-00 - 72-99	65	13	M10
73-00 - 75-99	66	13	M11
88-00 - 91-99	32	13	M12
92-00 - 113-99	33	13	M12
114-00 - 145-99	34	15	N13
181st Pl		13	M12
92-00 - 92-99	23	13	M12
143-00 - 144-99	13	15	N14
181st St		13	M10
48-00 - 72-99	65	13	M10
73-00 - 75-99	66	13	M11
88-00 - 92-99	23	13	M12
140-00 - 147-99	13	15	N14
182nd Pl		13	M12
88-00 - 92-99	23	13	M12
143-00 - OUT	13	15	N14
182nd St		13	M10
48-00 - 72-99	65	13	M10
73-00 - 75-99	66	13	M11
88-00 - 93-99	23	13	M12
139-00 - 150-99	13	15	N15
183rd Pl	23	13	M12
183rd St		13	M10
48-00 - 72-99	65	13	M10
73-00 - 75-99	66	13	M11
88-00 - 93-99	23	13	M12
137-00 - 147-99	13	15	N15
184th Pl	23	13	M12
184th St		13	M10
48-00 - 72-99	65	13	M10
73-00 - 75-99	66	13	M11
88-00 - 102-99	23	13	M12
104-00 - 104-99	12	13	M12
141-00 - 147-99	13	15	N14
185th St		13	M10
48-00 - 72-99	65	13	M10
73-00 - 75-99	66	13	M11
88-00 - 102-99	23	13	M12
104-00 - 104-99	12	13	N12
141-00 - 146-99	13	15	N14
186th La	65	13	M10
186th St		13	M10
48-00 - 72-99	65	13	M10
73-00 - 75-99	66	13	M11
88-00 - 103-99	23	13	M12
104-00 - OUT	12	13	N12
187th Pl	23	13	M11
187th St		13	M10
25-00 - 47-99	58	10	M 9
48-00 - 72-99	65	13	M10
73-00 - 75-99	66	13	M10
88-00 - 103-99	23	13	N12
104-00 - 105-99	12	13	N12
188th St		13	M10
25-00 - 47-99	58	10	M 9
48-00 - 72-99	65	13	M10
73-00 - 75-99	66	13	M10
80-00 - 103-99	23	13	N12
104-00 - 105-99	12	13	N12
189th St		10	M 9
25-00 - 47-99	58	10	M 9
48-00 - 72-99	65	13	M10
73-00 - 75-99	66	13	M10
80-00 - 103-99	23	13	N11
104-00 - 120-99	12	13	N12
190th La	65	13	M10
190th Pl	12	13	N12
190th St		10	M 9
25-00 - 47-99	58	10	M 9
48-00 - 72-99	65	13	M10
73-00 - 75-99	66	13	M10
80-00 - 97-99	23	13	N11
116-00 - 120-99	12	15	N13
121-00 - 122-99	13	15	N13
191st St		10	M 9
25-00 - 47-99	58	10	M 9
85-00 - 103-99	23	13	N11
104-00 - 120-99	12	15	N13
121-00 - 122-99	13	15	N13
192nd St		10	M 9
25-00 - 47-99	58	10	M 9
48-00 - 72-99	65	13	M10
73-00 - 75-99	66	13	M10
80-00 - 103-99	23	13	N11
104-00 - 120-99	12	15	N13
121-00 - 122-99	13	15	N13
193rd La	65	13	M10
193rd St		10	M 9
25-00 - 47-99	58	10	M 9
48-00 - 72-99	65	13	M10
73-00 - 75-99	66	13	M10
80-00 - 103-99	23	13	N11
104-00 - 120-99	12	15	N13
121-00 - 124-99	13	15	N13
194th La	65	13	M10
194th St		10	M 9
25-00 - 47-99	58	10	M 9
48-00 - 72-99	65	13	M10
73-00 - 75-99	66	13	M10
99-00 - 103-99	23	13	N13
104-00 - 120-99	12	15	N13
121-00 - 122-99	13	15	N13
195th La	65	13	M10
195th Pl	23	13	N11
195th St		10	M 9
25-00 - 47-99	58	10	M 9
48-00 - 72-99	65	10	M 9
73-00 - 75-99	66	13	M10
88-00 - 103-99	23	13	N11
104-00 - 120-99	12	13	N12
121-00 - 122-99	13	15	N13
196th Pl		10	M 9
25-00 - 47-99	58	10	M 9
48-00 - 72-99	65	13	M10
73-00 - 75-99	66	13	M10
196th St		10	M 9
25-00 - 47-99	58	10	M 9
48-00 - 72-99	65	13	M10
73-00 - 75-99	66	13	M10
88-00 - 103-99	23	13	N11
104-00 - 120-99	12	13	N12
121-00 - 122-99	13	15	N13
197th St		10	M 9
25-00 - 47-99	58	10	M 9
48-00 - 72-99	65	13	M10
73-00 - 75-99	66	13	M10
87-00 - 103-99	23	13	N11
104-00 -120-99	12	13	N12
121-00 - 123-99	13	15	N13
198th St		10	M 9
25-00 - 47-99	58	10	M 9
48-00 - 72-99	65	13	M10
73-00 - 75-99	66	13	M10
88-00 - 103-99	23	13	N11
104-99 - 120-99	12	13	N12
121-00 - OUT	13	15	N13
199th St		10	M 9
25-00 - 47-99	58	10	M 9
48-00 - 72-99	65	13	M10
73-00 - 75-99	66	13	M10
88-00 - 103-99	23	13	N11
104-00 - 120-99	12	13	N12
121-00 - OUT	13	15	N13
200th St		10	M 8
13-00 - 31-99	60	10	M 8
32-00 - 47-99	61	10	M 9
48-00 - 79-99	64	13	M13
99-00 - 103-99	23	13	N11
104-00 - 120-99	12	13	N12
121-00 - OUT	13	15	N13
201st Pl	12	15	N13
201st St		10	M 8
13-00 - 31-99	60	10	M 8
32-00 - 47-99	61	10	M 9
48-00 - 79-99	64	13	N12
88-00 - 103-99	23	13	N11
104-00 - 120-99	12	13	N12
121-00 - OUT	13	15	N13
202nd St		10	M 8
13-00 - 31-99	60	10	M 8
32-00 - 47-99	61	10	M 9
48-00 - 79-99	64	10	M 9
87-00 - 103-99	23	13	N11
104-00 - 120-99	12	13	N12
203rd Pl	60	10	M 8
203rd St		10	M 8
13-00 - 31-99	60	10	M 8
32-00 - 47-99	61	10	M 9
48-00 - 79-99	64	10	M 9
90-00 - 103-99	23	13	N11
104-00 - 119-99	12	13	N12
204th St		10	M 8
13-00 - 31-99	60	10	M 8
32-00 - 47-99	61	10	M 9
48-00 - 79-99	64	13	M10
87-00 - 103-99	23	13	N11
104-00 - 119-99	12	13	N12
205th Pl		13	N12
100-00 - 103-99	23	13	N12
104-00 - 109-99	12	13	N12
205th St		10	M 8
13-00 - 31-99	60	10	M 8
32-00 - 47-99	61	10	M 9
48-00 - 79-99	64	13	M10
88-00 - 103-99	23	13	N11
104-00 - 118-99	12	13	N12
206th St		10	M 8
13-00 - 31-99	60	10	M 8
32-00 - 47-99	61	10	M 9
48-00 - 79-99	64	10	M 9
80-00 - 89-99	27	13	N11
90-00 - 94-99	28	13	N11
95-00 - 113-99	29	13	N12
114-00 - 118-99	11	13	O12
207th St		10	M 8
13-00 - 31-99	60	10	M 8
32-00 - 47-99	61	10	M 9
48-00 - 79-99	64	10	M 9
80-00 - 89-99	27	13	N11
90-00 - 94-99	28	13	N11
95-00 - 113-99	29	13	N12
114-00 - 116-99	11	13	O12
208th Pl	60	10	M 8
208th St		10	M 8
13-00 - 31-99	60	10	M 8
32-00 - 47-99	61	10	M 9
48-00 - 79-99	64	13	N10
80-00 - 89-99	27	13	N11
90-00 - 94-99	28	13	N11
95-00 - 113-99	29	13	N12
114-00 - 116-99	11	13	O12
209th Pl		10	M 8
12-00 - 29-99	60	10	M 8
109-00 - 111-99	29	13	O12
209th St		10	M 8
13-00 - 31-99	60	10	M 8
32-00 - 47-99	61	10	M 9
48-00 - 79-99	64	13	N10
80-00 - 89-99	27	13	N11
90-00 - 94-99	28	13	N11
95-00 - 113-99	29	13	N12
114-00 - 116-99	11	13	O12
210th Pl		10	M 8
12-00 - 29-99	60	10	M 8
89-00 - 89-99	27	13	N11
90-00 - 94-99	28	13	N11
210th St		10	M 8
13-00 - 31-99	60	10	M 8
32-00 - 47-99	61	10	M 9
48-00 - 79-99	64	13	N10
80-00 - 89-99	27	13	N10
90-00 - 94-99	28	13	N11
95-00 - 113-99	29	13	O12
114-00 - 116-99	11	13	O12
211th Ct *(off 104th Av)	29	13	O12
211th Pl		13	N11
90-00 - 94-99	28	13	N11
95-00 - 104-99	29	13	O11
211th St		10	M 8
13-00 - 31-99	60	10	M 8
32-00 - 47-99	61	10	M 9
48-00 - 79-99	64	10	N 9
80-00 - 89-99	27	13	N10
90-00 - 94-99	28	13	N11
95-00 - 113-99	29	13	N12
114-00 - OUT	11	13	O12
212th Pl		13	N11
88-00 - 89-99	27	13	N11
90-00 - 94-99	28	13	O11
95-00 - 109-99	29	13	O12
212th St		10	M 8
13-00 - 31-99	60	10	M 8
32-00 - 47-99	61	10	M 9
48-00 - 79-99	64	10	N 9
80-00 - 89-99	27	13	N10
90-00 - 94-99	28	13	N11
95-00 - 113-99	29	13	O12
114-00 - OUT	11	13	O12
213th St		10	M 8
13-00 - 31-99	60	10	M 8
32-00 - 47-99	61	10	M 9
48-00 - 79-99	64	10	N 9
80-00 - 89-99	27	13	N10
90-00 - 94-99	28	13	O11
95-00 - 113-99	29	13	O12
214th La	61	10	N 8
214th Pl		10	M 8
14-00 - 31-99	60	10	M 8
32-00 - 47-99	61	10	N 9
90-00 - 94-99	28	13	O11
214th St		10	M 8
14-00 - 31-99	60	10	M 8
32-00 - 47-99	61	10	N 9
48-00 - 79-99	64	10	N 9
80-00 - 89-99	27	13	N10
90-00 - 94-99	28	13	O11
95-00 - 113-99	29	13	O12
215th Pl		10	M 8
14-00 - 31-99	60	10	N 8
32-00 - 47-99	61	10	N 9
80-00 - 89-99	27	13	O11
90-00 - OUT	28	13	O11
215th St		10	M 8
14-00 - 31-99	60	10	M 8
32-00 - 47-99	61	10	N 9
48-00 - 79-99	64	10	N 9
80-00 - 89-99	27	13	N10
90-00 - 94-99	28	13	O11
95-00 - 113-99	29	13	O12
216th St		10	M 8
14-00 - 31-99	60	10	M 8
32-00 - 47-99	61	10	N 9
48-00 - 79-99	64	10	N 9
80-00 - 89-99	27	13	O11
90-00 - 94-99	28	13	O11
95-00 - 113-99	29	13	O12
217th La	29	13	O11
217th Pl	29	13	O11
217th St		10	M 8
14-00 - 31-99	60	10	M 8
32-00 - 47-99	61	10	N 9
48-00 - 79-99	64	13	N10
80-00 - 89-99	27	13	O11
90-00 - 94-99	28	13	O11
95-00 - 113-99	29	13	O12
115-00 - 120-99	11	15	O13
130-00 - 135-99	13	15	N13
218th Pl		13	O11
80-00 - 89-99	27	13	O11
90-00 - 94-99	28	13	O11
102-00 - OUT	29	13	O11
218th St		10	N 8
14-00 - 31-99	60	10	N 8
32-00 - 47-99	61	10	N 9
48-00 - 79-99	64	10	N 9
81-00 - 89-99	27	13	O10
90-00	28	13	O11
95-00 - 104-99	29	13	O11
115-00 - 120-99	11	15	O13
130-00 - OUT	13	15	N14
219th St		10	N 9
32-00 - 47-99	61	10	N 9
48-00 - 79-99	64	10	N 9
80-00 - 89-99	27	13	N10
90-00 - 94-99	28	13	O11
95-00 - 113-99	29	13	O12
114-00 - 120-99	11	15	O13
130-00 - 141-99	13	15	N14
220th Pl		10	N 9
32-00 - 47-99	61	10	N 9
48-00 - 79-99	64	13	N10
135-00 - 137-99	13	15	O14
220th St		10	N 9
32-00 - 47-99	61	10	N 9
48-00 - 79-99	64	13	N10
80-00 - 89-99	27	13	O11
90-00 - 94-99	28	13	O11
95-00 - 108-99	29	13	O12
114-00 - 120-99	11	13	O12
130-00 - 146-99	13	15	O13

QUEENS

STREET INDEX AND POSTAL ZONES

STREET NAME AND HOUSE NUMBERS	ZONE NO.	MAP NO.	MAP GRID
221st Pl		13	O11
80-00 - 89-99	27	13	O11
90-00 - 94-99	28	13	O11
221st St		10	N 9
32-00 - 47-99	61	10	N 9
48-00 - 79-99	64	13	N10
80-00 - 89-99	27	13	O11
90-00 - 94-99	28	13	O11
95-00 - 113-99	29	13	O12
114-00 - 120-99	11	15	O13
130-00 - 145-99	13	15	N14
222nd St		10	N 9
32-00 - 47-99	61	10	N 9
48-00 - 79-99	64	10	N 9
80-00 - 89-99	27	13	N10
90-00 - 94-99	28	13	O11
95-00 - 113-99	29	13	O12
114-00 - 120-99	11	15	O13
130-00 - 146-99	13	15	O14
223rd Pl	64	13	N10
223rd St		10	N 9
32-00 - 47-99	61	10	N 9
48-00 - 79-99	64	10	N 9
80-00 - 89-99	27	13	N10
95-00 - 113-99	29	13	O11
114-00 - 120-99	11	13	O12
130-00 - 147-99	13	15	O14
224th St		10	N 9
57-00 - 69-99	64	10	N 9
91-00 - 94-99	28	13	O11
95-00 - 113-99	29	13	O12
114-00 - 120-99	11	15	O13
130-00 - 147-99	13	15	O14
225th St		10	N 9
48-00 - 79-99	64	10	N 9
92-00 - 92-99	26	13	O11
94-00 - 94-99	28	13	O11
95-00 - 112-99	29	13	O12
114-00 - 120-99	11	15	O13
130-00 - 148-99	13	15	O14
226th St		10	N 9
48-00 - 79-99	64	10	N 9
94-00 - 94-99	28	13	O11
114-00 - 120-99	11	15	O13
128-00 - 148-99	13	15	O14
227th St		13	O12
101-00 - 113-99	29	13	O12
114-00 - 120-99	11	15	O13
130-00 - OUT	13	15	O14
228th St		10	N 9
48-00 - 79-99	64	10	N 9
114-00 - 120-99	11	15	O13
130-00 - 148-99	13	15	O14
229th St		10	N 9
48-00 - 79-99	64	10	N 9
81-00 - 83-99	27	13	O10
114-00 - 120-99	11	15	O13
130-00 - 148-99	13	15	O14
230th Pl	13	15	O14
230th St		10	N 9
48-00 - 79-99	64	10	N 9
80-00 - 80-99	27	13	O10
114-00 - 120-99	11	15	O13
130-00 - 148-99	13	15	O14
231st St		10	N 9
43-00 - 45-99	63	10	N 9
48-00 - 79-99	64	10	N 9
80-00 - 86-99	27	13	O10
114-00 - 120-99	11	15	O13
130-00 - 148-99	13	15	O14
232nd St		10	N 9
48-00 - 79-99	64	10	N 9
80-00 - 88-99	27	13	O10
115-00 - 120-99	11	15	O13
129-00 - 148-99	13	15	O14
233rd Pl	63	10	N 8
233rd St		10	N 9
38-00 - 38-99	63	10	N 9
48-00 - 79-99	64	10	O 9
80-00 - 86-99	27	13	O10
114-00 - 120-99	11	15	O13
121-00 - OUT	22	15	O13
234th Pl	22	15	O14
234th St		10	N 8
25-00 - 44-99	63	10	N 8
80-00 - 89-99	27	13	O10
116-00 - 120-99	11	15	O13
121-00 - OUT	22	15	O13
235th Ct	27	13	O10
235th St		10	N 8
25-00 - 44-99	63	10	N 8
80-00 - 89-99	27	13	O10
117-00 - 120-99	11	15	O13
121-00 - OUT	22	15	O13
236th St		13	O10
80-00 - 82-99	27	13	O10
88-00 - 89-99	26	13	O11
118-00 - 120-99	11	15	O13
121-00 - OUT	22	15	O13
237th St		13	O10
80-00 - 80-99	27	13	O10
81-00 - 89-99	26	13	O11
119-00 - 120-99	11	15	P13
121-00 - OUT	22	15	O13
238th St		13	O11
88-00 - 95-99	26	13	O11
119-00 - 120-99	11	15	P13
121-00 - 128-99	22	15	O13
239th St		13	O11
85-00 - 95-99	26	13	O11
120-00 - OUT	11	15	O13
240th Pl	62	10	O 9
240th St		10	N 9
25-00 - 44-99	63	10	N 9
45-00 - 71-99	62	10	O 9
83-00 - 95-99	26	13	O10
147-00 - OUT	22	15	O15
241st St		10	O 9
45-00 - 53-99	62	10	O 9
82-00 - 94-99	26	13	O10
134-00 - 146-99	22	15	O14
242nd St		10	O 9
25-00 - 44-99	63	10	O 9
45-00 - 72-99	62	10	O 9
80-00 - 95-99	26	13	O10
131-00 - 138-99	22	15	O14
243rd St		10	O 9
25-00 - 44-99	63	10	O 9
45-00 - 72-99	62	10	O 9
80-00 - 95-99	26	13	O10
130-00 - 146-99	22	15	P13
244th St		10	O 9
25-00 - 44-99	63	10	O 9
45-00 - 73-99	62	10	O 9
80-00 - 93-99	26	13	O10
130-00 - 138-99	22	15	P14
245th La	62	10	O 9
245th Pl	62	10	O 9
245th St		10	O 9
45-00 - 71-99	62	10	O 9
91-00 - 93-99	26	13	P11
133-00 - 146-99	22	15	P14
246th Cres	62	10	O 9
246th Pl	62	10	O 9
246th St		10	O 9
66-00 - 66-99	30	10	O 9
80-00 - 93-99	26	13	P10
134-00 - 140-99	22	15	P14
247th St		10	O 8
12-96	26	10	O 9
25-00 - 44-99	63	10	O 9
45-00 - 66-99	62	10	O 9
77-00 - 92-99	26	13	P11
138-00 - 155-99	22	15	N14
248th St		10	O 8
25-00 - 44-99	63	10	O 8
45-00 - 66-99	62	10	O 9
80-00 - 89-99	26	13	P10
138-00 - 155-99	22	15	O14
249th St		10	O 8
25-00 - 44-99	63	10	O 8
75-00 - 89-99	26	13	P10
137-00 - 146-99	22	15	P14
250th St		10	O 8
25-00 - 44-99	63	10	O 8
45-00 - 66-99	62	10	O 9
75-00 - 89-99	26	13	P10
137-00 - 142-99	22	15	P14
251st Pl	62	10	O 9
251st St		10	O 9
45-00 - 66-99	62	10	O 9
75-00 - 87-99	26	13	P10
137-00 - OUT (also called Caney La)	22	15	O14
252nd St		10	O 9
45-00 - 66-99	62	10	O 9
70-00 - 87-99	26	13	P10
253rd Pl	22	15	O15
253rd St		10	O 9
45-00 - 66-99	62	10	O 9
83-00 - 87-99	26	13	P10
137-00 - OUT	22	15	O14
254th St		10	O 9
25-00 - 44-99	63	10	O 8
45-00 - 66-99	62	10	O 9
79-00 - 85-99	4	10	P10
86-00 - 87-99	26	13	P10
139-00 - 144-99	22	15	O14
255th St		10	O 9
33-00 - 38-99	63	10	O 8
45-00 - 66-99	62	10	O 9
75-00 - 83-99 (Floral Park)	4	10	P 9
140-00 - 149-99	22	15	O15
256th St		10	O 9
57-00 - 68-99	62	10	O 9
79-00 - 83-99	4	13	P10
84-00 - 87-101	1	13	P10
137-00 - OUT	22	15	P14
257th St		13	P10
79-00 - 83-99	4	13	P10
84-00 - 87-86 (Floral Park)	1	13	P10
141-00 - 149-00	22	15	O15
258th St		13	P10
79-00 - 83-99 (Floral Park)	4	13	P10
84-00 - 87-69 (Floral Park)	1	13	P10
149-00 - OUT	22	15	P15
259th St		13	P10
79-00 - 83-99	4	13	P10
84-00 - 87-69 (Floral Park)	1	13	P10
147-00 - OUT	22	15	P15
260th Pl	4	10	P 9
260th St		10	O 9
55-00 - 59-99	62	10	O 9
69-00 - 83-99	4	13	P10
84-00 - 87-32 (Floral Park)	1	13	P10
261st St		10	P 9
69-00 - 83-99 (Floral Park)	4	13	P10
84-00 - 86-59 (Floral Park)	1	13	P10
262nd St		10	P 9
57-00 - 60-99	62	10	P 9
77-00 - 83-99 (Floral Park)	4	13	P10
84-00 - OUT (Floral Park)	1	13	P10
149-00 - 149-98	22	15	P15
263rd St		10	P 9
57-00 - 58-99	62	10	P 9
73-00 - 83-99 (Floral Park)	4	13	P10
84-00 - OUT (Floral Park)	1	13	P10
264th St		10	P 9
58-00 - 60-99	62	10	P 9
76-00 - 83-99 (Floral Park)	4	13	P10
84-00 - OUT (Floral Park)	1	13	P10
265th St		10	P 9
76-01 - 77-99 (New Hyde Park)	40	10	P 9
78-00 - 83-99 (Floral Park)	4	13	P10
84-00 - OUT (Floral Park)	1	13	P10
266th St		10	P 9
76-01 - 77-99 (New Hyde Park)	40	13	P10
78-00 - 83-99 (Floral Park)	4	13	P10
84-00 - OUT (Floral Park)	1	13	P10
267th St		10	P 9
76-01 - 77-99 (New Hyde Park)	40	10	P 9
78-00 - 83-99 (Floral Park)	4	13	P10
84-00 - OUT (Floral Park)	1	13	P10
268th St		10	P 9
76-01 - 77-99 (New Hyde Park)	40	13	P10
78-00 - 83-99 (Floral Park)	4	13	P10
84-00 - OUT	1	13	P10
269th St (New Hyde Park)	40	10	P 9
270th St (New Hyde Park)	40	10	P 9
271st St (New Hyde Park)	40	10	P 9

BROOKLYN

STREET INDEX AND POSTAL ZONES

NOTE: To obtain ZIP code for Brooklyn, add 112 before two digit postal zone numbers and 1120 before single digit postal zone numbers.

STREET NAME AND HOUSE NUMBERS	ZONE NO.	MAP NO.	MAP GRID
A			
Abbey Ct	29	25	F18
Aberdeen St	7	21	G13
Academy Park Pl	17	20	D13
Adams St	1	20	C13
Adelphi St		20	D13
1-325 & 2-336	5	20	D13
327-OUT & 338-OUT	38	20	D13
Adler Pl	8	21	H13
Agate Ct	13	20	E13
Ainslie St	11	19	E12
Aitken Pl	1	20	C13
Alabama Av	7	21	G14
Albany Av		20	E13
1-33	16	20	E13
34-469	13	20	E14
470-1500	3	20	E14
1501-OUT	10	22	E16
Albee Sq	1	20	C13
Albemarle Rd		20	D15
1-1299	18	20	D15
1300-OUT	26	20	D15
Albemarle Ter	26	20	D15
Alben Sq	19	22	C16
Alice Ct	13	20	E13
Allen Av	29	25	F18
Alton Pl	10	22	E16
Amber St	8	14	J 14
Amboy St	12	21	G15
Amersfort Pl	10	22	E16
Ames La	36	21	G15
Amherst St	35	24	E19
Amity St	1	20	C13
Anchorage Pl *(off Plymouth St)	1	19	C12
Anna Ct	7	21	G15
Anthony St	22	19	F11
Apollo St	22	19	E11
Applegate Ct	23	24	D18
Archie C Ketchum Sq	23	22	C17
Ardsley Loop	39	21	H15
Argyle Rd		20	D15
1-530	18	22	D15
531-OUT	30	22	D16
Arion Pl	6	19	E12
Arkansas Dr	34	23	G17
Arlington Av		21	G13
1-240	7	21	G13
241-OUT	8	21	H13
Arlington Pl	16	20	E13
Ash St	22	19	E10
Ashford St	7	21	H14
Ashland Pl		20	D13
1-169	1	20	D13
170-OUT	17	20	D13
Aster Ct	29	25	F18
Atkins Av	8	21	H14
Atlantic Av		20	C13
1-346	1	20	C13
347-733 & 348-752	17	20	D13
735-1081 & 754-1130	38	20	D13
1083-1453 & 1132-1518	16	20	E14
1455-1727 & 1520-1800	13	20	E14
1729-2463 & 1802-2464	33	21	F14
2465-2957 & 2466-2950	7	21	G14
2959-3599 & 2952-3598	8	21	H13
3600-OUT	24	24	B19
Atlantic Av (Sea Gate)	24	24	B19
Atlantic Commons	17	20	D13
Atwater Ct	23	24	D19
Auburn Pl	5	20	D13
Aurelia Ct	10	22	E16
Autumn Av	8	21	H13
Autumn La	8	21	J 14
Avenue A		21	F15
1-9599	36	23	F15
9600-OUT	12	21	F15
Avenue B	36	21	F15
Avenue C	18	22	D16
Avenue D		22	E16
1-3299	26	22	E16
3300-5999	3	23	F15
6000-OUT	36	23	G15
Avenue F	18	22	D16
Avenue H		22	D16
1-1999	30	23	F16
2000-4399	10	22	E16
4400-OUT	34	23	F16
Avenue I		22	D16
1-1999	30	22	D16
2000-4399	10	22	E16
4400-OUT	34	23	F16
Avenue J		22	D16
1-1999	30	22	D16
2000-4399	10	22	E16
4400-7499	34	23	F16
7500-OUT	36	23	G16
Avenue K		22	E16
1-1999	30	22	D17
2000-4399	10	22	E16
4400-7499	34	23	F16
7500-OUT	36	23	G16
Avenue L		22	E17
1-1999	30	22	D17
2000-3999	10	22	E17
4000-7499	34	23	F16
7500-OUT	36	23	G16
Avenue M		22	E17
1-1999	30	22	D17
2000-3499	10	22	E17
3500-7499	34	23	F17
7500-OUT	36	23	G16
Avenue N		22	E17
1-1999	30	22	D17
2000-3199	10	22	E17
3200-7499	34	23	F17
7500-OUT	36	23	G16
Avenue O		22	D17
1-199	4	22	D17
200-1999	30	22	D17
2000-2699	10	22	E17
2700-OUT	34	23	F17
Avenue of Puerto Rico	6	19	E12
Avenue P		22	D17
1-391	4	22	D17
392-1099	23	22	D17
1100-2964	29	22	E17
2965-OUT	34	23	F17
Avenue R		22	E17
1-1199	23	22	D17
1200-3064	29	22	E17
3065-OUT	34	23	F17
Avenue S		24	D18
1-1199	23	24	D18
1200-3199	29	24	E18
3200-OUT	34	25	F17
Avenue T		24	D18
1-1199	23	24	D18
1200-3299	29	24	E18
3300-OUT	34	25	F17
Avenue U		24	D18
1-1199	23	24	D18
1200-3299	29	24	E18
3300-OUT	34	25	G17
Avenue V		24	D18
1-1199	23	24	D18
1200-3399	29	24	E18
3400-OUT	34	25	G17
Avenue W		24	D18
1-1199	23	24	D18
1200-3399	29	24	E18
3400-OUT	34	25	G17
Avenue X		24	D18
1-499	23	24	D18
500-3186	35	24	E18
3187-3399	29	25	F18
3400-OUT	34	23	G17
Avenue Y		24	D18
61-550	23	24	E18
551-3399	35	25	E18
3400-OUT	34	25	G17
Avenue Z		24	C19
1-282	14	24	C19
283-753	23	24	D18
754-3399	35	24	E18
Aviation Rd	34	25	H19
B			
Bainbridge St	33	21	F13
Balfour Pl	25	20	E14
Baltic St		20	B13
1-399	1	20	B13
400-OUT	17	20	C13
Bancroft Pl	33	21	F14
Bank St	36	21	G15
Banker St	22	19	E11
Banner Av	35	24	D19
Barberry Ct	7	21	G13
Barbey St	7	21	G13
Barlow Dr N	34	23	G17
Barlow Dr S	34	23	G17
Bartel Pritchard Sq	15	20	C14
Bartlett Pl	29	25	F18
Bartlett St	6	19	E12
Barwell Ct	9	22	A17
Bassett Av	34	23	G17
Bassett Wk	34	23	G17
Batchelder St		24	E18
1-2399	29	24	E18
2400-OUT	35	24	E18
Bath Av		24	B17
1-1599	28	24	B17
1600-OUT	14	24	B18
Battery Av		22	B17
1-83	28	22	B17
84-OUT	9	22	B17
Baughman Pl	34	23	F17
Bay Av		22	E17
1-1999	30	22	E17
2000-OUT	10	22	E17
Bay Cliff Ter	20	22	A16
Bay Pkwy		24	C18
1-5499	30	22	D17
5500-7499	4	24	C17
7500-OUT	14	24	C18
Bay Ridge Av		22	A16
1-899	20	22	A16
900-1599	19	22	B16
1600-OUT	4	22	C17
Bay Ridge Pkwy		22	A16
1-699	9	22	A16
700-1599	28	22	B16
1600-OUT	4	22	C17
Bay Ridge Pl	9	22	A16
Bay St	31	20	B14
Bay View Av	24	24	C19
Bay 7th St	28	22	B17
Bay 8th St	28	22	B17
Bay 10th St	28	22	B17
Bay 11th St	28	22	B17
Bay 13th St	14	24	B17
Bay 14th St	14	24	B17
Bay 16th St	14	24	B18
Bay 17th St	14	24	B18
Bay 19th St	14	24	B18
Bay 20th St	14	24	B18
Bay 22nd St	14	24	C18
Bay 23rd St	14	24	C18
Bay 25th St	14	24	C18
Bay 26th St	14	24	C18

STREET NAME AND HOUSE NUMBERS	ZONE NO.	MAP NO.	MAP GRID
Bay 28th St	14	24	C18
Bay 29th St	14	24	C18
Bay 31st St	14	24	C18
Bay 32nd St	14	24	C18
Bay 34th St	14	24	C18
Bay 35th St	14	24	C18
Bay 37th St	14	24	C18
Bay 38th St	14	24	C18
Bay 40th St	14	24	C18
Bay 41st St	14	24	C18
Bay 43rd St	14	24	C18
Bay 44th St	14	24	C18
Bay 46th St	14	24	C18
Bay 47th St	14	24	C18
Bay 48th St	14	24	C19
Bay 49th St	14	24	C19
Bay 50th St	14	24	C19
Bay 52nd St	14	24	C19
Bay 53rd St	14	24	C19
Bay 54th St	14	24	C19
Bayard St		19	E11
1-50	11	19	E11
51-OUT	22	19	E11
Bayview Pl	36	21	G15
Beach Wk	35	24	D19
Beach 37th St	24	24	C19
Beach 38th St	24	24	B19
Beach 40th St	24	24	B19
Beach 42nd St	24	24	B19
Beach 43rd St	24	24	B19
Beach 44th St	24	24	B19
Beach 45th St	24	24	B19
Beach 46th St	24	24	B19
Beach 47th St	24	24	B19
Beach 48th St	24	24	B19
Beach 49th St	24	24	B19
Beach 50th St	24	24	B19
Beach 51st St	24	24	B19
Beacon Ct	29	25	F18
Beadel St	22	19	E11
Beard St	31	20	B14
Beaumont St	35	24	E19
Beaver St	6	19	E12
Bedell La	36	21	G15
Bedford Av		19	D11
1-70	22	19	E11
71-679 & 72-684	11	19	D12
681-723 & 686-730	6	19	D12
725-1029 & 732-1058	5	20	E13
1031-1535 & 1060-1546	16	20	E13
1537-2005 & 1548-2004	25	20	E14
2006-2639	26	20	E15
2640-3663	10	22	E16
3664-4446 & 3665-4443	29	24	E18
4448-OUT & 4445-OUT	35	24	E18
Bedford Pl	16	20	E13
Beekman Pl	25	20	D15
Belmont Av		21	G14
1-200	12	21	G14
201-698	7	21	G14
699-1299	8	21	H14
Belt Pkwy (see Shore Pkwy)		24	B19
Belt Pkwy (see Shore Pkwy)		25	G18
Belvidere St	6	19	E12
Bennett Ct	9	22	B16
Bennett Pl	31	20	C14
Benson Av		22	B17
1-1599	28	24	B17
1600-OUT	14	24	C18
Bergen Av	34	23	F16
Bergen Ct	34	23	G16
Bergen Pl	20	22	A16
Bergen St		20	C13
1-131 & 2-136	1	20	C13
133-563 & 138-558	17	20	C13
565-949 & 560-946	38	20	D13
951-1159 & 948-1158	16	20	E14
1160-1730	13	20	E14
1731-OUT	33	21	F14
Berkeley Pl	17	20	D14
Berriman St	8	21	H14
Berry St	11	19	D11
Bethel Loop	39	21	H15
Beverly Rd		20	D15
1-1299	18	20	D15
1300-3299	26	20	E15
3300-OUT	3	21	F15
Bevy Ct	29	25	F18
Bijou Av	29	25	F18
Billings Pl	23	24	D18
Bills Pl	18	20	C15
Blake Av		21	F14
1-480	12	21	F14
481-958	7	21	G14
959-1499	8	21	H14
Blake Ct	35	24	D19
Bleecker St		21	F13
1-182	21	21	F13
183-1699	37	19	F12
Bliss Ter	20	22	A16
Boardwalk E	35	24	D19
Boardwalk W	24	24	C19
Boerum Pl	1	20	C13
Boerum St	6	19	E12
Bogart St	6	19	F12
Bokee Ct	23	24	D19
Bond St		20	C13
1-50	1	20	C13
51-285 & 52-294	17	20	C13
287-OUT & 296-OUT	31	20	C13
Bouck Ct	23	24	D18
Boulevard Ct	23	24	D18
Bowery St	24	24	C19
Bowne St	31	20	B13
Box St	22	19	E10
Boynton Pl	23	24	D18
Bradford St	7	21	G14
Bragg Ct	35	25	F19
Bragg St		25	F18
1-2399	29	25	F18
2400-OUT	35	25	F18
Branton St	36	21	F15
Brevoort Pl	16	20	E13
Bridge Plz Ct *(bounded by Concord & Nassau Sts, bet Flatbush Av Ext & Jay St)	1	19	C12
Bridge St	1	20	C13
Bridgewater St	22	19	E11
Brigham St		25	F18
1-2399	29	25	F18
2400-OUT	35	25	F19
Brighton Beach Av	35	24	D19
Brighton Ct		24	D18
1-60	23	24	D18
61-OUT	35	24	D18
Brighton 1st La *(off Brighton 1st St)	35	24	D19
Brighton 1st Pa *(off Brighton 1st St)	35	24	D19
Brighton 1st Pl	35	24	D19
Brighton 1st Rd	35	24	D19
Brighton 1st St	35	24	D19
Brighton 1st Ter *(off Brighton 1st St)	35	24	D19
Brighton 1st Wk	35	24	D19
Brighton 2nd La *(off Brighton 2nd St)	35	24	D19
Brighton 2nd Pa *(off Brighton 2nd St)	35	24	D19
Brighton 2nd Pl *(off Brighton 2nd St)	35	24	D19
Brighton 2nd St	35	24	D19
Brighton 2nd Wk	35	24	D19
Brighton 3rd Ct *(off Brighton 3rd St)	35	24	D19
Brighton 3rd La *(off Brighton 3rd St)	35	24	D19
Brighton 3rd Pl *(off Brighton 3rd St)	35	24	D19
Brighton 3rd Rd	35	24	D19
Brighton 3rd St	35	24	D19
Brighton 3rd Ter *(off Brighton 3rd St)	35	24	D19
Brighton 3rd Wk	35	24	D19
Brighton 4th Ct *(off Brighton 4th St)	35	24	D19
Brighton 4th La *(off Brighton 4th St)	35	24	D19
Brighton 4th Pl *(off Brighton 4th St)	35	24	D19
Brighton 4th Rd	35	24	D19
Brighton 4th St	35	24	D19
Brighton 4th Ter	35	24	D19
Brighton 4th Wk	35	24	D19
Brighton 5th Ct *(off Brighton 5th St)	35	24	D19
Brighton 5th La *(off Brighton 5th St)	35	24	D19
Brighton 5th Pl *(off Brighton 5th St)	35	24	D19
Brighton 5th St	35	24	D19
Brighton 5th Wk	35	24	D19
Brighton 6th Ct *(off Brighton 6th St)	35	24	D19
Brighton 6th La *(off Brighton 6th St)	35	24	D19
Brighton 6th Pl *(off Brighton 6th St)	35	24	D19
Brighton 6th St	35	24	D19
Brighton 6th Wk *(off Brighton 6th St)	35	24	D19
Brighton 7th Ct *(off Brighton 7th St)	35	24	D19
Brighton 7th La *(off Brighton 7th St)	35	24	D19
Brighton 7th St	35	24	D19
Brighton 7th Wk	35	24	D19
Brighton 8th Ct *(off Brighton 8th St)	35	24	D19
Brighton 8th La *(off Brighton 8th St)	35	24	D19
Brighton 8th Pl *(off Brighton 8th St)	35	24	D19
Brighton 8th St	35	24	D19
Brighton 10th Ct	35	24	D19
Brighton 10th La	35	24	D19
Brighton 10th Pa	35	24	D19
Brighton 10th St	35	24	E19
Brighton 10th Ter	35	24	D19
Brighton 11th St	35	24	E19
Brighton 12th St	35	24	E19
Brighton 13th St	35	24	E19
Brighton 14th St	35	24	E19
Brighton 15th St	35	24	E19
Brightwater Av	35	24	E19
Brightwater Ct	35	24	D19
Bristol St		21	G14
1-654	12	21	G14
655-OUT	36	21	G15
Broadway		19	D12
1-506	11	19	D12
507-945 & 508-932	6	19	E12
947-1557 & 934-1560	21	19	F12
1559-OUT & 1562-OUT	7	21	G13
Brookdale Plz *(bounded by Rockaway Pkwy, Av A and Linden Blvd)	12	21	F15
Brooklyn Av		20	E14
1-117 & 2-120	16	20	E14
119-373 & 122-374	13	20	E14
375-568	25	20	E14
569-1400	3	20	E15
1401-OUT	10	22	E16
Brooklyn-Queens Expwy		19	C12
		20	C13
		19	D12
Brooklyn Terminal Market	36	21	F15
Broome St	22	19	E11
Brown St		24	E18
1-2399	29	24	E18
2400-OUT	35	24	E18
Bryant St	31	20	B14
Buckingham Rd (E 16th St)		20	D15
1-638	26	22	D15
639-1599	30	22	D17
Buffalo Av		21	F14
1-130	33	21	F14
131-OUT	13	21	F14
Bulwer Pl	7	21	G13
Burnett St	29	22	E17
Bush St	31	20	B14
Bushwick Av		19	E12
1-97	11	19	E12
99-641 & 98-638	6	19	E12
643-1243 & 640-1242	21	21	F13
1244-OUT	7	21	F13
Bushwick Pl	6	19	E12
Butler Pl	38	20	D14
Butler St		20	C13
1-132	31	20	C13
133-OUT	17	20	C13

C

STREET NAME AND HOUSE NUMBERS	ZONE NO.	MAP NO.	MAP GRID
Cadman Plz	1	19	C12
Cadman Plz E	1	19	C12
Cadman Plz W	1	20	C13
Calder Pl	15	20	C14
Calhoun St	11	19	E11
Calyer St	22	19	D11
Cambridge Pl	38	20	D13
Cameron Ct	4	22	C17
Campus Pl	8	21	H13
Campus Rd	10	22	E16
Canada Av	35	24	E19
Canal Av	24	24	C19
Canarsie La	3	21	F15
Canarsie Rd	36	23	G16
Canarsie Veterans Cir	36	23	H16
Canton Ct	29	25	F18
Carlton Av		20	D13
1-341	5	20	D13
342-OUT	38	20	D13
Carlton Ct *(off Surf Av)	24	24	B19
Carroll St		20	B13
1-410	31	20	C13
411-873 & 412-898	15	20	C14
875-1225 & 900-1252	25	20	E14
1227-OUT & 1254-OUT	13	20	E14
Cary Ct	30	22	D17
Cass Pl	35	24	E19
Catharine St	11	19	E11
Cathedral Pl	1	19	C12
Caton Av		20	D15
1-1299	18	20	D15
1300-OUT	26	20	D15
Caton Pl	18	20	D15
Cedar St	30	22	D17
Cedar St	21	19	F12
Celeste Ct	29	25	F18
Central Av		19	F12
1-105 & 2-110	6	19	F12
107-525 & 112-550	21	19	F12
527-OUT & 552-OUT	7	21	G13
Centre Mall *(Red Hook Housing)	31	20	B14
Centre St	31	20	B14
Channel Av	29	25	F18
Chapel St	1	19	C12
Charles Pl	21	19	F12
Chase Ct	36	21	F15
Chauncey St		21	F13
1-600	33	21	F13
601-OUT	7	21	G13
Cheever Pl	31	20	C13
Cherry St	22	19	E11
Chester Av	18	20	C15
Chester Ct	25	20	D15
Chester St		21	G14
1-699	12	21	G15
700-OUT	36	21	G15
Chestnut Av	30	22	D17
Chestnut St	8	21	H13
Christopher Av	12	21	G14
Church Av		20	D15
1-1299	18	20	D15
1300-3299	26	20	E15
3300-5999	3	21	F15
6000-9299	36	21	F15
9300-OUT	12	21	F15
Church La	36	23	G16
Clara St	18	20	C15
Clarendon Rd		20	E15
1-3299	26	20	E15
3300-5999	3	23	F15
6000-OUT	36	23	F15
Clark St	1	19	C12
Clarkson Av		20	E15
1-366	26	20	E15
367-979	3	20	E15
980-OUT	12	21	F15
Classon Av		19	D13
1-70	11	19	D12
71-359 & 72-342	5	20	D13
361-845 & 344-852	38	20	D13
847-OUT & 854-OUT	25	20	D14
Claver Pl	38	20	D13
Clay St	22	19	E10
Clermont Av		20	D13
1-338	5	20	D13
339-OUT	38	20	D13
Cleveland St	8	21	H14
Clifford Pl	22	19	E11
Clifton Pl		20	D13
1-176	38	20	D13
177-OUT	16	20	E13
Clinton Av		20	D13
1-325 & 2-340	5	20	D13
327-OUT & 342-OUT	38	20	D13
Clinton St		20	C13
1-299 & 2-314	1	20	C13
301-OUT & 316-OUT	31	20	C13
Clinton Wharf	31	20	B13
Clove Rd	25	20	E14
Clymer St	11	19	D12
Cobble Hill St	1	20	C13
Cobeck Ct	23	24	D18
Coffey St	31	20	B14
Colby Ct	23	24	D19
Coleman St	34	23	F17
Coleridge St	35	24	E19
Coles St	31	20	B13
Colin Pl	23	24	D18
College Pl	1	19	C12
Colonial Ct	9	22	A16
Colonial Gardens	9	22	A17
Colonial Rd		22	A17
1-6899	20	22	A16
6900-OUT	9	22	A17
Columbia Ct *(off Nassau Ct)	35	24	D19
Columbia Hgts	1	19	C12
Columbia Pl	1	20	C13
Columbia St		20	C13
1-115 & 2-124	1	20	C13
117-OUT & 126-OUT	31	20	B14
Columbus Pl	33	21	F14
Commerce St	31	20	B13
Commercial St	22	19	D10
Commercial Wharf	31	20	B13
Concord St	1	19	C12
Conduit Blvd (Southern Pkwy)	8	21	H13
Coney Island Av		22	D17
1-909 & 2-912	18	22	D16
911-1939 & 914-1940	30	22	D17
1941-2668	23	24	D18
2669-OUT	35	24	D19
Congress St	1	20	C13
Conklin Av	36	21	G15
Conover St	31	20	B14
Conselyea St	11	19	E11
Conway St		21	G13
1-20	33	21	G13
21-OUT	7	21	G13
Cook St	6	19	E12
Cooke Ct	7	21	G13
Cooper St		21	G13
1-251 & 2-270	7	21	G13
253-OUT & 272-OUT	37	21	G13
Corbin Pl	35	24	E19
Cornelia St		19	F13
1-300	21	19	F13
301-OUT	37	19	G12
Corso Ct *(at Van Sicklen off Avenue V)	23	24	D18
Cortelyou Rd		22	D16
1-1299	18	22	D16
1300-3299	26	22	D16
3300-OUT	3	22	E15
Court Sq	1	20	C13
Court St		20	C13
1-15 & 17-25	1	20	C13
16 Only	41	20	C13
27-261 & 28-248	1	20	C13
26 Only	42	20	C13
263-OUT & 250-OUT	31	20	C13
Coventry Rd	36	21	F15
Covert St		21	F13
1-270	7	21	G13
271-OUT	37	21	G13
Cox Pl	8	21	H13
Coyle St		25	E18
1-2399	29	25	E18
2400-OUT	35	25	F18
Cozine Av		21	H15
1-414	7	21	H15
415-OUT	8	14	J14
Cranberry St	1	19	C12
Crawford Av	23	24	D18
Creamer St	31	20	B14
Crescent St	8	21	H14
Crooke Av	26	20	D15
Cropsey Av		24	B18
1-1599	28	24	B17
1600-3019	14	24	B18
3020-OUT	24	24	C19
Crosby Av	7	21	G13
Croton Loop	39	21	H15
Crown St		21	E14
1-492	25	21	E14
493-OUT	13	21	E14
Crystal St	8	21	H14
Cumberland St		20	D13
1-275 & 2-292	5	20	D13
277-OUT & 294-OUT	38	20	D13
Cumberland Wk *(Walt Whitman Houses)	5	20	D13
Cypress Av	37	19	F12
Cypress Av (Sea Gate)	24	24	B19
Cypress Ct	8	21	H13
Cypress Hills St	8	21	H13
Cyrus Av	29	25	F18

D

STREET NAME AND HOUSE NUMBERS	ZONE NO.	MAP NO.	MAP GRID
Dahill Rd		22	D16
1-799	18	22	D16
800-1600	4	22	D17
1601-OUT	23	22	D17
Dahl Ct	4	22	C17
Dahlgren Pl	28	22	A17
Dakota Pl	34	23	G17
Danforth St	8	21	H13
Dank Ct	23	24	D18
Dare Ct	29	25	F18
Dean St		20	C13
1-135	1	20	C13
137-571 & 136-578	17	20	C13
573-1049 & 580-1048	38	20	D13
1050-1419	16	20	E14
1420-1730	13	20	E14
1731-OUT	33	21	F14
Dearborn Ct	25	20	E14
Debevoise Av		19	E11
1-60	11	19	E11
61-OUT	22	19	E11
Debevoise St	6	19	E12
Decatur St		21	E13
1-147 & 2-140	16	21	E13
149-901 & 142-900	33	21	F13
903-1303 & 902-1312	7	21	G13
1305-OUT & 1314-OUT	37	19	G13
Degraw St		20	B13
1-397 & 2-424	31	20	C13
399-OUT & 426-OUT	17	20	C13
De Kalb Av		20	C13
1-121 & 2-116	1	20	C13
123-165 & 118-166	17	20	D13
167-607 & 168-616	5	20	D13
609-765 & 618-762	16	20	E13
767-1387 & 764-1388	21	20	E13
1389-OUT	37	19	F12
De Koven Ct	30	22	D16
Delamere Pl		22	E17
1-500	26	20	E15
501-1599	10	22	E16
1600-2399	29	22	E17
2400-OUT	35	24	E18
Delavan St	31	20	B13
Delmar Loop	39	21	H15
Delmonico Pl	6	19	E12
Dennet Pl	31	20	C14
Denton Pl	15	20	C14
De Sales Pl	7	21	G13
Desmond Ct	35	24	D18
Devoe St	11	19	E11
Devon Av	29	25	F18
Dewey Pl	33	21	F14
De Witt Av		21	G15
302-OUT	7	21	G15
1-301	36	21	G15
Diamond St	22	19	E11
Dickinson St	11	19	E11
Dictum Ct	29	25	F18
Dikeman St	31	20	B14
Dinsmore Pl	8	21	H13
Ditmars St	21	19	F12
Ditmas Av		22	D16
1-1299	18	22	D16
1300-3299	26	22	D16
3300-5999	3	22	E16
6000-OUT	36	21	F15
Division Av	11	19	D12
Division Pl	22	19	E11
Dobbin St	22	19	E11
Dock St	1	19	C12
Dodworth St	21	21	F13
Dooley St	35	24	E18
Doone Ct	35	24	E18
Dorchester Rd		22	D16
1-1299	18	22	D16
1300-OUT	26	22	D16
Dorset St	36	21	F15
Doscher St	8	21	H13
Doughty St	1	19	C12
Douglass Ct	31	20	C13
Douglass St		20	C13
1-111 & 2-118	31	20	C13
113-OUT & 120-OUT	17	20	C13
Dover St	35	24	E19
Downing St	38	20	D13
Drew St	8	21	J14
Driggs Av		19	D12
1-400	11	19	D12
401-OUT	22	19	E11
Duffield St	1	20	C13
Dumont Av		21	G14
1-480	12	21	G14
481-967	7	21	G14
968-1549	8	21	H14
Dunham Pl	11	19	D12

STREET NAME AND HOUSE NUMBERS	ZONE NO.	MAP NO.	MAP GRID
Dunne Ct	35	24	D18
Dunne Pl	35	24	E19
Dupont St	22	19	E10
Durland Pl	36	21	G15
Duryea Ct	19	22	C17
Duryea Pl	26	20	E15
Dwight St	31	20	B14
Dyker Pl	28	22	B17

E

STREET NAME AND HOUSE NUMBERS	ZONE NO.	MAP NO.	MAP GRID
Eagle St	22	19	D10
East New York Av		21	E14
1-606	25	21	E14
607-961 & 608-944	3	21	E14
963-1761 & 946-1756	12	21	F14
1763-OUT & 1758-OUT	7	21	G14
East 1st St	23	24	D18
East 2nd St		22	D16
1-799	18	22	D16
800-1668	30	22	D17
1669-OUT	23	24	D18
East 3rd St		22	D16
1-820	18	22	D16
821-1699	30	22	D17
1700-OUT	23	24	D18
East 4th St		22	D16
1-805	18	22	D16
806-1699	30	22	D17
1700-OUT	23	24	D18
East 5th St		22	D16
1-799	18	22	D16
800-1699	30	22	D17
1700-OUT	23	24	D18
East 6th St	35	24	D19
East 7th St		22	D17
1-734	18	22	D16
735-1675 & 736-1688	30	22	D17
1677-2415 & 1690-2416	23	24	D18
2417-OUT	35	24	D18
East 8th St		22	D17
1-649	18	22	D16
650-1599	30	22	D17
1600-OUT	23	24	D18
East 9th St		22	D17
1-599	18	22	D16
600-1600	30	22	D17
1601-OUT	23	24	D18
East 10th St		20	D17
1-100	18	22	D15
101-1599	30	22	D17
1600-OUT	23	22	D17
East 11th St		24	D18
529-OUT	35	24	D18
East 12th St		22	D16
531-1599	30	22	D16
1600-2399	29	22	D17
2400-OUT	35	24	E18
East 13th St		22	D17
531-1599	30	22	D16
1600-2399	29	22	D17
2400-OUT	35	24	E18
East 14th St		22	D16
531-1599	30	22	D16
1600-2399	29	24	E18
2400-OUT	35	24	E18
East 15th St		22	D16
1-638	26	22	D16
639-1599	30	22	D16
1600-2399	29	24	E18
2400-OUT	35	24	E18
East 16th St		22	D16
1-638	26	22	D16
639-1599	30	22	D16
1600-2399	29	24	E18
East 17th St		22	D16
1-640	26	22	D16
641-1606	30	22	D16
1607-2399	29	24	E18
2400-OUT	35	24	E18
East 18th St		22	D16
1-633	26	22	D15
634-1603	30	22	D16
1604-2399	29	24	E18
2400-OUT	35	24	E18
East 19th St		22	D16
1-615	26	22	D15
616-1599	30	22	D16
1600-2399	29	24	E18
2400-OUT	35	24	E18
East 21st St		22	D15
1-690	26	22	D15
691-1716	10	22	E16
1717-2446	29	24	E18
2447-OUT	35	24	E18
East 22nd St		22	E15
1-615	26	22	E15
616-1652	10	22	E16
1653-2399	29	24	E18
2400-OUT	35	24	E18
East 23rd St (Delamere Pl)		22	E15
1-500	26	22	E15
501-1599	10	22	E16
1600-2399	29	24	E18
2400-OUT	35	24	E18
East 24th St (Mansfield Pl)		22	E16
1-1551	10	22	E16
1552-2399	29	24	E18
2400-OUT	35	24	E18
East 25th St	26	22	E16
East 26th St		22	E16
1-490	26	22	E16
491-1500	10	22	E16
1501-2399	29	24	E18
2400-OUT	35	24	E18
East 27th St		22	E16
1-1500	10	22	E16
1501-2399	29	24	E18
2400-OUT	35	24	E18
East 28th St		22	E16
1-490	26	22	E16
491-1489	10	22	E16
1490-2399	29	24	E18
2400-OUT	35	24	E18
East 29th St		22	E16
1-490	26	20	E15
491-1459	10	22	E16
1460-2399	29	24	E18
2400-OUT	35	24	E18
East 31st St		22	E15
1-490	26	22	E15
491-1412	10	22	E16
1413-OUT	34	22	E17
East 32nd St		22	E15
1-490	26	22	E15
491-1399	10	22	E16
1400-OUT	34	22	E17
East 33rd St	34	22	E17
East 34th St		22	E15
1-710	3	22	E15
711-1445	10	22	E16
1446-OUT	34	22	E17
East 35th St		22	E15
1-710	3	22	E15
711-1370	10	22	E16
1371-OUT	34	22	E17
East 36th St		22	E16
1-1269	10	22	E16
1270-OUT	34	22	E17
East 37th St		22	E15
1-718	3	22	E15
719-1402	10	22	E16
1403-OUT	34	23	F17
East 38th St		22	E15
1-667 & 2-656	3	22	E15
669-1301 & 658-1300	10	22	E16
1302-OUT	34	23	F17
East 39th St		22	E15
1-720	3	22	E15
721-OUT	10	22	E16
East 40th St		22	E15
1-668	3	22	E15
669-1299	10	22	E16
1300-OUT	34	23	F16
East 41st St	34	23	F16
East 42nd St		20	E15
1-744	3	23	E15
745-OUT	10	23	E16
East 43rd St		23	E15
1-744	3	23	E15
745-1399	10	23	F16
1400-OUT	34	23	F17
East 45th St		23	E15
1-1093 & 2-1104	3	23	E15
1095-OUT & 1106-OUT	34	23	F17
East 46th St		23	E15
1-1099	3	23	E15
1100-OUT	34	23	F17
East 48th St		23	F15
1-1053	3	23	F15
1054-OUT	34	23	F17
East 49th St		23	F15
1-1050	3	23	F15
1051-OUT	34	23	F17
East 51st St		23	F15
1-1070	3	23	F15
1071-OUT	34	23	F17
East 52nd St		23	F15
1-949	3	23	F15
950-OUT	34	23	F17
East 53rd Pl	34	23	F17
East 53rd St		23	F15
1-899	3	23	F15
900-OUT	34	23	F17
East 54th St		23	F15
1-740	3	23	F15
741-OUT	34	23	F17
East 55th St		23	F15
1-710	3	23	F15
711-OUT	34	23	F17
East 56th St		23	F15
1-680	3	23	F15
681-OUT	34	23	F17
East 57th Pl	34	23	F17
East 57th St		23	F15
1-579	3	23	F15
580-OUT	34	23	F17
East 58th St		23	F15
1-654	3	23	F15
655-OUT	34	23	F17
East 59th Pl	34	23	G17
East 59th St		23	F15
1-584	3	23	F15
585-OUT	34	23	F17
East 60th Pl	34	23	G17
East 60th St	34	23	F17
East 61st St	34	23	F17
East 63rd St	34	23	F17
East 64th St	34	23	F17
East 65th St	34	23	F17
East 66th St	34	23	G17
East 67th St	34	23	G17
East 68th St	34	23	G17
East 69th St	34	23	F16
East 70th St	34	23	G17
East 71st St	34	23	G17
East 72nd St	34	23	F16
East 73rd St	34	23	F16
East 74th St	34	23	G17
East 76th St	36	23	F16
East 77th St	36	23	F16
East 78th St	36	23	F16
East 79th St	36	23	F16
East 80th St	36	23	F16
East 81st St	36	23	F16
East 82nd St	36	23	F16
East 83rd St	36	23	G16
East 84th St	36	23	G16
East 85th St	36	23	G16
East 86th St	36	21	F15
East 87th St	36	21	F15
East 88th St	36	21	F15
East 89th St	36	21	F15
East 91st St		21	G16
1-479	12	21	F15
480-OUT	36	23	G16
East 92nd St		23	G16
1-499	12	21	F15
500-OUT	36	23	G16
East 93rd St		23	G16
1-521	12	21	F15
522-OUT	36	23	G16
East 94th St		23	G16
1-542	12	21	F15
543-OUT	36	23	G16
East 95th St		23	G16
1-571	12	21	F15
572-OUT	36	23	G16
East 96th St		21	F14
1-588	12	21	F15
589-OUT	36	23	G16
East 98th St		21	G15
1-640	12	21	F15
641-OUT	36	21	G15
East 99th St	36	21	G15
East 100th St	36	21	G15
East 101st St	36	21	G15
East 102nd St	36	21	G15
East 103rd St	36	21	G15
East 104th St	36	21	G15
East 105th Dr *(off Seaview Av)	36	23	H16
East 105th St	36	21	G15
East 105th Wk	36	21	G15
East 106th St	36	21	G15
East 107th St	36	21	G15
East 108th St	36	21	G15
Eastern Pkwy		20	D14
1-327 & 2-200	38	20	D14
329-617 (odd only)	16	20	E14
202-618 (even only)	25	20	E14
619-1290	13	20	E14
1291-2010	33	21	F14
2011-OUT	7	21	G13
Eaton Ct	29	25	F18
Ebony Ct	29	25	F18
Eckford St	22	19	E11
Edwards Ct *(off W 20th St)	24	24	C19
Eldert La	8	21	J13
Eldert St		21	F13
1-290	7	21	F13
291-OUT	37	21	G13
Elizabeth Pl	1	19	C12
Ellery St	6	19	E12
Elm Av	30	22	D17
Elm Pl	1	20	C13
Elmira Loop	39	21	H15
Elmwood Av	30	22	D16
Elton St	8	21	H14
Emerald St	8	14	J14
Emerson Pl	5	20	D13
Emmers La	35	24	E18
Emmons Av	35	24	E19
Empire Blvd		20	E14
1-588	25	20	E14
589-OUT	13	20	E14
Engert Av	22	19	E11
Erasmus St	26	20	E15
Eric Pl	20	22	B16
Erie Basin	31	20	B14
Erskine St	8	21	H15
Esplanade	35	24	E19
Essex St	8	21	H14
Estate Rd	23	22	D17
Etna Av	8	21	H13
Euclid Av	8	21	H13
Evans St	1	19	C12
Everett Av	29	25	F18
Evergreen Av		19	F13
1-141 & 2-174	6	19	F12
143-585 & 176-640	21	21	F13
587-OUT & 642-OUT	7	21	G13
Everit St	1	19	C12
Exeter St	35	24	E19

F

STREET NAME AND HOUSE NUMBERS	ZONE NO.	MAP NO.	MAP GRID
Fair St	1	20	C13
Fairview Pl	26	20	E15
Falmouth St	35	24	E19
Fanchon Pl	7	21	G13
Fane Ct	29	25	F18
Fane Ct S	29	25	F18
Farr Pl	10	23	E16
Farragut Pl	10	22	E16
Farragut Rd		22	E16
1-4199	10	22	E16
4200-5599	3	23	F16
5600-5999	34	23	F16
6000-OUT	36	23	G15
Fayette St	6	19	E12
Fenimore St		20	E15
1-450	25	20	E15
451-OUT	3	20	E15
Ferris St	31	20	B13
Ferry Pl	31	20	B13
Fillmore Av		23	F17
1-2999	29	23	F17
3000-OUT	34	23	F17
Fillmore Pl	11	19	D11
Fiske Pl	15	20	D14
Flatbush Av		20	D15
1-343 & 2-302	17	20	C13
345-449 & 304-450	38	20	D13
451-713 & 452-722	25	20	D14
715-1339 & 724-1296	26	20	E15
1341-1949 & 1298-1944	10	22	E16
1951-OUT & 1946-OUT	34	23	F17
Flatbush Av Ext	1	19	C12
Flatlands Av		23	E17
1 - 5999	34	23	E17
6000 - 109-99	36	23	G16
110-00 - 124-10	7	21	H15
124-11 - OUT	8	21	H15
Flatlands 1st St	36	21	G15
Flatlands 2nd St	36	21	G15
Flatlands 3rd St	36	21	H15
Flatlands 4th St	36	21	H15
Flatlands 5th St	36	21	H15
Flatlands 6th St	36	21	H15
Flatlands 7th St	36	23	H16
Flatlands 8th St	36	23	H16
Flatlands 9th St	36	23	H16
Flatlands 10th St	36	23	H16
Fleet Al	1	19	C12
Fleet Pl	1	20	C13
Fleet St	1	20	C13
Fleet Wk (Raymond V Ingersoll Houses)	1	20	C13
Florence Av	29	25	F18
Floyd Bennett Field (US Naval Air Station)	34	25	G18
Floyd St	6	19	E12
Flushing Av		19	D12
1-535 & 2-518	5	19	D12
537-1029 & 520-1002	6	19	E12
1031-1699 & 1004-1698	37	19	F12
Folsom Pl	8	21	H13
Forbell St	8	21	J14
Force Tube Av	8	21	H13
Ford St		21	F14
1-50	13	21	F14
51-2399	29	24	E18
2400-OUT	35	25	F18
Forest Pl	9	22	A17
Forrest St	6	19	E12
Fort Greene Pl	17	20	D13
Fort Hamilton Pkwy		22	A17
1-4099	18	20	C15
4100-6899	19	22	C16
6900-7799	28	22	B17
7800-OUT	9	22	A17
Fort Hill Pl	28	22	A17
Foster Av		22	D16
1-1999	30	22	D16
2000-3299	10	22	E16
3300-5399	3	23	F16
5400-5999	34	23	F16
6000-OUT	36	23	G15
Fountain Av	8	21	H14
Frank Ct	29	25	F18
Franklin Av		20	D13
1-20	11	19	D12
21-303 & 22-296	5	20	D13
305-819 & 298-802	38	20	E14
821-OUT & 804-OUT	25	20	D14
Franklin Ct *(off Kent Av)	5	20	D13
Franklin St	22	19	D11
Fraser Sq	34	22	E17
Freeman St	22	19	D10
Freeport Loop	39	21	H15
Friel Pl	18	20	D15
Front St	1	19	C12
Frost St		19	E11
1-255 & 2-260	11	19	E11
257-OUT & 262-OUT	22	19	E11
Fuller Pl	15	20	D15
Fulton St		20	C13
1-589 & 2-542	1	20	C13
591-781 & 544-712	17	20	D13
783-1149 & 714-1132	38	20	D13
1151-1569 & 1134-1558	16	20	E13
1571-1699 & 1560-1752	13	21	E13
1701-2449 & 1754-2448	33	21	F13
2450-2958	7	21	G13
2959-3499	8	21	H13
Furman Av	7	21	G13
Furman St	1	20	C13

G

STREET NAME AND HOUSE NUMBERS	ZONE NO.	MAP NO.	MAP GRID
Gain Ct	29	25	F18
Gallatin Pl	1	20	C13
Garden Pl	1	20	C13
Garden St	6	19	E12
Gardner Av		19	F11
1-209 & 2-206	37	19	F12
211-395 & 208-396	11	19	F11
397-OUT	22	19	F11
Garfield Pl	15	20	C14
Garland Ct	29	25	F18
Garnet St	31	20	C14
Garrison St *(off Front St)	1	19	C12
Gates Av		20	E13
1-273 & 2-260	38	20	D13
275-551 & 262-528	16	20	E13
553-1423 & 530-1422	21	21	F13
1424-OUT	37	19	F12
Gatling Pl	9	22	B17
Gaylord Dr N	34	23	G17
Gaylord Dr S	34	23	G17
Gelb Wk *(off W 5th St)	24	24	D19
Gelston Av	9	22	A17
Gem St	22	19	E11
Geneva Loop	39	21	H15
George St		19	F12
1-96	6	19	F12
97-1599	37	19	F12
Georgia Av	7	21	G14
Gerald Ct	35	24	D18
Gerald H Chambers Sq	35	24	E19
Gerritsen Av	29	22	E17
Gerry St	6	19	E12
Gibbons St	22	19	F11
Gilmore Ct	35	24	D19
Girard St	35	24	E19
Glen St	8	21	H13
Glendale Ct	34	23	F16
Glenmore Av		21	G14
1-200	12	21	G14
201-696	7	21	G14
697-1279	8	21	H14
Glenmore Plz		21	G14
Glenwood Rd		22	D16
1-1999	30	22	D16
2000-4399	10	22	E16
4400-4599	3	23	F16
4600-5999	34	23	F16
6000-OUT	36	23	G16
Gold St	1	19	C12
Goodwin Pl	21	21	F13
Gotham Av	29	25	F18
Gowanus Expwy		20	B15
Gowanus Expwy		22	B16
Gowanus Expwy		20	C14
Grace Ct	1	20	C13
Grace Ct Al	1	20	C13
Grafton St	12	21	F14
Graham Av		19	E12
1-270	6	19	E12
271-449 & 272-454	11	19	E12
451-OUT & 456-OUT	22	19	E11
Grand Army Plz	38	20	D14
Grand Av		20	D13
1-265 & 2-272	5	20	D13
267-OUT & 274-OUT	38	20	D14
Grand St	11	19	D11
Grand St Ext	11	19	E12
Granite St	7	21	G13
Grant Av	8	21	H13
Grant Sq	16	20	E14
Granville Payne Av (Penn Av)	7	21	G14
Grattan St		19	F12
1-46	6	19	F12
47-OUT	37	19	F12
Gravesend Neck Rd		24	E18
1-1044	23	24	D18
1045-OUT	29	24	E18
Green St	22	19	E10
Greene Av		20	D13
1-353 & 2-346	38	20	D13
355-599 & 348-598	16	20	E13
600-1282	21	20	E13
1283-OUT	37	19	F12
Greenpoint Av	22	19	E11
Greenwood Av	18	20	D15
Grove Pl	1	20	C13
Grove St		21	F13
1-210	21	21	F13
211-1599	37	19	F12
Guernsey St	22	19	E11
Guider Av	35	24	D19
Gunnison Ct	35	24	E19
Gunther Pl	33	21	F14

H

STREET NAME AND HOUSE NUMBERS	ZONE NO.	MAP NO.	MAP GRID
Hale Av	8	21	H13
Hall St	5	20	D13
Halleck St	31	20	B14
Halsey St		20	E13
1-361 & 2-400	16	21	E13
363-971 & 402-970	33	21	F13
973-1205 & 972-1262	7	21	F13
1207-OUT & 1264-OUT	37	21	G13
Hamilton Av		20	B13
1-406	31	20	B13
407-OUT	32	20	C14
Hamilton Pl	15	20	C14
Hamilton Wk	9	22	A17
Hampton Av	35	24	E19
Hampton Pl	13	20	E14
Hancock St		21	E13
1-439 & 2-432	16	21	E13
441-969 & 434-970	33	21	F13
971-1298	21	21	F13
1299-1599	37	21	G13
Hanover Pl	1	20	C13

STREET NAME AND HOUSE NUMBERS	ZONE NO.	MAP NO.	MAP GRID
Hanson Pl		20	D13
1-only	43	20	D13
2-OUT	17	20	D13
Harbor Ct	9	22	A17
Harbor La	9	22	A16
Harbor View Ter	9	22	A16
Harden St	34	23	F17
Haring St		24	E18
1-2399	29	24	E18
2400-OUT	35	24	E18
Harkness Av	35	25	F18
Harman St		21	F13
1-190	21	21	F13
191-OUT	37	19	F12
Harover Ct *(off Rodman St)	24	24	D19
Harrison Al *(off Evans St)	1	19	C12
Harrison Av		19	E12
1-77	11	19	E12
78-OUT	6	19	E12
Harrison Pl		19	F12
1-41	6	19	E12
42-OUT	37	19	F12
Hart Pl	24	24	C19
Hart St		20	E13
1-395 & 2-412	6	20	E13
397-739 & 414-738	21	19	F12
740-OUT	37	19	F12
Harway Av	14	24	C18
Harwood Pl	3	23	F16
Hastings St	35	24	E19
Hattie Jones Ct	13	20	E13
Hausman St	22	19	E11
Havemeyer St	11	19	D12
Havens Pl	33	21	G14
Hawthorne St		20	E15
1-400	25	20	E15
401-OUT	3	20	E15
Hazel Ct	29	25	F18
Heath Pl	7	21	G13
Hefferman Sq	19	20	C15
Hegeman Av		21	G15
1-330	12	21	G15
331-850	7	21	H14
851-OUT	8	21	H14
Hemlock St	8	21	H13
Henderson Wk	24	24	D19
Hendrickson Pl	34	23	F17
Hendrickson St	34	23	F17
Hendrix St	7	21	H14
Henry St		20	C13
1-425 & 2-422	1	19	C12
427-OUT & 424-OUT	31	20	C13
Herbert St	22	19	E11
Herkimer Ct	16	20	E13
Herkimer Pl	16	20	E13
Herkimer St		20	E13
1-364	16	20	E13
365-699	13	21	E13
700-1518	33	21	F14
1519-OUT	7	21	G14
Herzl St	12	21	F15
Hewes St	11	19	D12
Heyward St		19	D12
1-75 & 2-60	11	19	D12
77-OUT & 62-OUT	6	19	E12
Hicks St		19	C12
1-449 & 2-434	1	19	C12
451-OUT & 436-OUT	31	20	B14
High St	1	19	C12
Highland Av	24	24	B19
Highland Blvd	7	21	G13
Highland Pl	8	21	H13
Highland View Av	24	24	C19
Highlawn Av	23	24	C18
Hill St	8	21	H13
Hillel Pl	10	22	E16
Himrod St		19	F12
1-180	21	19	F12
181-OUT	37	19	F12
Hinckley Pl	18	20	D15
Hinsdale St	7	21	G14
Holly St	8	21	H14
Holmes La	36	23	G16
Homecrest Av		24	D18
1-2399	29	24	D18
2400-OUT	35	24	E18
Homecrest Ct	23	24	D18
Hooper St	11	19	D12
Hope St	11	19	E12
Hopkins St	6	19	E12
Hopkinson Av (Thomas S. Boyland St)		21	F14
1-401 & 2-418	33	21	F14
403-1049 & 420-1048	12	21	F14
1050-OUT	36	21	G15
Horace Ct	18	20	D15
Hornell Loop	39	21	H15
Howard Al	1	19	C12
Howard Av		21	F13
1-79 & 2-76	21	21	F13
81-569 & 78-570	33	21	F13
571-OUT	12	21	F14
Howard Pl	15	20	C15
Hoyt St		20	C13
1-89	1	20	C13
90-286	17	20	C13
287-OUT	31	20	C13
Hoyt's La	36	21	G15
Hubbard Pl	10	22	E16
Hubbard St	35	24	D19
Hudson Av	1	19	C12
Hudson Wk *(Raymond V Ingersoll Houses)	1	20	C13
Hull St	33	21	F13
Humboldt St		19	E12
1-290	6	19	E12
291-477 & 292-488	11	19	E12
479-OUT & 490-OUT	22	19	E11
Hunter Av	14	24	C18
Hunterfly Pl	33	21	F14
Huntington St	31	20	B14
Hunt's La	1	20	C13
Huron St	22	19	D11
Hutchinson Ct	23	24	D18
Hyman Ct	29	25	F18

I

STREET NAME AND HOUSE NUMBERS	ZONE NO.	MAP NO.	MAP GRID
Imlay St	31	20	B13
Independence Av	28	24	B18
India St	22	19	D11
Indiana Pl	34	23	G17
Ingraham St		19	F12
1-56	6	19	F12
57-OUT	37	19	F12
Interborough Pkwy	7	21	G13
Interstate Hwy 278 (Brooklyn-Queens Expwy)		19	C12
Ira Ct	29	25	F18
Irving Av	37	19	F12
Irving Pl	38	20	D13
Irving St	31	20	B13
Irvington Pl	30	22	D16
Irwin St	35	24	E19
Ivan Ct	29	25	F18
Ivy Hill Rd	11	19	F11

J

STREET NAME AND HOUSE NUMBERS	ZONE NO.	MAP NO.	MAP GRID
Jackie Robinson Pkwy	7	21	G13
Jackson Ct	9	22	A17
Jackson Pl	15	20	C14
Jackson St	11	19	E11
Jaffray St	35	24	E19
Jamaica Av		21	G13
1-422	7	21	G13
443-1004	8	21	H13
Jardine Pl	33	21	G14
Java St	22	19	E11
Jay St	1	20	C13
Jefferson Av		21	E13
1-35	38	21	E13
36-344	16	21	E13
345-1366	21	21	F13
1367-OUT	37	19	G12
Jefferson House *(off Surf Av)	24	24	B19
Jefferson St		19	E12
1-227	6	19	E12
228-OUT	37	19	F12
Jerome Av		24	E18
1-35	8	24	E18
36-3399	35	24	E18
Jerome St	7	21	H14
Jewel St	22	19	E11
Jewell McKoy La	13	21	F13
Jewell Sq	7	21	G14
Jodie Ct	3	21	F15
John Barry Blvd	35	24	E19
John St	1	19	C12
Johnson Av		19	E12
1-405	6	19	E12
406-OUT	37	19	F12
Johnson Pl	26	20	E15
Johnson St	1	20	C13
Jones Wk	24	24	D19
Joralemon St	1	20	C13
Joval Ct	29	25	F18
Judge St	11	19	E12
Juliana Pl	11	19	D12
Junius St	12	21	G14
Just Ct	29	25	F18

K

STREET NAME AND HOUSE NUMBERS	ZONE NO.	MAP NO.	MAP GRID
Kane Pl	33	21	F14
Kane St	31	20	B13
Kansas Pl	34	23	G17
Karweg Pl	8	21	H13
Kathleen Pl	35	24	D18
Kaufman Pl	36	23	G16
Kay Ct	29	25	F18
Keap St	11	19	D12
Keen Ct	29	25	F18
Kenilworth Pl	10	22	E16
Kenmore Ct *(off Voorhies Av)	35	24	E18
Kenmore Pl	26	20	D15
Kenmore Ter	26	20	D15
Kensington St	35	24	E19
Kensington Wk	24	24	C19
Kent Av		19	D11
1-760	11	19	D12
761-OUT	5	20	D13
Kent St	22	19	E11
Kermit Pl	18	20	D15
Kiely Pl	8	21	H13
Kimball St	34	23	F17
King St	31	20	B13
Kings Hwy		22	C17
1-124	14	22	C17
125-1099	23	22	D17
1100-3099	29	22	E17
3100-5301	34	22	E17
5302-5999	3	21	F15
6000-OUT	12	21	F15
Kings Pl	23	24	D18
Kingsborough 1st Wk *(Kingsborough Houses)	33	21	F14
Kingsborough 2nd Wk *(Kingsborough Houses)	33	21	F14
Kingsborough 3rd Wk *(Kingsborough Houses)	33	21	F14
Kingsborough 4th Wk *(Kingsborough Houses)	33	21	F14
Kingsborough 5th Wk *(Kingsborough Houses)	33	21	F14
Kingsborough 6th Wk *(Kingsborough Houses)	33	21	F14
Kingsborough 7th Wk *(Kingsborough Houses)	33	21	F14
Kingsland Av		19	E11
1-83 & 2-76	11	19	E11
85-OUT & 78-OUT	22	19	E11
Kingston Av		20	E14
1-383 & 2-376	13	20	E14
385-541 & 378-540	25	20	E14
542-OUT	3	20	E15
Kingsway Pl	34	23	F16
Knapp St		25	F18
1-2399	29	25	F18
2400-OUT	35	25	F18
Knickerbocker Av		19	F12
1-518	37	19	F12
519-761	21	21	F13
762-OUT	7	21	G13
Knight Ct	29	25	F18
Kosciusko St		20	E13
1-87 & 2-90	5	20	E13
89-229 & 92-230	16	20	E13
231-OUT	21	20	E13
Kossuth Pl	21	21	F13
Krier Pl	36	21	G15

L

STREET NAME AND HOUSE NUMBERS	ZONE NO.	MAP NO.	MAP GRID
Lacon Ct	29	25	F18
Lady Moody Sq	23	24	D18
Lafayette Av		20	D13
1-129 & 2-118	17	20	D13
131-449 & 120-448	38	20	D13
451-573 & 450-586	5	20	E13
575-695 & 588-698	16	20	E13
697-OUT & 700-OUT	21	20	E13
Lafayette St *(off Debevoise Pl)	1	20	C13
Lafayette Wk	9	22	A17
Lake Pl	23	24	D18
Lake St	23	24	D18
Lama Ct *(at W 5th St off Avenue V)	23	24	D18
Lamont Ct	25	20	E14
Lancaster Av	23	24	D18
Landis Ct	29	25	F18
Langham St	35	24	E19
Laurel Av	24	24	B19
Lawn Ct	35	24	E19
Lawrence Av	30	22	D16
Lawrence St	1	20	C13
Lawton St	21	19	F13
Lee Av		19	D12
1-199 & 2-196	11	19	D12
201-OUT & 198-OUT	6	19	E12
Lefferts Av		20	E14
1-557 & 2-554	25	21	E14
559-883 & 556-884	3	21	E14
885-OUT	13	21	F14
Lefferts Pl	38	20	D13
Legion St	12	21	F14
Leif Ericson Dr		22	A16
Leiv Eiriksson Sq	20	22	B16
Lenox Rd		21	E15
1-374	26	21	E15
375-950	3	21	E15
951-OUT	12	21	F15
Leonard St		19	E12
1-210	6	19	E12
211-401 & 212-394	11	19	E12
403-OUT & 396-OUT	22	19	E11
Lester Ct	29	25	F18
Lewis Av		20	E13
1-115 & 2-120	6	20	E13
117-331 & 122-334	21	20	E13
333-OUT & 336-OUT	33	20	E13
Lewis Pl	18	20	D15
Lexington Av		21	E13
1-125 & 2-116	38	21	D13
127-425 & 118-410	16	21	E13
427-OUT & 412-OUT	21	21	E13
Liberty Av		21	G14
1-175	12	21	G14
176-675	7	21	G14
676-1240	8	21	H13
Lieutenant Kenneth E Aimee Triangle	29	22	E17
Lincoln Av	8	21	H13
Lincoln Pl		20	D14
1-261 & 2-266	17	20	D14
263-571 & 268-560	38	20	D14
573-871 & 562-872	16	20	E14
873-1540	13	20	E14
1541-OUT	33	21	F14
Lincoln Rd	25	20	E14
Linda Ct	36	23	F15
Linden Blvd		21	E15
1-335	26	21	E15
336-966	3	21	E15
967-1720	12	21	F15
1721-2250	7	21	H15
2251-OUT	8	21	H14
Linden St		19	F13
1-253	21	19	F13
254-OUT	37	19	F12
Linwood St	8	21	H13
Little Nassau St	5	19	D12
Little St	1	19	C12
Livingston Plz	1	20	C13
Livingston St		20	C13
1-251 & 2-270	1	20	C13
253-OUT & 272-OUT	17	20	C13
Livonia Av		21	F14
1-450	12	21	F14
451-OUT	7	21	G14
Lloyd Ct	23	24	D18
Lloyd St	26	20	E15
Locust Av	30	22	D17
Locust St	6	19	E12
Logan St	8	21	H14
Lois Av	29	25	F18
Lombardy St	22	19	E11
Lorimer St		19	E12
1-480	6	19	E12
481-740	11	19	E11
741-OUT	22	19	E12
Loring Av	8	21	H14
Lorraine St	31	20	B14
Losee Ter	35	24	E19
Lott Av	12	21	G15
Lott Pl	34	22	E17
Lott St	26	20	E15
Lotts La	18	22	C16
Louis Pl	33	21	F14
Louisa St	18	20	C15
Louise Ter	9	22	A16
Louisiana Av		21	G15
1-599	7	21	G15
600-OUT	39	21	H15
Love La	1	19	C12
Lowe Sq	12	21	F14
Ludlam Pl	25	20	E14
Luquer St	31	20	B13
Lyme Av	24	24	B19
Lynch St		19	D12
1-17	11	19	D12
18-OUT	6	19	E12

M

STREET NAME AND HOUSE NUMBERS	ZONE NO.	MAP NO.	MAP GRID
MacDougal St	33	21	F13
Mackay Pl	9	22	A16
Mackenzie St	35	24	E19
Macon St		20	E13
1-339 & 2-320	16	21	E13
341-OUT & 322-OUT	33	21	F13
Madeline Ct	20	22	A16
Madison Pl	29	22	E17
Madison St		20	E13
1-76	38	20	D13
77-350	16	20	E13
351-1300	21	20	E13
1301-OUT	37	19	G12
Madoc Av	29	25	F18
Main St	1	19	C12
Malbone St	25	20	E14
Malcolm X Blvd		21	F13
1-222	21	21	F13
233-374	33	21	F13
Malta St	7	21	G14
Manhattan Av		19	E12
1-231 & 2-240	6	19	E12
233-409 & 242-414	11	19	E12
411-1299 & 416-1298	22	19	E11
Manhattan Av (Sea Gate)	24	24	B19
Manhattan Ct		24	D18
1-59	23	24	D18
60-OUT	35	24	D18
Manor Ct	35	24	D18
Mansfield Pl (E 24th)		22	E17
1-1551	10	24	E17
1552-2399	29	24	E18
2400-OUT	35	24	E18
Maple Av	24	24	B19
Maple St		20	E14
1-548	25	20	E15
549-OUT	3	20	E14
Marconi Pl	33	21	F14
Marcus Garvey Blvd		20	E13
1-153	6	19	E12
166-383	21	20	E13
383-467	16	20	E13
Marcy Av		19	D12
1-331 & 2-344	11	19	D12
333-665 & 346-664	6	19	E12
666-OUT	16	20	E13
Marginal St	32	20	B15
Marginal St E	7	21	G13
Marginal St W	7	21	G13
Marine Av	9	22	A17
Marine Pkwy	34	22	E17
Marion St	33	21	F13
Marlborough Ct *(off Foster Av)	33	22	D16
Marlborough Rd	26	20	D15
Marshall St	1	19	C12
Martense Ct	26	20	D15
Martense St	26	20	E15
Martin Luther King Jr. Pl	6	19	E12
Maspeth Av	11	19	E11
Mater Ct *(off Brighton Beach Av)	35	24	E19
Matthews Ct	18	20	D15
Matthews Pl	36	23	G16
Maujer St	6	19	E12
Mayfair Dr N	34	23	G17
Mayfair Dr S	34	23	G17
McClancy Pl	7	21	H14
McDonald Av		22	D16
1-953	18	22	D16
954-1799	30	22	D17
1800-OUT	23	24	D18
McDonough St		21	E13
1-209 & 2-220	16	21	E13
211-OUT & 222-OUT	33	21	F13
McGuinness Blvd	22	19	E11
McGuinness Blvd S	22	19	E11
McKeever Pl	25	20	D14
McKenny St *(off Vine St)	1	19	C12
McKibbin St	6	19	E12
McKinley Av	8	21	H13
Meadow St		19	E12
1-80	6	19	E12
81-OUT	37	19	F12
Meeker Av		19	E11
1-390	11	19	E11
391-OUT	22	19	E11
Melba Ct	29	25	F18
Melrose St		19	E12
1-285 & 2-300	6	19	E12
287-OUT & 302-OUT	37	19	F12
Menahan St		21	F13
1-170	21	21	F13
171-OUT	37	19	F12
Merceine St *(off Front St)	1	19	C12
Merit Ct	29	25	F18
Mermaid Av	24	24	C19
Mesereau Ct *(off Emmons Av)	35	24	E18
Meserole Av	22	19	E11
Meserole St		19	E12
1-377 & 2-392	6	19	E12
379-OUT & 394-OUT	37	19	F12
Metropolitan Av		19	D11
1-1125	11	19	D11
1126-4599	37	19	F11
Miami Ct	25	20	E14
Micieli Pl	18	20	C15
Middagh St	1	19	C12
Middleton St	6	19	E12
Midwood St		21	E15
1-545	25	21	E15
546-OUT	3	20	E14
Milford St	8	21	H14
Mill Av	34	23	F17
Mill Basin	34	23	G17
Mill La	34	23	F17
Mill Rd	14	24	C18
Mill St	31	20	B14
Miller Av	7	21	G13
Miller Pl	7	21	G13
Milton St	22	19	D11
Minna St	18	20	C15
Moffat St		21	G13
1-283 & 2-290	7	21	G13
285-OUT & 292-OUT	37	21	G13
Monaco Pl	33	21	G14
Monitor St	22	19	E11
Monroe Pl	1	20	C13
Monroe St		20	E13
1-63 & 2-68	38	20	D13
65-337 & 70-354	16	20	E13
339-OUT & 356-OUT	21	20	E13
Montague St	1	20	C13
Montague Ter	1	20	C13
Montana Pl	34	23	G17
Montauk Av	8	21	H14
Montauk Ct	35	24	D19
Montgomery Pl	15	20	D14
Montgomery St		21	E14
1-668	25	21	E14
669-OUT	13	21	E14
Montieth St	6	19	E12
Montrose Av	6	19	E12
Monument Wk *(Raymond V Ingersoll Houses)	5	19	C12
Moore Pl	29	22	E17
Moore St	6	19	E12
Morgan Av		19	F12
1-265 & 2-272	37	19	F12
267-423 & 274-418	11	19	E12
425-OUT & 420-OUT	22	19	E11
Morgan St	22	19	E11
Morton St	11	19	D12
Mother Gaston Blvd		21	G14
0-228	33	21	G14
231-OUT	12	21	G14
Moultrie St	22	19	E11
Murdock Ct	23	24	D19
Myrtle Av		20	C13
1-278	1	20	C13
279-751 & 280-754	5	20	D13
753-1173 & 756-1132	6	20	E13
1175-1373 & 1134-1350	21	19	F12
1375-5399 & 1352-5398	37	19	F12
Myrtle La	34	23	G16

N

STREET NAME AND HOUSE NUMBERS	ZONE NO.	MAP NO.	MAP GRID
Narrows Av		22	A17
1-6899	20	22	A16
6900-OUT	9	22	A17
Nassau Av	22	19	E11
Nassau St	1	19	C12

STREET NAME AND HOUSE NUMBERS	ZONE NO.	MAP NO.	MAP GRID
National Dr	34	23	G17
Nautilus Av	24	24	B19
Navy St	1	20	C13
Navy Wk *(Raymond V Ingersoll Houses)	1	20	C13
Nelson St	31	20	B14
Neptune Av		24	C19
1-389 & 2-396	35	24	D19
391-OUT & 398 out	24	24	D19
Neptune Ct *(off W End Av)	35	24	E19
Neptune Ter *(off Neptune Av)	24	24	D19
Nevins St		20	C13
1-303 & 2-298	17	20	C13
305-OUT & 300-OUT	15	20	C14
New Dock St	1	19	C12
New Jersey Av	7	21	G14
New Lots Av		21	G14
1-160	12	21	G15
161-760	7	21	G14
761-OUT	8	21	H14
New Utrecht Av		22	C17
1-6899	19	22	C16
6900-7299	28	22	C17
7300-7499	4	22	C17
7500-OUT	14	22	C17
New York Av		20	E14
1-298	16	20	E14
299-392	13	20	E14
393-584	25	20	E14
585-1400	3	20	E15
1401-2199	10	22	E16
2200-OUT	34	22	E17
Newel St	22	19	E11
Newkirk Av		22	D16
1-1399	30	22	D16
1400-3299	26	22	E16
3300-OUT	3	22	E16
Newkirk Av Plz *(off Newkirk Av)	26	22	D16
Newport St		21	G15
1-400	12	21	G15
401-OUT	7	21	G14
Newton St	22	19	E11
Nichols Av	8	21	H13
Nixon Ct	23	24	D19
Noble St	22	19	D11
Noel Av	29	25	F18
Nolans La	36	21	G15
Noll St		19	E12
1-158	6	19	E12
159-OUT	37	19	F12
Norfolk St	35	24	E19
Norman Av	22	19	E11
Norman Pl	7	21	G13
North Conduit Av	8	21	J14
North Elliot Pl	5	19	D12
North Elliot Wk *(Walt Whitman Houses)	5	20	D13
North Henry St	22	19	E11
North Oxford St	5	19	D12
North Oxford Wk *(Walt Whitman Houses)	5	20	D13
North Portland Av	5	20	D13
North 1st St	11	19	D11
North 2nd St	11	19	D11
North 3rd St	11	19	D11
North 4th St	11	19	D11
North 5th St	11	19	D11
North 6th St	11	19	D11
North 7th St	11	19	D11
North 8th St	11	19	D11
North 9th St	11	19	D11
North 10th St	11	19	D11
North 11th St	11	19	D11
North 12th St	11	19	D11
North 13th St	11	19	D11
North 14th St	11	19	D11
North 15th St	22	19	D11
Norwood Av	8	21	H13
Nostrand Av		20	E13
1-135 (odd only)	6	19	E12
137-259 & 2-290	5	20	E13
261-791 & 292-832	16	20	E13
793-1261 & 834-1268	25	20	E14
1263-1925 & 1270-1926	26	20	E15
1927-2799 & 1928-2802	10	22	E16
2801-3693 & 2804-3694	29	22	E17
3695-OUT	35	24	E18
Nova Ct	29	25	F18

O

STREET NAME AND HOUSE NUMBERS	ZONE NO.	MAP NO.	MAP GRID
Oak St	22	19	D11
Oakland Pl	26	20	E15
O'Brien Pl	8	21	H13
Ocean Av		22	D15
1-325	25	22	D15
326-1060	26	22	D15
1061-2099	30	22	E17
2100-2812	29	24	E18
2813-OUT	35	24	E19
Ocean Beachside Ct *(off Brighton Beach Av)	35	24	E19
Ocean Ct		24	D18
1-51	23	24	D18
52-OUT	35	24	D18
Ocean Pkwy		22	D16
1-619 & 2-630	18	22	D16
621-1599 & 632-1608	30	22	D17
1601-2399 & 1610-2398	23	24	D18
2400-OUT	35	24	D19
Ocean View Av		24	B19
1-3799	35	24	D19
3800-OUT	24	24	B19
Oceanic Av	24	24	B19
Ohio Wk	34	23	G17
Old Fulton St *(Cadman Plz W bet Furman St and Henry St)	1	19	C12
Old Mill Rd	8	21	H14
Old New Utrecht Rd		22	C16
1-4099	18	22	C16
4100-OUT	4	22	C16
Olean St	10	22	E17
Olive St	11	19	E12
Oliver St	9	22	A17
Opal Ct	29	25	F18
Orange St	1	19	C12
Orient Av	11	19	E11
Oriental Blvd	35	24	E19
Oriental Ct *(off W End Av)	35	24	E19
Osborn St	12	21	G14
Otsego St	31	20	B14
Overbaugh Pl	10	22	E16
Ovington Av		22	A16
1-699	9	22	B16
700-899	28	22	B16
900-OUT	19	22	B16
Ovington Ct	4	22	C17
Owls Head Ct	20	22	A16
Oxford St	35	24	E19

P

STREET NAME AND HOUSE NUMBERS	ZONE NO.	MAP NO.	MAP GRID
Pacific St		20	C13
1-331	1	20	C13
333-777 & 332-736	17	20	C13
779-1145 & 738-1120	38	20	D13
1147-1503 & 1122-1460	16	20	E14
1505-1795 & 1462-1750	13	20	E14
1797-OUT & 1752-OUT	33	21	F14
Paerdegat Av N	36	23	G16
Paerdegat Av S	34	23	F16
Paerdegat 1st St	36	23	F16
Paerdegat 2nd St	36	23	G16
Paerdegat 3rd St	36	23	G16
Paerdegat 4th St	36	23	G16
Paerdegat 5th St	36	23	G16
Paerdegat 6th St	36	23	G16
Paerdegat 7th St	36	23	G16
Paerdegat 8th St	36	23	G16
Paerdegat 9th St	36	23	G16
Paerdegat 10th St	36	23	G16
Paerdegat 11th St	36	23	G16
Paerdegat 12th St	36	23	G16
Paerdegat 13th St	36	23	G16
Paerdegat 14th St	36	23	G16
Paerdegat 15th St	36	23	G16
Paidge Av	22	19	E10
Palm Ct	25	20	E14
Palmetto St		21	F13
1-280	21	21	F13
281-OUT	37	19	F12
Parade Pl	26	20	D15
Park Av		19	E12
1-45	1	19	D12
47-569 & 46-560	5	19	D12
571-OUT & 562-OUT	6	19	E12
Park Cir	18	20	D15
Park Pl		20	D14
1-159 & 2-168	17	20	D14
161-637 & 170-638	38	20	D14
639-912	16	20	E14
913-1570	13	20	E14
1571-OUT	33	21	F14
Park St	6	19	E12
Parkes Cadman Plz	1	19	C12
Parkside Av	26	20	D15
Parkside Ct	26	20	D15
Parkville Av	30	22	D16
Parkway Ct		24	D18
1-41	23	24	D18
42-OUT	35	24	D18
Parrott Pl	28	22	B17
Patchen Av		21	F13
1-179 & 2-176	21	21	F13
181-OUT & 178-OUT	33	21	F13
Pearl St	1	20	C13
Pearson St	34	23	F17
Pembroke St	35	24	E19
Penn St	11	19	D12
Pennsylvania Av		21	G14
1-1140	7	21	G14
1141-OUT	39	21	H15
Percival St	31	20	B14
Peri La	34	23	G16
Perry Av	35	24	E19
Perry Pl	16	20	E13
Perry Ter	9	22	A16
Perry Wk	35	24	E19
Pierrepont Pl	1	20	C13
Pierrepont Plz	1	19	C13
Pierrepont St	1	20	C13
Pilling St	7	21	G13
Pine St	8	21	H13
Pineapple St	1	19	C12
Pioneer St	31	20	B13
Pitkin Av		21	G14
1-1454	33	21	F14
1455-1900	12	21	F14
1901-2385	7	21	G14
2386-2999	8	21	H14
Plaza St E	38	20	D14
Plaza St W	17	20	D14
Pleasant Pl	33	21	G14
Plumb Beach Av	29	25	F18
Plumb 1st St	29	25	F18
Plumb 2nd St	29	25	F18
Plumb 3rd St	35	25	F18
Plymouth St	1	19	C12
Poe Pl	6	19	E12
Polar St	24	24	B19
Polhemus Pl	15	20	D14
Poly Pl	9	22	B17
Poole La	35	24	E19
Pope John Paul II Sq *(sec of Humboldt St bet Driggs Av to Broome St)	22	19	E11
Poplar Av	24	24	B19
Poplar St	1	19	C12
Portal St	33	21	F14
Porter Av		19	E11
1-226	37	19	F12
227-OUT	22	19	E11
Post Ct	29	25	F18
Powell St	12	21	G14
Powers St	11	19	E12
Prescott Pl	33	21	F14
President St		20	B13
1-436	31	20	C13
437-969 & 438-958	15	20	C14
971-1261 & 960-1262	25	20	D14
1263-OUT	13	20	E14
Preston Ct		23	F16
1-7999	34	23	F16
8000-OUT	36	21	F15
Prince St	1	20	C13
Prospect Av		20	D15
1-618	15	20	C14
619-OUT	18	20	D15
Prospect Expwy		20	C14
Prospect Park SW		20	D15
1-78	15	20	D15
79-OUT	18	20	D15
Prospect Park W	15	20	C15
Prospect Pl		20	D13
141-605 & 152-604	38	20	D14
606-878	16	20	E14
879-1546	13	20	E14
1547-OUT	33	21	F14
Prospect St	1	19	C12
Provost St	22	19	E11
Pulaski St		20	E13
1-409 & 2-420	6	20	E13
411-OUT & 422-OUT	21	20	E13
Putnam Av		20	E13
1-129	38	20	D13
153-423 & 130-422	16	20	E13
424-1396	21	21	F13
1397-1599	37	11	G12

Q

STREET NAME AND HOUSE NUMBERS	ZONE NO.	MAP NO.	MAP GRID
Quay St	22	19	D11
Quentin Rd		22	D17
1-1099	23	22	D17
1100-3008	29	22	E17
3009-OUT	34	22	E17
Quentin St	35	25	F19
Quincy St		20	E13
1-106	38	20	D13
107-396	16	20	E13
397-OUT	21	20	E13

R

STREET NAME AND HOUSE NUMBERS	ZONE NO.	MAP NO.	MAP GRID
Rabbi Joel Teitelbaum Pl	11	19	D12
Radde Pl	33	21	F14
Raleigh Pl	26	20	E15
Ralph Av		21	F13
1-127	21	21	F13
128-625	33	21	F14
626-757	12	21	F14
759-1853 & 758-1864	36	23	F16
1855-OUT & 1866-OUT	34	23	F17
Randolph St	37	19	F12
Rapelye St	31	20	B13
Red Cross Pl	1	19	C12
Red Hook La	1	20	C13
Reed St	31	20	B14
Reeve Pl	18	20	D15
Regent Pl	26	20	D15
Remsen Av		21	F15
1-479	12	21	F15
480-OUT	36	21	F15
Remsen St	1	20	C13
Revere Pl	13	20	E14
Rewe St	11	19	F11
Richards St	31	20	B14
Richardson St		19	E11
1-153 & 2-160	11	19	E11
155-OUT & 162-OUT	22	19	E11
Richmond St	8	21	H13
Ridge Blvd		22	A16
1-6899	20	22	A16
6900-OUT	9	22	A16
Ridge Ct	9	22	A16
Ridgecrest Ter	9	22	A16
Ridgewood Av		21	H13
1-72	7	21	H13
73-600	8	21	H13
Ridgewood Pl	27	19	F12
Riegelmann Boardwalk	24	24	C19
River St	11	19	D11
Riverdale Av		21	F14
1-425	12	21	F14
426-OUT	7	21	G14
Robert Pl	7	21	G13
Robert St	7	21	G13
Rochester Av		21	F14
1-127	33	21	F14
128-OUT	13	21	F14
Rock St	6	19	F12
Rockaway Av		21	G14
1-325	33	21	G14
326-1021	12	21	G14
1022-OUT	36	21	G15
Rockaway Pkwy		21	F14
1-601	12	21	F14
602-OUT	36	21	G15
Rockwell Pl	17	20	D13
Roder Av	30	22	D17
Rodney St	11	19	D12
Roebling St	11	19	D12
Rogers Av		20	E14
1-199 & 2-176	16	20	E14
201-633 & 178-634	25	20	E14
635-1280	26	20	E15
1281-OUT	10	22	E16
Roosevelt Ct *(off 30th St)	32	20	B15
Roosevelt Pl	33	21	F14
Rose St	36	21	G15
Ross St	11	19	D12
Rost Pl	36	23	G16
Royce Pl	34	23	G16
Royce St	34	23	G16
Rubins La *(off Sea Breeze Av)	24	24	D19
Ruby St	8	21	J14
Rugby Rd		22	D16
1-530	26	22	D15
531-OUT	30	22	D16
Russell St	22	19	E11
Rutherford Pl	14	24	B18
Rutland Rd		20	E15
1-400	25	20	E15
401-914	3	20	E15
915-OUT	12	21	F14
Rutledge St	11	19	D12
Ryder Av	30	22	D17
Ryder St	34	23	F17
Ryerson St	5	20	D13

S

STREET NAME AND HOUSE NUMBERS	ZONE NO.	MAP NO.	MAP GRID
Sackett St		20	C13
1-516	31	20	C13
517-OUT	17	20	C13
Sackman St		21	G14
1-160	33	21	G14
161-OUT	12	21	G14
St. Andrews Pl	16	20	E13
St. Charles Pl	16	20	E14
St. Edward's St		20	D13
1-125	5	20	D13
126-OUT	1	20	D13
St. Felix St	17	20	D13
St. Francis Pl	16	20	E14
St. James Pl		20	D13
1-50	5	20	D13
51-OUT	38	20	D13
St. Johns Pl		20	D14
1-267	17	20	D14
269-621 & 268-624	38	20	D14
623-925 & 626-924	16	20	E14
927-1571 & 926-1588	13	20	E14
1573-OUT & 1590-OUT	33	21	F14
St. Jude Pl	36	23	H16
St. Mark's Av		20	C13
1-135 & 2-144	17	20	C13
137-537 & 146-552	38	20	D14
539-759 & 554-778	16	20	E14
761-1315 & 780-1316	13	20	E14
1317-OUT	33	21	F14
St. Mark's Pl	17	20	C13
St. Nicholas Av	37	19	F12
St. Paul's Ct	26	20	D15
St. Paul's Pl	26	20	D15
Sandford St	5	20	E13
Sands St	1	19	C12
Sapphire St	8	21	J14
Saratoga Av		21	F14
1-475	33	21	F14
476-OUT	12	21	F14
Schaefer St		21	G13
1-259 & 2-256	7	21	G13
261-OUT & 258-OUT	37	21	G13
Schenck Av	7	21	H14
Schenck Ct	7	21	G13
Schenck Pl	36	21	G16
Schenck St	36	23	H16
Schenectady Av		21	F14
1-430	13	21	F14
431-1529	3	21	F15
1530-OUT	34	23	F17
Schermerhorn St		20	C13
1-257 & 2-250	1	20	C13
259-OUT & 252-OUT	17	20	C13
Scholes St		19	E12
1-376	6	19	E12
377-OUT	37	19	F12
School La	36	21	G15
Schroeders Av	39	21	H15
Schweikerts Wk	24	24	C19
Scott Av		19	F12
1-215	37	19	F12
216-OUT	22	19	F11
Sea Breeze Av	24	24	D19
Sea Breeze Ct *(off W End Av)	35	24	E19
Sea Gate Av	24	24	B19
Sea Pl	24	24	C19
Seabreeze Wk	35	24	D19
Seabring St	31	20	B13
Seacoast Ter	35	24	E19
Seaview Av		23	G16
1 - 112-44	36	23	G16
112-45 -OUT	39	21	H15
Seaview Ct	36	23	H16
Seaview Loop	8	21	H15
Seba Av	29	25	F18
Sedgwick Pl	20	22	A16
Sedgwick St	31	20	B13
Seeley St	18	20	C15
Seigel St	6	19	E12
Senator St	20	22	A16
Seneca Av	37	19	F12
Seton Pl	30	22	D16
Sharon St	11	19	E11
Sheepshead Bay Rd		24	E18
1-999	24	24	D19
1000-1148 & 1001-1153	29	24	E18
1150-OUT & 1155-OUT	35	24	E18
Sheffield Av	7	21	G14
Shell Rd		24	D19
1-2819 & 2-2840	23	24	D19
2821-OUT & 2842-OUT	24	24	D19
Shepherd Av	8	21	H13
Sheridan Av	8	21	H14
Sherlock Pl	33	21	G14
Sherman St		20	D15
1-70	15	20	D15
71-OUT	18	20	D15
Shore Blvd	35	24	E19
Shore Ct	9	22	A17
Shore Pkwy (Leif Ericson Dr)		24	B18
1-1118	28	24	B18
1119-2341 & 1120-2318	14	24	C18
2343-2799 & 2320-2798	23	24	D19
2800-4000	35	24	E19
4001-5000	34	23	G17
5001-6999	36	23	H16
Shore Rd		22	A16
1-6899	20	22	A16
6900-OUT	9	22	A16
Shore Rd Ext		24	B18
1-1118	28	24	B18
1119-OUT	14	24	B18
Shore Road Dr	20	22	A16
Shore Road La	9	22	A16
Sidney Pl	1	20	C13
Siegel St	6	19	E12
Sigourney St	31	20	B14
Skidmore Av	36	23	G16
Skidmore La	36	23	G16
Skidmore Pl	36	23	G16
Skillman Av	11	19	E11
Skillman St	5	20	D13
Sloan Pl	23	24	D18
Slocum Pl	18	22	D16
Smith St		20	C14
1-223 & 2-220	1	20	C14
225-OUT & 222-OUT	31	20	C14
Smith's La	36	21	G15
Snediker Av	7	21	G14
Snyder Av		20	E15
1-3299	26	20	E15
3300-OUT	3	20	E15
Somers St	33	21	G13
South Conduit Av	17	21	J14
South Elliott Pl	17	20	D13
South Oxford St	17	20	D13
South Portland Av	17	20	D13
South 1st St	11	19	D11
South 2nd St	11	19	D12
South 3rd St	11	19	D12
South 4th St	11	19	D12
South 5th Pl	11	19	D12
South 5th St	11	19	D12
South 6th St	11	19	D12
South 7th St	11	19	D12
South 8th St	11	19	D12
South 9th St	11	19	D12
South 10th St	11	19	D12
South 11th St	11	19	D12
Southgate Ct	23	24	D18
Spencer Ct	5	20	E13
Spencer Pl	16	20	E13
Spencer St	5	20	E13
Stagg St		19	E12
1-376	6	19	E12
377-OUT	37	19	F12
Stagg Wk	6	19	F12
Stanhope St		19	F12
1-156	21	19	F12
157-OUT	37	19	F12
Stanley Av		21	G15
1-820	7	21	G15
821-OUT	8	21	H14
Stanton Rd	35	25	F19
Stanwix St	6	19	E12
Starr St		19	F12
1-50	21	19	F12
51-OUT	37	19	F12
State St		20	C13
1-309 & 2-334	1	20	C13
311-OUT & 336-OUT	17	20	C13
Stephen's Ct	26	22	E16

STREET NAME AND HOUSE NUMBERS	ZONE NO.	MAP NO.	MAP GRID
Sterling Pl		20	D14
1-159 & 2-184	17	20	D14
161-649 & 186-650	38	20	D14
651-940	16	20	E14
941-1603 & 942-1610	13	20	E14
1605-OUT & 1612-OUT	33	21	F14
Sterling St	25	20	E14
Steuben St	5	20	D13
Stewart Av		19	F12
1-227 & 2-234	37	19	F12
229-399 & 236-400	11	19	F11
401-6899	22	19	F11
6900-OUT	9	22	A17
Stewart St	7	21	G13
Stillwell Av		24	C19
1-1599	4	24	C17
1600-2649	23	24	C18
2650-OUT	24	24	C19
Stillwell's Pl	36	23	G16
Stockholm St		19	F12
1-160	21	19	F12
161-OUT	37	19	F12
Stockton St	6	19	E12
Stoddard Pl	25	20	E14
Stone Ave (Mother Gaston Blvd)		21	G14
1-230	33	21	G14
231-OUT	12	21	G14
Story Ct *(off Story St)	18	20	C15
Story St	18	20	C15
Stratford Rd	18	20	D16
Strauss St	12	21	F15
Strickland Av	34	23	F17
Strong Pl	31	20	C13
Stryker Ct	23	24	D18
Stryker St	23	24	D18
Stuart St	29	22	E17
Stuyvesant Av		21	F13
1-287 & 2-300	21	21	F13
289-OUT & 302-OUT	33	21	F13
Sullivan Pl	25	20	D14
Sullivan St	31	20	B13
Summit St	31	20	B13
Sumner Av (Marcus Garvey Blvd)		20	E13
1-165	6	20	E13
166-383	21	20	E13
384-OUT	16	20	E13
Sumner Pl	6	19	E12
Sumpter St	33	21	F13
Sunnyside Av	7	21	G13
Sunnyside Ct	7	21	G13
Sunset Ct	24	24	B19
Surf Av	24	24	B19
Sutter Av		21	H14
1-470	12	21	F14
471-950	7	21	G14
951-1599	8	21	H14
Sutton St	22	19	E11
Suydam Pl	33	21	F14
Suydam St		19	F12
1-200	21	19	F12
201-OUT	37	19	F12
Sylvan Ter *(off W 33rd St)	24	24	C19
T			
Taaffe Pl	5	20	D13
Tabor Ct *(off 13th Av)	19	22	B16
Tampa Ct	25	20	E14
Tapscott St	12	21	F14
Taylor St	11	19	D12
Tech Pl	1	20	C13
Tehama St	18	20	C15
Temple Ct	18	20	D15
Temple Sq	17	20	C13
Ten Eyck St		19	E12
1-375 & 2-382	6	19	E12
377-OUT & 384-OUT	37	19	F12
Ten Eyck Wk *(Williamsburg Housing)	6	19	F12
Tennis Ct	26	20	D15
Terrace Pl	18	20	C15
Thames St		19	F12
1-25 & 2-28	6	19	F12
27-OUT & 30-OUT	37	19	F12
Thatford Av	12	21	G14
Thatford St	12	21	G14
Thomas S Boyland St (Hopkinson Av)		21	F13
1 - 418	33	21	F13
444 - 1049	12	21	G15
Thomas St	22	19	F11
Thornton St	6	19	E12
Throop Av		20	E13
1-325 & 2-350	6	20	E13
327-543 & 352-574	21	20	E13
545-OUT & 576-OUT	16	20	E13
Tieman's La	36	21	G15
Tiffany Pl	31	20	B13
Tilden Av		20	E15
1-3299	26	20	E15
3300-OUT	3	20	E15
Tillary St	1	20	C13
Tompkins Av		20	E13
1-205 & 2-202	6	20	E13
207-OUT & 204-OUT	16	20	E13
Tompkins Pl	31	20	C13
Townsend St	22	19	F11
Troutman St		19	F12
1-215	6	19	F12
216-OUT	37	19	F12

STREET NAME AND HOUSE NUMBERS	ZONE NO.	MAP NO.	MAP GRID
Troy Av		20	E14
1-430	13	20	E14
431-1575	3	20	E15
1576-OUT	34	23	F16
Troy Pl	34	23	F16
Truckleman's La	36	21	G15
Truxton St	33	21	G13
Tudor Ter *(off W 37th St)	24	24	B19
Turnbull Av	36	21	G15
Turner Pl	18	20	D15
Twin Pines Dr	39	21	H15
U			
Underhill Av	38	20	D14
Union Av		19	E12
1-185 & 2-168	6	19	E12
187-OUT & 170-OUT	11	19	E12
Union St		20	B13
1-515 & 2-476	31	20	C13
517-971 & 478-922	15	20	C14
973-1325 & 924-1300	25	20	E14
1327-1901 & 1302-1850	13	20	E14
1903-1991 & 1852-1928	33	21	F14
1993-OUT & 1930-OUT	12	21	F14
Utica Av		21	F14
1-50	33	21	F14
51-440	13	21	F14
441-1460	3	21	F15
1461-OUT	34	23	F16
V			
Van Brunt St	31	20	B13
Van Buren St	21	20	E13
Van Dam St	22	19	E11
Van Dyke St	31	20	B14
Van Sicklen St	23	24	D18
Van Siclen Av		21	G13
1-1022	7	21	G13
1023-OUT	39	21	H15
Van Siclen Ct	7	21	G13
Van Sinderen Av	7	21	G14
Vandalia Av		21	H15
1-414	39	21	H15
415-OUT	8	21	H15
Vanderbilt Av		20	D13
1-331	5	20	D13
332-OUT	38	20	D14
Vanderbilt St	18	20	D15
Vanderveer Pl	26	20	E16
Vanderveer St	7	21	G13
Vandervoort Av		19	E11
1-405	11	19	E11
406-OUT	22	19	E11
Vandervoort Pl	37	19	F12
Varet St	6	19	E12
Varick Av		19	F12
1-258	37	19	F12
259-400	11	19	F11
401-OUT	22	19	E11
Varick St	22	19	E11
Varkens Hook Rd	36	23	G16
Verandah Pl	1	20	C13
Vermont Av	7	21	G13
Vermont Ct	7	21	G13
Vermont St	7	21	G14
Vernon Av		20	E13
1-399	6	20	E13
400-OUT	21	20	E13
Verona Pl	16	20	E13
Verona St	31	20	B13
Veronica Pl	26	20	E15
Veterans Av	34	23	F17
Victor Rd	3	22	E16
Village Ct	23	24	D18
Village Rd E	23	24	D18
Village Rd N	23	24	D18
Village Rd S	23	24	D18
Vine St	1	19	C12
Virginia Pl	13	20	E14
Visitation Pl	31	20	B13
Vista Pl	20	22	B16
Voorhies Av	35	24	E18
W			
Wakeman Pl	20	22	A16
Waldorf Ct	30	22	D16
Walker St	7	21	H15
Wallabout St		19	D12
1-97 & 2-148	11	19	D12
99-OUT & 150-OUT	6	19	E12
Wallaston Ct	4	22	C17
Walsh Ct	30	22	D16
Walton St	6	19	E12
Walworth St	5	20	D13
Warren Pl	1	20	B13
Warren St		20	C13
1-396	1	20	C13
397-OUT	17	20	C13
Warsoff Pl	5	19	E12
Warwick St	7	21	H14
Washington Av		20	D13
1-350	5	20	D13
351-811 & 352-860	38	20	D13
813-OUT & 862-OUT	25	20	D14
Washington Pk	5	20	D13
Washington Plz	11	19	D12
Washington St	1	19	C12
Washington Wk *(Walt Whitman Houses)	5	20	C13
Water St	1	19	C12

STREET NAME AND HOUSE NUMBERS	ZONE NO.	MAP NO.	MAP GRID
Waterbury St	6	19	E12
Watkins St	12	21	G14
Waverly Av		20	D13
1-335	5	20	D13
336-OUT	38	20	D13
Weber's Ct	35	24	E19
Weber's Ter	35	24	E19
Webster Av	30	22	D16
Webster Pl	15	20	C14
Weirfield St		21	F13
1-289	21	21	F13
290-OUT	37	11	G12
Weldon St	8	21	H13
Wellington Ct	30	22	D16
Wells St	8	21	H13
West Av	24	24	D19
West Brighton Av	24	24	D19
West End Av	35	24	E19
West St		19	D10
1-399	22	19	D10
400-OUT	23	24	D18
West 1st St		24	D17
1-1599	4	24	D17
1600-2699	23	24	D17
2700-OUT	24	24	D19
West 2nd Pl	24	24	D19
West 2nd St		24	D17
1-1599	4	24	D17
1600-2699	23	24	D18
2700-OUT	24	24	D19
West 3rd St		24	D17
1-1599	4	24	D17
1600-2699	23	24	D18
2700-OUT	24	24	D19
West 4th St		24	D17
1-1599	4	24	D17
1600-OUT	23	24	D18
West 5th St		24	D17
1-1600	4	24	D17
1601-2699	23	24	D18
2700-OUT	24	24	D19
West 6th St		24	D17
1-1599	4	24	D17
1600-2699	23	24	D18
2700-OUT	24	24	D19
West 7th St		24	D18
1-1600	4	24	C17
1601-OUT	23	24	D18
West 8th St		24	D18
1-1599	4	24	C17
1600-2699	23	24	D18
2700-OUT	24	24	D19
West 9th St		24	D18
1-213	31	20	B14
214-1599	4	24	C17
1600-OUT	23	24	D18
West 10th St		24	D18
1-1599	4	24	C17
1600-2699	23	24	C18
2700-OUT	24	24	D19
West 11th St		24	C18
1-1599	4	24	C17
1600-OUT	23	24	C18
West 12th St		24	C18
1-1599	4	24	C17
1600-2699	23	24	C18
2700-OUT	24	24	D19
West 13th St	23	24	C18
West 15th Pl	14	24	C19
West 15th St		24	C19
1-2659	14	24	C19
2660-OUT	24	24	C19
West 16th St		24	C19
1-2699	14	24	C19
2700-OUT	24	24	C19
West 17th St		24	C19
1-2699	14	24	C19
2700-OUT	24	24	C19
West 19th St		24	C19
1-2699	14	24	C19
2700-OUT	24	24	C19
West 20th St		24	C19
1-2699	14	24	C19
2700-OUT	24	24	C19
West 21st St		24	C19
1-2799	14	24	C19
2800-OUT	24	24	C19
West 22nd St		24	C19
1-2699	14	24	C19
2700-OUT	24	24	C19
West 23rd St	24	24	C19
West 24th St	24	24	C19
West 25th St	24	24	C19
West 26th St	24	24	C19
West 27th St	24	24	C19
West 28th St	24	24	C19
West 29th St	24	24	C19
West 30th St	24	24	C19
West 31st St	24	24	C19
West 32nd St	24	24	C19
West 33rd St	24	24	C19
West 34th St	24	24	C19
West 35th St	24	24	C19
West 36th St	24	24	C19
West 37th St	24	24	C19
Westbury Ct	25	20	D15
Westerly La	9	22	A16
Westminster Rd	18	22	D16
Wharton Pl	8	21	H13
Whipple St	6	19	E12
White St	6	19	E12
Whitman Dr	34	23	G17
Whitney Av	29	25	F18

STREET NAME AND HOUSE NUMBERS	ZONE NO.	MAP NO.	MAP GRID
Whitney Pl	23	24	D18
Whitty La	3	23	F16
Whitwell Pl	15	20	C14
Will Pl	7	21	G15
William J Hennesy Sq	35	24	D19
Williams Av	7	21	G14
Williams Ct	35	24	E18
Williams Pl	7	21	G14
Williamsburg Pl	11	19	D12
Williamsburg St E	11	19	D12
Williamsburg St W		19	D12
1-344	11	19	D12
345-OUT	5	19	D12
Willmohr St	12	21	F15
Willoughby Av		20	D13
1-438	5	20	D13
439-840	6	20	E13
841-1100	21	19	F12
1101-OUT	37	19	F12
Willoughby St	1	20	C13
Willow Pl	1	20	C13
Willow St	1	19	C12
Wilson Av		19	F12
1-333 & 2-318	37	19	F12
335-527 & 320-512	21	21	F13
529-OUT & 514-OUT	7	21	G13
Wilson St	11	19	D12
Windsor Pl		20	C14
1-254	15	20	C14
255-OUT	18	20	D15
Winthrop St		20	E15
1-370	25	20	E15
371-965	3	20	E15
966-OUT	12	21	F14
Withers St		19	E11
1-275 & 2-272	11	19	E11
277-OUT & 274-OUT	22	19	E11
Wogan Ter	9	22	A17
Wolcott St	31	20	B14
Wolf Pl	23	24	D18
Woodbine St		21	F13
1-280	21	21	F13
281-1599	37	19	F12
Woodhull St	31	20	B13
Woodpoint Rd	11	19	E11
Woodrow Ct *(off 30th St)	32	20	B15
Woodruff Av	26	20	D15
Woods Pl	26	20	E15
Woodside Av	23	22	D17
Wortman Av		21	G15
1-433	7	21	G14
434-OUT	8	21	H14
Wortman Dr	7	21	H15
Wyckoff Av	37	19	F12
Wyckoff St		20	C13
1-129 & 2-132	1	20	C13
131-OUT & 134-OUT	17	20	C13
Wyona St	7	21	G14
Wythe Av	11	19	D11
Wythe Pl	11	19	D12
Y			
York St	1	19	C12
NUMBERED STREETS			
1st Av		20	B15
1-5299	32	20	B15
5300-6899	20	20	B15
6900-OUT	9	22	A16
1st Ct	23	24	D18
1st Pl	31	20	C13
1st St *(Fort Hamilton Manor)	9	22	A17
1st St		20	C14
1-105	31	20	C14
106-OUT	15	20	C14
2nd Av		20	B15
1-216	15	20	C14
217-5299	32	20	B15
5300-6899	20	20	B15
6900-OUT	9	22	A16
2nd Pl	31	20	C13
2nd St		20	C14
1-166	31	20	C14
167-OUT	15	20	C14
3rd Av		22	A17
1-250	17	20	C13
251-617 & 252-612	15	20	C14
619-4399 & 614-4398	32	20	B15
4400-6899	20	20	B15
6900-OUT	9	22	A16
3rd Pl	31	20	C13
3rd St		20	C14
1-166	31	20	C14
167-OUT	15	20	C14
4th Av		22	A17
1-213 & 2-222	17	20	C13
215-617 & 224-630	15	20	C14
619-4399 & 632-4398	32	20	B15
4400-6899	20	20	B15
6900-OUT	9	22	A17
4th Pl	31	20	C14
4th St		20	C14
1-113	31	20	C14
114-OUT	15	20	C14
5th Av		22	A17
1-206	17	20	D13
207-723	15	20	C14
724-4399	32	20	C15
4400-6899	20	20	B15
6900-OUT	9	22	B16

STREET NAME AND HOUSE NUMBERS	ZONE NO.	MAP NO.	MAP GRID
5th St		20	C14
1-76	31	20	C14
77-OUT	15	20	C14
6th Av		22	B16
1-207 & 2-204	17	20	D14
209-759 & 206-758	15	20	C15
760-4399	32	20	C15
4400-6899	20	22	B16
6900-OUT	9	22	B16
6th St	15	20	C14
7th Av		22	B17
1-94	17	20	D14
95-630	15	20	C15
631-4399	32	20	C15
4400-6899	20	22	B16
6900-7898 (even)	9	22	B16
6901-OUT (odd)	28	22	B17
7th St	15	20	C14
8th Av		20	D14
1-72	17	20	D14
73-2599	15	20	D14
2600-4399	32	20	C15
4400-6899	20	22	B16
6900-OUT	28	22	B16
8th St	15	20	C14
9th Av		22	B16
1-330	15	20	D14
331-4399	32	20	C15
4400-OUT	20	22	B16
9th St		20	C14
1-39	31	20	B14
40-OUT	15	20	C14
10th Av (John P Devaney Blvd)		22	B16
1-2100	15	20	C15
2101-6899	19	22	C16
6900-OUT	28	22	B17
10th St	15	20	C14
11th Av		22	B16
1-1690	15	20	D15
1691-2099	18	22	D15
2100-6899	19	22	C16
6900-OUT	28	22	B17
11th St	15	20	C14
12th Av		22	B17
1-4099	18	22	C16
4100-6899	19	22	C16
6900-OUT	28	22	B17
12th St	15	20	C14
13th Av		22	B17
1-4099	18	22	C16
4100-6899	19	22	C16
6900-OUT	28	22	B17
13th St	15	20	C14
14th Av		22	C16
1-4099	18	22	C16
4100-6899	19	22	C16
6900-OUT	28	22	B17
14th St	15	20	C14
15th Av		22	C17
1-4099	18	22	C16
4100-6899	19	22	C16
6900-OUT	28	22	B17
15th St	15	20	C14
16th Av		22	C17
1-4099	18	22	C16
4100-7499	4	22	C17
7500-OUT	14	22	B17
16th St		20	C14
1-587 & 2-558	15	20	C14
589-OUT & 560-OUT	18	20	D15
17th Av		24	B18
1-7499	4	22	C17
7500-OUT	14	24	B18
17th Ct	14	24	B18
17th St		20	C14
1-115 & 2-108	32	20	C14
117-559 & 110-566	15	20	C14
561-OUT & 568-OUT	18	20	D15
18th Av		24	B18
1-4399	18	22	D16
4400-7499	4	22	C17
7500-OUT	14	24	B18
18th St		20	C14
1-115 & 2-108	32	20	C14
117-567 & 110-556	15	20	C14
569-OUT & 558-OUT	18	20	D15
19th Av		24	C17
1-7499	4	24	C17
7500-OUT	14	24	B18
19th La	14	24	B18
19th St		20	C14
0-223	32	20	C14
237-500	15	20	C15
541-699	18	20	D15
20th Av		22	C17
1-7499	4	22	C17
7500-OUT	14	22	C17
20th Dr	14	24	B18
20th La	14	24	C18
20th St		20	C14
1-236	32	20	C14
237-540	15	20	C15
541-OUT	18	20	D15
21st Av		22	C17
1-7499	4	22	C17
7500-OUT	14	22	C17
21st Dr	14	24	C18
21st La	14	24	C18
21st St		20	C14
1-236	32	20	C14
237-OUT	15	20	C15
22nd St		20	C14
1-236	32	20	C14
237-OUT	15	20	C15

STREET NAME AND HOUSE NUMBERS	ZONE NO.	MAP NO.	MAP GRID
23rd Av		24	C18
1-7499	4	22	D17
7500-OUT	14	24	C18
23rd St		20	C14
1-236	32	20	C14
237-OUT	15	20	C15
24th Av		24	C18
1-7499	4	22	D17
7500-OUT	14	24	C18
24th St	32	20	C14
25th Av	14	24	C18
25th St	32	20	C14
26th Av	14	24	C18
26th St	32	20	C15
27th Av	14	24	C18
27th St	32	20	C15
28th Av	14	24	C18
28th St	32	20	C15
29th St	32	20	C15
30th St	32	20	C15
31st St	32	20	B15
32nd St	32	20	B15
33rd St	32	20	B15
34th St	32	20	B15
35th St		20	B15
1-899	32	20	B15
900-OUT	18	22	C16
36th St		20	B15
1-899	32	20	C15
900-OUT	18	22	C16
37th St		20	B15
1-899	32	20	C15
900-1099	19	20	C15
1100-OUT	18	22	C16
38th St		20	B15
1-899	32	20	C15
900-1099	19	20	C15
1100-OUT	18	22	C16
39th St		20	B15
1-899	32	20	B15
900-1099	19	20	C15
1100-OUT	18	22	C16
40th St		20	B15
1-899	32	20	B15
900-1099	19	20	C15
1100-OUT	18	22	C16
41st St		20	B15
1-899	32	20	B15
900-1099	19	20	C15
1100-OUT	18	22	C16
42nd St		20	B15

STREET NAME AND HOUSE NUMBERS	ZONE NO.	MAP NO.	MAP GRID
1-899	32	20	B15
900-1599	19	22	C16
1600-OUT	4	22	C16
43rd St		20	B15
1-899	32	20	B15
900-1599	19	22	C16
1600-OUT	4	22	C16
44th St		20	B15
1-299	32	20	B15
300-899	20	20	B15
900-1599	19	22	C16
1600-OUT	4	22	C16
45th St		20	B15
1-899	20	20	B15
900-1599	19	22	C16
1600-OUT	4	22	C16
46th St		20	B15
1-899	20	20	B15
900-1599	19	22	C16
1600-OUT	4	22	C16
47th St		20	B15
1-199	32	20	B15
200-899	20	20	B15
900-1599	19	22	C16
1600-OUT	4	22	C16
48th St		20	B15
1-199	32	20	B15
200-899	20	20	B15
900-1599	19	22	C16
1600-OUT	4	22	C16
49th St		20	B15
1-199	32	20	B15
200-899	20	20	B15
900-1599	19	22	C16
1600-OUT	4	22	C16
50th St		20	B15
1-199	32	20	B15
200-899	20	20	B15
900-1599	19	22	C16
1600-OUT	4	22	C16
51st St		20	B15
1-199	32	20	B15
200-899	20	20	B15
900-1599	19	22	C16
1600-OUT	4	22	C16
52nd St		20	B15
1-199	32	20	B15
200-899	20	20	B15
900-1599	19	22	C16
1600-OUT	4	22	C16
53rd St		20	B15

STREET NAME AND HOUSE NUMBERS	ZONE NO.	MAP NO.	MAP GRID
1-199	32	20	B15
200-899	20	20	B15
900-1599	19	22	C16
1600-OUT	4	22	C16
54th St		20	B15
1-899	20	22	B16
900-1599	19	22	C16
1600-OUT	4	22	C16
55th St		20	B15
1-899	20	22	B16
899-1599	19	22	C16
1600-OUT	4	22	C16
56th Dr	34	23	G17
56th St		20	B15
1-899	20	22	B16
900-1599	19	22	C16
1600-OUT	4	22	C16
57th St		20	B15
1-899	20	20	B16
900-1599	19	22	C16
1600-2999	4	22	C16
58th St		22	B16
1-899	20	22	B16
900-1599	19	22	C16
1600-OUT	4	22	C17
59th St		22	B16
1-899	20	22	B16
900-1599	19	22	C16
1600-2999	4	22	C17
60th St		22	B16
1-899	20	22	B16
900-1599	19	22	C16
1600-OUT	4	22	C17
61st St		22	B16
1-899	20	22	B16
900-1599	19	22	C16
1600-OUT	4	22	C17
62nd St		22	B16
1-899	20	22	B16
900-1599	19	22	B16
1600-OUT	4	22	C17
63rd St		22	B16
1-899	20	22	B16
900-1599	19	22	B16
1600-OUT	4	22	C17
64th St		22	B16
1-899	20	22	B16
900-1599	19	22	B16
1600-OUT	4	22	C17
65th St		22	B16
1-899	20	22	B16

STREET NAME AND HOUSE NUMBERS	ZONE NO.	MAP NO.	MAP GRID
900-1599	19	22	B16
1600-OUT	4	22	C17
66th St		22	B16
1-899	20	22	B16
900-1599	19	22	B16
1600-OUT	4	22	C17
67th St		22	B16
1-899	20	22	B16
900-1599	19	22	B16
1600-OUT	4	22	C17
68th St		22	A16
1-899	20	22	A16
900-1599	19	22	B16
1600-OUT	4	22	C17
70th St		22	A16
1-699	9	22	A16
700-1599	28	22	B16
1600-2999	4	22	C17
71st St		22	A16
1-699	9	22	A16
700-1599	28	22	B16
1600-2999	4	22	C17
72nd Ct	9	22	A16
72nd St		22	A16
1-699	9	22	A16
700-1599	28	22	B16
1600-2999	4	22	C17
73rd St		22	A16
1-699	9	22	A16
700-1599	28	22	B16
1600-2999	4	22	C17
74th St		22	A16
1-699	9	22	A16
700-1599	28	22	B16
1600-2999	4	22	C17
75th St (Bay Ridge Pkwy)	9	22	A16
76th St		22	A16
1-699	9	22	A16
700-1599	28	22	B17
1600-2999	14	22	C17
77th St		22	A16
1-699	9	22	A16
700-1599	28	22	B17
1600-2999	14	22	C17
78th St		22	A16
1-699	9	22	A16
700-1599	28	22	B17
1600-2999	14	22	C17
79th St		22	A16
1-699	9	22	A16
700-1599	28	22	B17
1600-2999	14	22	C17

STREET NAME AND HOUSE NUMBERS	ZONE NO.	MAP NO.	MAP GRID
80th St		22	A16
1-699	9	22	A16
700-1599	28	22	B17
1600-2999	14	22	C17
81st St		22	A16
1-679	9	22	A16
680-1599	28	22	B17
1600-2999	14	22	C17
82nd St		22	A16
1-668	9	22	A16
669-1599	28	22	B17
1600-2999	14	22	C17
83rd St		22	A16
1-663	9	22	A16
664-1599	28	22	B17
1600-2999	14	22	C17
84th St		22	A16
1-650	9	22	A16
651-1599	28	22	B17
1600-2999	14	22	C17
85th St		22	A16
1-656	9	22	A16
657-1599	28	22	B17
1600-2999	14	22	C17
86th St		22	A16
1-673 & 2-610	9	22	A16
675-1599 & 612-1598	28	22	B17
1600-2599	14	22	B17
2600-2999	23	24	C18
87th St	9	22	A17
88th St		22	A17
1-623	9	22	A17
624-2999	28	22	B17
89th St	9	22	A17
90th St		22	A17
1-620	9	22	A17
621-OUT	28	22	B17
91st St	9	22	A17
92nd St		22	A17
1-599	9	22	A17
600-OUT	28	22	B17
93rd St	9	22	A17
94th St	9	22	A17
95th Av	8	21	J13
95th St	9	22	A17
96th St	9	22	A17
97th St	9	22	A17
98th St	9	22	A17
99th St	9	22	A17
100th St	9	22	A17
101st Av	8	21	J13
101st St	9	22	A17

STATEN ISLAND

STREET INDEX AND POSTAL ZONES

NOTE: To obtain ZIP code for Staten Island, add 103 before two digit postal zone numbers and 1030 before single digit postal zone numbers.

A

STREET NAME AND HOUSE NUMBERS	ZONE NO.	MAP NO.	MAP GRID
A St	14	26	J 4
Abbey Rd	8	28	H 8
Abbott St	5	27	P 4
Abby Pl	1	27	M 2
Abingdon Av	8	28	H 8
Abingdon Ct	8	28	H 8
Acacia Av	8	31	J 9
Academy Av	7	30	C12
Academy Pl	1	27	O 1
Ackerman St	8	31	J 9
Acorn Ct	9	30	E 9
Acorn St	6	29	L 8
Ada Dr		26	H 3
1-299	14	26	H 3
300-OUT	3	26	H 3
Ada Pl	1	27	N 3
Adam Ct	14	28	J 6
Adams Av	6	29	M 6
Adelaide Av	6	29	L 8
Adele Ct	4	27	O 3
Adele St	5	29	N 5
Adelphi Av	12	30	D11
Adlai Cir	12	31	H 9
Adlers La	7	30	C12
Admiralty Loop	9	30	E11
Adrianne La	3	26	J 3
Adrienne Pl	8	31	J 9
Agda Av	6	29	M 8
Agnes Pl	5	29	O 6
Ainsworth Av	8	31	K 9
Akron St	14	26	H 4
Alabama Pl	14	27	L 3
Alan Loop	4	27	N 4
Alaska Pl	14	28	H 7
Alaska St	10	27	L 2
Alban St	10	27	M 2
Albans Pl	12	31	H 9
Albany Av	3	26	H 3
Albee Av	12	31	G 9
Albert Ct	3	26	H 3
Albert St	1	27	L 4
Alberta Av	14	28	F 5
Albion Pl	2	26	K 2
Albourne Av	9	30	E10

STREET NAME AND HOUSE NUMBERS	ZONE NO.	MAP NO.	MAP GRID
Albourne Av E	12	30	F10
Albourne Ct	9	30	E10
Albright St	4	29	N 5
Alcott St	12	28	F 8
Alden Pl	1	27	N 2
Alderwood Pl	4	29	M 5
Alexander Av		28	G 8
Alexandra Pl *(connects Gower St to N Gannon Av)	14	27	L 4
Alexsandra Ct *(off Ladd Av)	12	28	H 8
Algonkin St	12	30	F10
Allegro St	12	31	G10
Allen Ct	10	27	L 2
Allen Pl	12	31	H10
Allendale Rd	5	29	O 5
Allentown La	9	30	C10
Allison Av	6	29	L 7
Allison Pl	6	29	L 7
Almond St	12	31	G 9
Alpine Av	1	27	M 4
Alpine Ct	10	27	L 3
Altamont St	6	29	L 6
Alter Av		29	M 5
1-200	4	29	M 5
201-OUT	5	29	N 6
Altoona Av	6	28	K 7
Aluminum Av	14	28	H 6
Alverson Av	9	28	E 8
Alverson Av	9	30	E 9
Alverson Loop	9	30	F 9
Alvine Av	12	31	G10
Alysia Ct	9	30	E 9
Amador St	3	26	H 3
Amanda Ct	12	28	G 8
Amaron La	22	30	C12
Amber St	6	28	K 7
Amboy Rd		30	B12
1-3550	6	29	L 7
3551-4275	8	31	J 9
4276-5540	12	31	H 9
5541-6974	9	30	F10
6975-OUT	7	30	C11
Amelia Ct	10	27	M 1
Amherst St	6	29	L 8
Amity Pl	3	26	H 2
Amity St	5	27	O 4
Amsterdam Av	14	26	H 4
Amsterdam Pl	14	28	H 5
Amy Ct	14	28	H 6

STREET NAME AND HOUSE NUMBERS	ZONE NO.	MAP NO.	MAP GRID
Amy La	14	28	J 5
Anaconda St	12	30	F 9
Anderson Av	2	26	K 2
Anderson Pl	3	26	H 2
Anderson St	5	27	O 4
Andes Pl	14	27	L 4
Andrea Ct	12	28	H 8
Andrea Pl	3	26	H 3
Andrease St	5	27	P 4
Andrews Av	6	28	K 7
Andrews St	5	29	O 6
Andros Av	3	26	H 2
Androvette Av	12	30	F10
Androvette St	9	30	C 9
Anita St	14	26	J 3
Ann St	2	26	K 2
Annadale Rd	12	28	G 8
Annfield Ct	4	29	M 5
Anthony Pl	2	26	K 3
Anthony St	9	30	E 9
Appleby Av	5	29	O 6
Arbutus Av	12	31	G10
Arbutus Way	12	31	G10
Arc Pl	6	29	L 7
Arcadia Pl	10	27	L 2
Archwood Av	12	30	G10
Arden Av	12	28	F 8
Ardmore Av	14	26	K 4
Ardsley St	6	28	K 7
Area Pl	14	27	L 4
Argonne St	5	29	O 5
Arielle La	14	28	H 6
Arkansas Av	8	28	J 8
Arlene Ct	14	26	H 3
Arlene St	14	26	H 3
Arlington Av	3	26	H 1
Arlington Ct	10	27	M 1
Arlington Pl	3	26	H 2
Arlo Rd	1	27	N 3
Armand St	14	26	J 3
Armour Pl	9	30	F11
Armstrong Av	8	28	H 8
Arnedo Pl	1	27	M 2
Arnold St	1	27	M 2
Arnprior St	2	26	J 3
Arrowood Ct	9	28	E 8
Arthur Av	1	29	O 5
Arthur Ct	10	27	L 3
Arthur Kill Rd		30	B11
1-241	6	28	J 7
242-699	8	28	J 8

STREET NAME AND HOUSE NUMBERS	ZONE NO.	MAP NO.	MAP GRID
700-2000	12	28	H 8
2001-4949	9	30	D 9
4950-OUT	7	30	C11
Arthur Pl	12	31	G 9
Ascot Av	6	28	K 6
Ash Pl	14	26	K 4
Ashland Av	9	30	E10
Ashland Av E	12	30	F10
Ashley La	9	30	E 9
Ashton Dr	12	30	F 9
Ashwood Ct	8	28	J 8
Ashworth Av	14	28	H 5
Aspen Knolls Way	12	28	G 8
Aspinwall St	7	30	B12
Astor Av	14	26	H 3
Athena Pl	14	27	L 4
Atlantic Av		29	N 5
1-199	4	29	N 5
200-OUT	5	29	N 6
Atmore Pl	6	28	K 8
Auburn Av	14	26	J 4
Augusta Av	12	31	H 9
Aultman Av	6	28	K 7
Ausable Av	1	27	M 2
Austin Av	5	29	O 5
Austin Pl	4	27	N 2
Avenue B	2	26	K 2
Averill Pl	7	30	C11
Aviston St	6	29	L 8
Avon Green	12	30	F 9
Avon La	14	26	K 4
Avon Pl	1	27	N 2
Aye Ct	14	26	H 3
Aymar Av	1	27	M 4
Azalea Ct	9	28	E 8

B

STREET NAME AND HOUSE NUMBERS	ZONE NO.	MAP NO.	MAP GRID
B St	14	28	J 5
Bache Av	6	29	L 7
Bache St	2	26	K 2
Baden Pl		29	N 7
1-49	5	29	N 7
50-OUT	6	29	N 7
Bailey Pl	3	26	H 1
Baker Pl	10	27	M 2
Balfour St	5	29	O 6
Ballard Av	12	30	F 9
Balsam Pl	9	30	E 9
Baltic Av	4	27	N 4
Baltic St	4	27	O 2

STREET NAME AND HOUSE NUMBERS	ZONE NO.	MAP NO.	MAP GRID
Baltimore St	8	31	J 9
Bamberger La	12	31	H 9
Bancroft Av	6	29	L 6
Bang Ter	5	27	P 4
Bangor St	14	28	J 6
Bank Pl	4	29	N 5
Bank St	1	27	N 1
Bar Ct	9	30	E 8
Barbara St	6	28	K 7
Barclay Av	12	31	H10
Barclay Cir	12	28	F 8
Bard Av		27	M 1
1-772	10	27	M 2
773-OUT	1	27	M 3
Bard Pl	1	27	M 3
Baring Pl	4	27	N 3
Barker St	10	27	L 2
Barlow Av		28	H 8
1-489	8	28	H 8
490-OUT	12	28	J 8
Barnard Av	7	30	C11
Baron Blvd	14	28	G 5
Barrett Av	2	26	K 3
Barrett La	10	27	L 1
Barrow Pl	9	30	E 9
Barry Ct	6	29	M 8
Barry St	9	28	E 8
Bartlett Av	12	31	H 9
Barton Av	6	29	M 6
Bartow La	12	30	D12
Bartow St	8	31	K 9
Bascom Pl	14	26	J 4
Bass St	14	26	K 4
Bates Av	14	28	G 5
Bath Av	5	29	N 5
Bathgate St	12	31	H10
Bay St		27	O 1
1-406	1	27	O 1
407-900	4	27	O 3
901-OUT	5	27	P 4
Bay Street Landing	1	27	O 2
Bay Ter	6	28	K 8
Bayard St	12	31	H 9
Bayport Pl	14	26	J 4
Bayview Av	9	30	E11
Bayview Pl	4	27	N 2
Bayview Ter	12	31	H11
Beach Av	6	29	L 7
Beach Rd	12	31	H 9
Beach St	4	27	O 3
Beachview Av	6	29	M 7

STREET NAME AND HOUSE NUMBERS	ZONE NO.	MAP NO.	MAP GRID
Beacon Av	6	29	L 7
Beacon Pl	6	29	M 8
Bean St	6	29	M 8
Bear St	4	29	N 5
Beard St	14	28	J 6
Bedell Av	7	30	C11
Bedell St	9	30	E11
Bedford Av	6	29	M 6
Bedford Pl	9	30	F 9
Bee Ct	14	26	H 3
Beebe St	1	27	M 4
Beechwood Av	1	27	N 1
Beechwood Pl	14	27	L 3
Beekman Cir	12	28	F 8
Beekman St	2	26	K 2
Beethoven St	5	27	O 4
Behan Ct	6	29	L 7
Belair Rd	5	27	O 4
Belden St	8	31	J 9
Belfast Av	6	29	L 7
Belfield Av	12	30	F 9
Bell St	5	27	O 4
Belle Dr	1	27	O 2
Bellhaven Pl	14	26	J 4
Belmar Dr E	14	28	J 6
Belmar Dr W	14	28	J 6
Belmont Pl	1	27	O 1
Bement Av	10	27	L 1
Bement Ct	10	27	L 1
Benedict Av	14	26	K 3
Benedict Rd	4	29	M 5
Benjamin Dr	3	26	H 3
Benjamin Pl	3	26	H 2
Bennet Pl	12	31	H10
Bennett Av	12	31	G10
Bennett St	2	26	K 2
Bennington St	12	31	J 10
Benson St	12	28	G 8
Bent St	12	31	H 9
Bentley St	7	30	B11
Benton Av	5	29	N 5
Benton Ct	6	28	K 8
Benziger Av	1	27	N 2
Beresford Av	14	28	F 5
Berglund Av	14	26	H 4
Berkley St	12	31	H10
Berne Pl	9	30	E 9
Berry Av	12	28	G 8
Berry Av W	12	28	G 8
Berry Ct	9	28	E 8
Bertha Pl	1	27	N 3
Bertram Av	12	31	G11
Berwick Pl	10	27	M 3
Berwin La	10	27	L 3
Beth Pl	8	31	J 9
Bethel Av	7	30	C11
Beverly Av	1	27	M 3
Beverly Rd	5	29	O 5
Bianca Ct	12	28	G 8
Bidwell Av	14	26	K 3
Billings St	12	28	G 8
Billiou St	12	30	F 10
Billiou St	12	31	G10
Billop Av	7	30	B12
Biltmore Pl	14	26	J 4
Bionia Av	5	29	O 5
Birch Av	1	27	M 3
Birch La	12	28	F 8
Birch Rd	3	26	H 3
Birchard Av	14	26	K 4
Bishop St	6	28	K 7
Bismark Av	1	27	N 1
Bismark Ct	1	27	N 1
Blackford Av	2	26	K 2
Blackhorse Av	4	29	L 5
Blaine Ct	10	27	L 3
Bland Pl	12	31	G10
Bleeker Pl	14	28	H 5
Block St	6	28	K 8
Bloomfield Av	14	26	G 4
Bloomfield Rd	14	26	G 4
Bloomingdale Rd	9	30	E 9
Blue Heron Dr	12	31	H10
Blueberry La	12	31	H10
Blythe Pl	6	28	K 8
Boardwalk Av	12	31	H11
Boating Pl	9	30	F11
Bodine St	10	27	L 2
Bogert Av	14	29	L 5
Bogota St	14	28	J 6
Bolivar St	14	29	L 5
Bombay St	9	30	E 9
Bond St	2	26	K 2
Boone St	14	28	K 5
Booth Av	12	31	G10
Borman Av	14	28	J 5
Borough Pl	1	27	O 1
Boscombe Av	9	30	C10
Bosworth St	10	27	L 3
Boulder St	12	30	F 9
Boulevard, The	14	26	K 3
Boundary Av	6	29	M 7
Bovanizer St	12	31	H 9
Bowden St	6	29	M 6
Bowdoin St	14	28	J 6
Bowen St	4	27	N 4
Bower Ct	9	28	E 8
Bowles Av	3	26	J 2
Bowling Green Pl	14	28	H 5
Boyce Av	6	28	K 7
Boyd St	4	27	O 3
Boylan St	12	28	G 8
Boyle Pl	6	28	K 7
Boyle St	6	29	L 6
Boynton St	9	30	E10
Brabant St	3	26	H 2
Bradford Av	9	30	E10
Bradley Av	14	26	K 4
Bradley Ct	14	29	K 5
Brady Pl	5	29	O 5
Braisted Av	14	28	J 6
Brandis Av	12	28	H 8
Brandis La	12	28	H 8
Brehaut Av	7	30	C11
Brenton Pl	14	27	L 4
Brentwood Av	1	27	M 2
Brewster St	4	27	O 2
Briarcliff Rd	5	29	O 5
Briarwood Rd	3	26	H 3
Bridgetown St	14	28	J 6
Brielle Av	14	28	K 5
Brighton Av	1	27	M 2
Brighton St	7	30	C12
Bristol Av	1	27	M 4
Britton Av	4	27	N 4
Britton La	6	29	M 8
Britton St	10	27	L 2
Broad St	4	27	N 3
Broadway	10	27	L 1
Brokenshell Rd	9	30	E11
Brook Av	6	29	L 8
Brook St	1	27	N 2
Brookfield Av	8	28	H 8
Brooks Pl	10	27	L 2
Brookside Av		27	L 3
1-109	10	27	L 3
110-OUT	14	27	L 3
Brookspond Pl	10	27	L 3
Brower Ct	8	31	J 9
Brown Av	4	27	N 2
Brown Pl	5	27	O 4
Brownell St	4	27	O 3
Browning Av	4	29	L 5
Bruckner Av	3	26	H 2
Brunswick St	14	28	J 6
Bryan St	7	30	B12
Bryant Av	6	29	M 7
Bryson Av		26	J 3
1-199	2	26	J 3
200-OUT	14	26	J 3
Buchanan Av	14	26	K 4
Buchanan St	1	27	N 1
Buel Av		29	M 6
1-123	4	29	M 6
124-OUT	5	29	N 6
Buffalo St	6	28	K 8
Buffington Av	12	31	G10
Bunnell Ct	12	28	F 8
Bunnell St	12	28	F 8
Burbank Av	6	29	L 7
Burchard Ct	12	31	G 9
Burden Av	2	26	K 2
Burgher Av		29	N 5
1-185	4	29	N 5
186-OUT	5	29	N 6
Burke Av	14	28	G 5
Burnside Av	2	26	K 3
Burton Av	9	30	E11
Burton Ct	6	28	K 6
Bush Av	3	26	H 2
Butler Av	7	30	B11
Butler Blvd	9	30	D12
Butler Ct	9	30	D11
Butler Pl	5	27	O 3
Butler St	9	30	D11
Butler Ter	1	27	N 2
Butterworth Av	1	27	M 4
Buttonwood Rd	4	29	M 5
Byrd Pl	8	31	J 10
Byrne Av	14	26	K 4

C

STREET NAME AND HOUSE NUMBERS	ZONE NO.	MAP NO.	MAP GRID
C St	14	28	J 5
Cabot Pl	5	27	O 4
Calcutta St	12	30	D11
Caldera Pl	1	27	M 2
Call St	6	28	K 7
Callan Av	4	29	M 5
Calvin Pl	4	27	N 4
Cambria St	5	29	O 5
Cambridge Av	14	26	J 3
Camden St	5	27	O 3
Cameron Av	5	29	O 5
Campbell Av	10	27	L 2
Campus Rd	1	27	N 4
Canal St	4	27	O 3
Candon Av	9	30	E 9
Candon Ct	9	30	E 9
Cannon Av	14	28	F 5
Cannon Blvd	6	29	L 7
Canoe Pl	5	29	N 7
Canon Dr	14	28	H 7
Canterbury Av	14	26	J 3
Canton Av	12	30	F 9
Cappellan St	12	31	G11
Cardiff St	12	30	F 9
Cardinal La	6	31	J 8
Carlin St	9	30	D 9
Carlton Av		30	E10
1-1549	12	30	F10
1550-OUT	9	30	E10
Carlton Blvd	12	31	G 9
Carlton Ct	12	30	F10
Carlton Pl	4	27	M 4
Carly Ct	9	30	D11
Carlyle Green	12	28	F 8
Carlyle St	1	27	N 1
Carmel Av	14	26	K 4
Carnegie Av	14	26	H 4
Caro St	14	26	K 4
Carol Ct	9	30	E11
Carol Pl	3	26	H 3
Carolina Ct	14	28	K 5
Carolina Pl	14	27	L 3
Caroline St	10	27	L 2
Carpenter Av	14	28	J 5
Carreau Av	14	28	H 5
Carroll Pl	1	27	N 1
Carteret St	7	30	B12
Cary Av	10	27	L 2
Cascade St	6	29	M 6
Cascio Pl	10	27	M 1
Case Av	9	30	F11
Casino Pl *(off Staten Island Blvd near Andes Pl)	14	27	L 4
Casper Av	14	28	G 5
Cassidy Pl	1	27	M 1
Castleton Av		26	K 2
1-699	1	27	N 2
700-1389	10	27	L 2
1390-OUT	2	26	K 2
Castleton Ct	1	27	N 2
Castleton Pk E	1	27	O 1
Castleton Pk N	1	27	O 1
Castleton Pk S	1	27	O 1
Castor Pl	12	30	F 9
Caswell Av	14	26	J 3
Caswell La	14	26	H 3
Catharine Ct	2	26	K 2
Catherine Pl	3	26	G 1
Catherine St	2	26	K 2
Catlin Av	4	27	N 2
Cattaragus St	1	27	M 4
Cayuga Av	1	27	M 4
Cebra Av		27	N 2
1-30	1	27	N 2
31-OUT	4	27	N 2
Cedar Av	5	29	O 5
Cedar Grove Av	6	31	L 9
Cedar Grove Beach Pl	6	29	M 8
Cedar Grove Ct	6	29	M 8
Cedar St	4	27	O 3
Cedar Ter	4	27	N 4
Cedarcliff Rd	1	27	N 3
Cedarview Av	6	28	K 7
Cedarwood Ct	3	26	H 3
Celina La	7	30	C12
Celtic Pl	6	29	M 8
Center Pl	6	29	M 8
Center St	6	28	J 7
Central Av	1	27	O 1
Centre Av	4	27	N 3
Challenger Dr *(off Ladd Av)	12	28	H 8
Champ Ct	9	30	D11
Champlain Av	6	28	K 8
Chandler Av	14	26	K 4
Chapin Av	4	29	M 5
Chappell St	10	27	L 2
Charles Av	2	26	K 2
Charles Ct	6	28	K 6
Charles Pl	3	26	J 2
Charleston Av	9	28	E 8
Charter Oaks Rd	4	29	M 6
Chelsea Rd	14	26	G 4
Chelsea St	7	30	C12
Chemical La	9	30	D 8
Cherokee St	5	29	N 7
Cherry Pl	14	28	K 5
Cherrywood Ct	8	28	J 8
Cheryl Av	12	28	G 8
Chesebrough St	12	31	H 9
Cheshire Pl	1	27	M 3
Chester Av	12	31	G11
Chester Pl	4	27	N 2
Chesterton Av	6	28	K 8
Chestnut Av	5	27	O 3
Chestnut Cir	12	28	F 8
Chestnut St	4	27	N 3
Cheston Pl	4	27	N 2
Cheves Av	14	26	K 3
Chicago Av	5	29	O 5
Chisholm St	12	30	F10
Christ St	5	29	N 5
Christine Ct	12	30	G10
Christopher La	14	26	J 3
Christopher St	3	26	H 2
Church Av	14	28	G 5
Church Ct	14	28	G 5
Church La	5	27	O 4
Church St	2	26	K 1
Churchill Av	9	30	D10
Cindra Av	8	31	J 10
Circle Loop	4	27	O 4
Circle Rd	4	29	M 5
City Blvd	1	27	M 2
Claire Ct	1	27	N 3
Claradon La	5	29	O 5
Clarence Pl	6	29	L 8
Clark La	4	27	N 2
Clark Pl	2	26	K 3
Clarke Av	6	28	J 7
Claudia Ct	3	26	J 3
Clawson St	6	29	L 7
Clayboard St	6	29	M 8
Claypit Rd	9	30	D 9
Clayton St	5	27	P 4
Clearmont Av	9	30	E10
Clermont Av	7	30	B12
Clermont Av	9	30	D12
Clermont Pl	14	26	K 4
Cletus St	5	29	M 6
Cleveland Av	8	31	J 9
Cleveland Pl	5	29	O 5
Cleveland St	1	27	N 1
Cliff Ct *(connects Cliff St and Nautilus St)	5	27	P 4
Cliff St	5	27	P 4
Cliffside Av	4	27	N 4
Cliffwood Av	4	29	L 5
Clifton Av	5	27	O 4
Clifton St	14	26	H 4
Clinton Av	1	27	M 1
Clinton B Fiske Av	14	26	K 3
Clinton Ct	1	27	M 2
Clinton Pl	2	26	K 2
Clinton Rd	8	31	J 9
Clinton St	4	27	O 2
Cloister Pl	6	29	L 7
Clove Lake Pl	10	27	L 2
Clove Rd		27	L 2
1-853	10	27	L 2
854-1600	1	27	M 3
1601-2075	4	27	N 4
2076-OUT	5	29	N 5
Clove Way	14	27	L 3
Cloverdale Av	8	31	J 9
Clovis Rd	8	31	J 9
Clyde Pl	1	27	N 2
Coale Av	14	26	K 4
Coddington Av	6	29	L 7
Cody Pl	12	28	F 8
Coke St	9	30	D10
Cold Spring Ct	4	29	M 5
Cole St	9	30	D11
Colfax Av	6	29	M 6
Colgate Pl	6	29	L 7
College Av		26	K 3
1-529 (odd)	14	26	K 3
2-520 (even)	14	26	K 3
522-OUT (even)	2	26	K 3
531-OUT (odd)	2	26	K 3
523-529 (odd)	14	26	K 3
530-OUT	2	26	K 3
College Ct	2	26	J 3
College Pl	4	29	M 5
Collfield Av		26	J 3
1-200	2	26	J 3
201-OUT	14	26	J 3
Collyer Av	12	31	G10
Colon Av	8	28	J 8
Colon St	12	31	G10
Colonial Av	14	28	J 5
Colonial Av	14	28	K 5
Colonial Ct	10	27	L 3
Colony St		29	N 7
1-109	5	29	N 7
110-OUT	6	29	N 7
Colorado Ct	14	27	L 3
Colorado St *(connects Kingsley Av and College Av)	14	27	L 3
Colton St	5	27	O 4
Columbia Av	5	29	O 5
Columbus Av	4	29	N 5
Columbus Pl	14	26	K 3
Combs Av	6	28	K 7
Comely St	12	31	G10
Commerce St	14	26	H 4
Commodore Dr	9	30	E11
Comstock Av	14	26	H 3
Concord La	4	27	M 5
Concord Pl	4	27	N 4
Confederation Pl	3	26	H 2
Conger St	5	29	P 5
Congress Av	4	27	O 2
Congress St	4	27	O 2
Conklin Av	3	26	J 2
Connecticut St	7	30	B12
Connor Av	6	28	K 7
Connors Av	14	29	L 6
Conrad Av	14	28	J 6
Constant Av	14	26	K 3
Continental Pl	3	26	H 2
Convent Av	9	30	E 9
Conyingham Av	1	27	M 2
Cooke St	14	26	H 3
Coonley Av	3	26	J 2
Coonley Ct	3	26	H 2
Cooper Av	5	29	N 5
Cooper Pl	9	30	F11
Cooper Ter	14	28	H 5
Copley St	14	28	J 6
Copperflagg La	4	29	M 6
Copperleaf Ter	4	29	M 6
Corbin Av	8	28	J 8
Cordelia Av	9	30	E11
Cordes Av	9	30	E11
Cornelia Av	12	30	F10
Cornelia St	4	29	N 5
Cornell Av	10	27	L 2
Cornell Pl	4	27	N 4
Cornell St	2	26	K 2
Cornish St	8	31	J 9
Cornwall Av	4	29	M 5
Corona Av	6	28	K 8
Correll Av		30	E 9
1-199	12	30	F 9
200-OUT	9	30	E 9
Corson Av	1	27	N 2
Cortelyou Av	12	28	H 8
Cortelyou Pl	1	27	N 1
Cortlandt St	2	26	K 2
Cottage Av	8	31	J 9
Cottage Pl	2	26	K 2
Cotter Av	6	28	K 8
Cottonwood Ct	8	28	J 8
Coughlan Av	10	27	L 3
Country Dr E	14	28	H 5
Country Dr N	14	28	H 5
Country Dr S	14	28	H 6
Country Dr W	14	28	H 6
Country La	12	28	F 8
Country Woods La	8	28	J 8
Coursen Ct	4	27	O 3
Coursen Pl	4	27	O 3
Court Pl *(bet Richmond Hill & Arthur Kill Rds, connects Richmond Rd to Center St)	6	28	J 7
Court St	4	27	O 3
Courtney Loop	5	27	P 4
Coventry Loop	12	30	F 9
Coventry Rd	4	29	M 6
Coverly Av		27	M 4
All Except 181	1	27	M 4
181 only	4	27	M 4
Coverly Av N *(off Coverly Av)	1	27	M 4
Coverly St	6	29	L 7
Cowen Pl	3	26	H 2
Crabbs La	14	28	F 5
Crabtree Av	9	30	D 9
Crafton Av	14	26	K 4
Craig Av	7	30	B12
Crane Ter	9	30	E11
Cranford Av	6	28	K 7
Cranford Ct	6	29	K 7
Cranford St	6	31	K 9
Crescent Av	1	27	N 1
Crest Loop	12	31	J 10
Creston Pl	4	27	N 2
Creston St	9	30	E11
Crittenden Pl	2	26	K 2
Croak Av	14	27	L 4
Crocheron Av	14	26	J 4
Crocker Ct	12	28	F 8
Croft Ct	6	28	K 8
Croft Pl	14	26	H 4
Cromer St	8	28	J 8
Cromwell Av		29	M 5
1-187	4	29	M 5
188-OUT	5	29	N 6
Cromwell Cir	4	29	M 6
Cross St	4	27	O 3
Crossfield Av	12	28	G 8
Crosshill St	1	27	M 3
Croton Av	1	27	M 3
Crowell Av	14	26	K 3
Crown Av	12	31	G 9
Crown Ct	12	31	G 9
Crown Pl	12	30	F 9
Crystal Av		26	K 3
1-300	2	26	K 3
301-OUT	14	26	K 3
Cuba Av	6	29	M 8
Cubberly Pl	6	29	L 7
Cunard Av	4	27	N 4
Cunard Pl	4	27	N 4
Cunningham Rd	9	30	D11
Currie Av	6	28	K 8
Curtis Av	10	27	L 3
Curtis Ct	10	27	M 2
Curtis Pl	1	27	N 1
Cypress Av	1	27	M 4
Cypress Loop	9	28	E 8

D

STREET NAME AND HOUSE NUMBERS	ZONE NO.	MAP NO.	MAP GRID
D St	14	28	J 5
Daffodil Ct	12	28	F 8
Daffodil La	14	28	H 6
Dahlia St	9	30	F 9
Daisy Way	6	28	K 6
Dakota Pl	14	26	K 3
Dale Av	6	29	L 7
Daleham St	8	28	J 8
Dalemere Rd	4	29	M 5
Dallas St	10	27	L 3
Dalton Av	6	28	K 7
Damon St	12	30	D11
Dana St	1	27	M 2
Daniel Low Ter	1	27	N 1
Darcey Av	14	26	J 4
Darien St	4	27	N 4
Darlington Av		30	E10
1-402	12	30	F10
403-OUT	9	30	E10
Darnell La	9	30	D10
David Pl	3	26	J 2
David St	8	31	J 10
Davidson Ct	3	26	H 2
Davidson St	3	26	H 2
Davis Av	10	27	M 1
Davis Ct	10	27	M 1
Dawson Cir	14	26	H 4
Dawson Ct	14	26	H 4
Dawson Pl	5	29	N 5
Dawson St	14	26	K 4
Dayna Dr	5	27	O 4
Deal Ct	5	27	O 4
Debbie St	14	26	J 4
Deborah Loop	12	31	G 9
Decatur Av	14	26	J 4

STREET NAME AND HOUSE NUMBERS	ZONE NO.	MAP NO.	MAP GRID
Decker Av	2	26	K 3
Deems Av	14	26	K 3
Deere Park Pl	1	27	M 4
De Groot Pl	10	27	L 2
De Hart Av	3	26	J 2
Deisius St	12	30	F10
De Kalb St	4	27	N 4
De Kay St	10	27	M 2
Delafield Av		27	L 2
1-240	1	27	M 2
241-OUT	10	27	L 2
Delafield Pl	10	27	L 1
De Laine Pl	14	26	H 3
Delaware Av		29	N 5
1-199	4	29	M 5
200-OUT	5	29	N 6
Delaware Pl	14	27	L 3
Delaware St	4	29	M 5
Delford St	4	27	N 3
Dellwood Rd	4	29	N 5
Delmar Av	12	30	F 9
Delmore St	14	26	K 3
Delphine Ter	5	29	O 5
Demopolis Av	8	31	H 9
Demorest Av	14	26	K 3
Denise Ct	12	31	G10
Denker Pl	14	28	J 6
Dennis Toricelli St	5	27	P 4
DeNoble La	1	27	M 4
Dent Rd	8	31	J 9
Denton Pl	14	26	J 4
Depew Pl	9	30	E10
Deppe Pl	14	26	J 3
Derby Ct	2	26	K 2
Dermody Pl	14	28	K 6
De Ruyter Pl	3	26	J 2
Deserre Av	12	30	F 9
Detroit Av	12	31	G 9
Devens St	14	26	J 3
Devine St	4	29	N 5
Devon Loop	14	28	H 6
Devon Pl	1	27	M 2
Dewey Av	8	28	J 8
Dewey Ct	8	28	J 8
Dewey Pl	8	28	J 8
Dewhurst St	14	28	K 5
Diana Tr	4	27	N 4
Diaz St	5	29	O 5
Dickie Av	14	26	K 3
Dierauf St	12	28	G 8
Di Marco Pl	6	29	L 7
Dina Ct	6	28	K 8
Dinsmore St	14	26	H 4
Di Renzo Ct	9	30	F11
Dissoway Pl	10	27	L 2
Ditson St	5	27	O 3
Divine St	4	29	N 5
Division St	14	26	J 4
Dix Pl	4	27	O 3
Dixon Av		26	J 2
1-100	2	26	J 2
101-OUT	3	26	J 2
Dixwell Av	12	31	G11
Doane Av	8	28	J 8
Dobbs Pl	1	27	M 4
Dock Rd	14	28	H 6
Dock St	4	27	O 3
Doe Ct	14	28	H 5
Doe Pl	10	27	L 2
Dogwood Av	5	29	O 6
Dogwood Dr	12	30	F 9
Dogwood La	5	29	O 5
Dole St	12	31	H11
Dolson Pl	3	26	H 2
Domain St	14	26	H 3
Don Ct	12	28	G 8
Donald Pl	10	27	M 1
Dongan Av	14	27	L 4
Dongan Hills Av		29	M 6
1-99	6	29	M 6
100-OUT	5	29	N 6
Dongan St	10	27	L 2
Donley Av	5	27	O 4
Donna Ct	14	28	H 6
Dora St	14	26	K 4
Dore Ct	10	27	L 3
Doreen Dr	3	26	H 3
Dorothea Pl	6	29	L 7
Dorothy St	14	28	K 5
Dorval Av	12	28	G 8
Dorval Pl	12	28	G 8
Doty Av	5	29	P 5
Douglas Av	10	27	L 3
Douglas Rd	4	27	N 4
Dover Green	12	28	F 8
Downes Av	12	31	G10
Downey Pl	3	26	H 2
Dr Martin Luther King Jr Expwy		26	J 3
Drake Av	14	27	L 3
Draper Pl	14	28	H 5
Dresden Pl	1	27	L 4
Dreyer Av	14	26	J 4
Driggs St	8	31	J10
Driprock St	10	26	K 2
Drumgoole Rd	12	31	G 9
Drumgoole Rd E		30	E10
1-1276	12	30	F10
1277-OUT	9	30	E10
Drumgoole Rd W		30	E10
1-1630	12	30	F10
1631-OUT	9	30	E10
Drury Av	5	29	P 5
Dryden Ct	2	26	K 2
Drysdale St	14	28	K 5
Duane Ct	1	27	N 2
Dublin Pl	3	26	H 2
Dubois Av	10	26	K 2
Dudley Av	1	27	M 4
Duer Av	5	29	P 5
Duer La	1	27	N 2
Dugdale St	6	29	L 8
Duke Pl	14	26	K 4
Dumont Av	5	29	N 5
Dunbar St	8	28	J 8
Duncan Rd	1	27	N 3
Duncan St	4	29	M 5
Dunham St	9	30	E10
Durant Av		28	K 8
1-310	6	28	K 8
311-OUT	8	28	K 9
Durgess St	4	29	N 5
Dutchess Av	4	29	M 5
Dwarf St	3	26	H 2
Dyson St	4	27	O 2

E

STREET NAME AND HOUSE NUMBERS	ZONE NO.	MAP NO.	MAP GRID
Eadie Pl	1	27	N 1
Eagan Av	12	31	H10
Eagle Rd	14	26	J 3
Earle Av	14	26	K 3
Earley Pl	7	30	B11
East Albourne Av	12	30	F10
East Ashland Av	12	30	F10
East Augusta Av	8	31	H 9
East Brandis Av	8	28	H 8
East Broadway	6	28	K 7
East Buchanan St	1	27	N 1
East Figurea Av	8	31	H 9
East Gurley Av	8	28	H 8
East Loop Rd	4	29	M 6
East Macon Av	8	28	H 8
East Perkiomen Av	8	28	H 8
East Raleigh Av	10	27	L 2
East Reading Av	8	28	H 8
East Scranton Av	8	28	H 8
East Stroud Av	8	28	H 8
East Tenafly Av	12	31	G10
East Tenafly Pl	12	31	G10
Eastentry Rd	4	29	M 6
Eastman St	12	31	H10
Eaton Pl	2	26	J 2
Ebbitts St	6	29	M 8
Ebey La	12	30	F 9
Ebony St	6	29	L 7
Echo Pl	14	26	J 3
Eddy St	1	27	N 3
Eden Ct	7	30	B11
Edgar Pl	4	27	N 4
Edgar Ter	1	27	N 2
Edgegrove Av		30	F10
1-846	12	31	G 9
847-OUT	9	30	F10
Edgewater St	5	27	O 3
Edgewood Rd	8	31	J 9
Edinboro Rd	6	28	J 7
Edison St	6	29	L 7
Edith Av	12	31	G11
Edna Pl	14	26	H 3
Edstone Dr	1	27	M 3
Edward Ct	14	28	J 6
Edward Curry Av	14	26	G 4
Edwin St	12	31	G10
Egan Av	14	27	L 4
Egbert Av	10	27	L 1
Egbert Av	10	26	K 3
Egbert Pl	5	27	P 4
Egbert Sq	2	26	J 3
Egmont Pl	1	27	N 1
Elaine Ct	4	27	M 5
Elbe Av	4	27	N 4
Elder Av	9	30	E11
Eldridge Av	2	26	K 3
Eleanor La	8	31	J 9
Eleanor Pl	3	26	J 3
Eleanor St	6	28	K 6
Elias Pl	14	26	K 3
Elie Ct	14	28	H 6
Elise Ct	6	29	K 8
Elizabeth Av	10	27	L 1
Elizabeth Ct	7	30	C11
Elizabeth Grove Rd	3	26	H 2
Elizabeth Pl	9	30	F11
Elizabeth St	10	27	L 2
Elk Ct	6	29	K 8
Elkhart St	8	28	J 8
Elks Pl	9	30	E 9
Ella Pl	6	29	L 8
Ellicott Pl	1	27	M 2
Ellington St	4	27	N 4
Ellis Pl	9	30	C 9
Ellis St	7	30	B11
Ellsworth Av	12	30	F 9
Ellsworth Pl	14	27	L 4
Elm Av	12	31	G11
Elm Pl	1	27	M 4
Elm St	10	27	L 1
Elma Av	5	29	O 5
Elmbank St	12	31	H10
Elmhurst Av	1	29	L 5
Elmira Av	14	26	K 3
Elmira St	6	29	L 8
Elmtree Av	6	29	M 7
Elmwood Av	8	31	J 9
Elmwood Park Dr	14	28	H 6
Elson Ct	14	26	H 3
Elson St	14	26	H 3
Eltinge St	4	29	N 5
Eltingville Blvd	12	31	H 9
Elverton Av	8	28	J 8
Elvin St	14	27	L 4
Elwood Av	14	28	H 6
Elwood Pl	1	27	M 2
Ely Av	12	31	G10
Ely St	1	27	N 2
Emeric Ct	3	26	J 2
Emerson Av	1	27	M 4
Emerson Ct	4	27	M 4
Emerson Dr	4	27	N 4
Emily La	12	28	G 8
Emmet Av	6	28	K 8
End Pl	12	28	G 8
Endor Av	1	27	M 4
Endview St	12	31	G 9
Enfield Pl	6	29	L 7
Engert St	9	28	E 8
Englewood Av	9	30	D10
Erastina Pl	3	26	J 2
Eric La	8	28	J 8
Erie St	9	30	E10
Errington Pl	4	27	O 3
Escanaba Av	8	31	H 9
Esmac Ct	4	29	M 5
Essex Dr	14	28	J 6
Esther Depew St	6	28	K 6
Eton Pl	14	26	H 4
Eugene Pl	12	31	G10
Eugene St	12	30	D11
Eunice Pl	3	26	J 3
Eva Av	6	29	M 8
Evan Pl	12	28	G 8
Evans St	14	28	J 6
Evelyn Pl	5	27	P 4
Everett Pl	9	30	E11
Evergreen Av		29	N 5
1-89	4	29	N 5
90-OUT	5	29	N 6
Evergreen St	8	28	J 8
Everton Av	12	30	F 9
Excelsior Av	9	30	E11
Exeter St	8	28	J 8
Eylandt St	12	30	F11

F

STREET NAME AND HOUSE NUMBERS	ZONE NO.	MAP NO.	MAP GRID
Faber St	2	26	K 2
Fabian St	12	31	G 9
Fahy Av	14	26	H 3
Fairbanks Av	6	28	K 8
Fairfield St	8	28	J 8
Fairlawn Av	8	31	K 9
Fairlawn Loop	8	31	K 9
Fairview Av	14	27	L 3
Fairview Pl	4	29	M 6
Fairway Av	4	27	O 3
Fairway La	1	27	M 3
Falcon Av	6	29	L 8
Fancher Pl	3	26	H 1
Fanning St	14	27	L 4
Farraday St	14	26	J 3
Farragut Av	14	26	H 3
Father Capodanno Blvd		29	N 7
1-924	5	29	O 6
925-OUT	6	29	N 7
Fawn La	6	31	J 8
Fayann La	7	30	C12
Fayette Av	5	29	N 5
Federal Pl	3	26	H 1
Feldmeyers La	14	28	F 5
Felton St	14	26	H 3
Fenway Cir	8	28	H 8
Fern Av	8	31	H 9
Ferndale Av	14	28	H 5
Ferndale Ct	14	28	J 5
Ferry St	2	26	K 1
Ficarelle Dr	9	30	E11
Fiedler Av	1	27	N 2
Field St	14	28	K 5
Fields Av	14	28	K 5
Fieldstone Rd	14	26	H 3
Fieldway Av	8	31	J 9
Figurea Av	12	31	H 9
Filbert Av	5	29	N 6
Filer St	12	31	G 9
Filipe La	6	31	J10
Fillat St	14	26	K 4
Fillmore Av	14	26	K 4
Fillmore Pl	5	27	O 4
Fillmore St	1	27	M 1
Fine Blvd	14	27	L 4
Fingal St	12	31	H10
Fingerboard Rd		29	O 5
1-900	5	29	O 5
901-OUT (odd)	4	29	N 5
902-958 (even)	5	29	N 5
Finlay Av	9	30	E11
Finlay St	7	30	B12
Finley Av	6	29	M 8
Firth Rd	14	26	H 4
Fisher Av	7	30	C11
Fisk Pl	14	26	J 4
Fiske Av	14	26	K 3
Fitzgerald Av	8	31	J10
Flagg Ct	4	29	M 6
Flagg Pl	4	29	M 6
Flagship Cir	9	30	E11
Fletcher St	5	27	O 4
Flint St	6	29	L 8
Florence Pl	9	30	E11
Florence St	8	31	J 9
Florida Av	5	29	P 5
Florida Ter	6	28	K 6
Flower Av	9	30	D12
Flower Ct	4	27	O 3
Floyd St	10	26	K 2
Foch Av	5	29	O 5
Fonda Pl	9	30	E10
Foote Av	1	27	M 4
Ford Pl	10	27	L 2
Fordel St	5	27	O 4
Forest Av		26	H 2
1-479	1	27	N 2
480-1238	10	27	M 2
1239-1700	2	27	K 3
1701-OUT	3	26	H 2
Forest Ct	3	26	H 2
Forest Green	12	28	F 8
Forest Hill Rd	14	26	K 4
Forest Rd	4	29	M 5
Forest St	14	26	H 4
Fornes Pl	12	31	G10
Forrestal Av	12	28	G 8
Forrestal Ct	12	28	G 8
Fort Hill Cir	1	27	N 1
Fort Hill Pk	1	27	N 1
Fort Pl	1	27	O 1
Foster Av	14	29	L 5
Foster Rd	9	30	E 9
Four Corners Rd	4	29	M 5
Fox Hill Ter	5	27	O 4
Fox Hunt Ct	1	27	M 3
Fox La	6	31	L 9
Foxbeach Av	6	31	L 9
Foxholm St	6	29	L 7
Francesca La	3	26	H 3
Francine Ct	6	29	L 7
Francine La	14	26	J 4
Francis Pl	4	27	M 5
Franklin Av	1	27	N 1
Franklin D Roosevelt Boardwalk	5	29	O 7
Franklin La	6	28	J 7
Franklin Pl	14	27	L 4
Fraser Av	12	28	F 8
Fraser St	14	28	J 6
Frean St	4	27	N 3
Frede St *(bet Felton St and Elson St, Connects Gauldy Av and Caswell Av)	14	26	H 3
Frederick St	14	26	K 4
Freeborn St		29	N 7
1-99	5	29	N 7
100-OUT	6	29	N 7
Freedom Av	14	28	H 5
Freeman Pl	10	27	L 3
Fremont Av	6	29	M 6
Fremont St	1	27	N 2
Front St	4	27	O 2
Fuller Ct	6	28	K 8
Fulton St	4	27	N 3
Furman St	12	31	G10
Furness Pl	14	28	J 6
Futurity Pl	12	28	G 8

G

STREET NAME AND HOUSE NUMBERS	ZONE NO.	MAP NO.	MAP GRID
Gadsen Pl	14	28	H 5
Gail Ct	6	29	L 7
Gales La	2	26	K 1
Galesville Ct	5	29	P 5
Gall Ct	4	29	N 5
Galloway Av	2	26	K 3
Gannon Av	14	26	J 4
Gansevoort Blvd	14	26	K 4
Garden Ct	4	29	M 5
Garden St	14	27	L 4
Gardenia La	14	28	H 6
Garfield Av	5	27	O 4
Garibaldi Av	6	29	M 8
Garretson Av		29	M 6
1-170	4	29	M 6
171-OUT	5	29	N 6
Garrison Av		26	K 3
All except 315	14	26	K 3
315 only	2	26	K 3
Garth Ct	6	28	K 8
Gary Ct	14	26	H 4
Gary Pl	14	28	H 5
Gary St	12	28	G 8
Gateway Dr	4	29	N 5
Gauldy Av	14	26	H 3
Gaynor St	9	30	D10
Geissel Pl	3	26	H 2
Geldner Av	6	29	L 7
Genesee Av		31	G 9
1-209	8	28	H 8
210-OUT	12	31	G 9
Genesee St	1	27	M 4
George La	9	30	E11
George St	7	30	C12
Gervil St	9	30	E 9
Getz Av	12	28	H 8
Geyser Dr	12	30	F 9
Gibson Av	8	28	J 8
Gibson Pl	8	28	J 8
Giegerich Pl	7	30	C12
Giffords Glen	8	31	J 9
Giffords La	8	28	J 8
Gigi St	3	26	J 2
Gil Ct	12	31	H 9
Gilbert Pl	9	30	E11
Gilbert St	6	28	K 7
Giles Pl	4	27	N 4
Gill Pl	1	27	M 2
Gillard Av	12	31	H 9
Gilroy St	9	30	F 9
Gina Ct	14	28	J 6
Giordan Ct	3	26	J 2
Girard St	7	30	B11
Gladwin Av	9	30	D 9
Glascoe Av	14	26	K 3
Glen Av	1	27	N 2
Glen Rd	14	28	J 5
Glen St	14	26	G 4
Glendale Av	4	29	N 5
Glenwood Av	1	27	M 4
Glenwood Pl	10	27	L 3
Globe Av	14	26	J 3
Glover St	8	31	J10
Goethals Rd N		26	G 2
1-899	14	26	H 3
900-OUT	3	26	G 2
Goff Av	9	30	E10
Gold Av	12	28	G 8
Golf View Ct	14	28	J 6
Goller Pl	14	26	H 4
Goodall St	8	31	J10
Goodell Av	14	27	L 4
Goodrich St	3	26	H 2
Goodwin Av	14	26	K 3
Gordon Pl	1	27	M 1
Gordon St	4	27	N 3
Gothic Pl	12	28	H 8
Governor Rd	14	27	L 4
Gower St	14	27	L 4
Grace Ct	1	27	M 1
Grace Rd	6	29	L 7
Grafe St	9	28	E 8
Graham Av	14	26	H 4
Graham Blvd	5	29	N 7
Grand Av	1	27	M 3
Grandview Av	3	26	H 1
Grandview Ter	8	31	J 9
Granite Av	3	26	J 2
Grant Pl	6	29	M 7
Grant St	1	27	O 2
Grantwood Av	12	28	G 8
Grasmere Av	4	27	N 4
Grasmere Ct	5	29	N 5
Grasmere Dr	5	27	O 4
Grattan Av	6	31	K 9
Graves St	14	26	K 4
Gray St	4	27	O 3
Grayson St	6	29	L 8
Great Kills La	6	31	M 9
Great Kills Rd	8	31	J 9
Greaves Av	8	28	J 8
Greaves Ct *(connects Exeter St and Greaves Av)	8	28	J 8
Greaves La	8	31	J 9
Greeley Av	6	29	L 6
Green Ct	10	27	L 3
Green St	10	27	M 2
Green Valley Rd	12	30	F 9
Greencroft Av	8	31	K 9
Greencroft La	8	31	K 9
Greenfield Av	4	27	O 3
Greenfield Ct	4	27	O 3
Greenleaf Av	10	27	L 3
Greenport St	4	29	M 5
Greentree La	14	26	H 4
Greenway Av	14	28	J 6
Greenway Dr	1	27	M 3
Greenwood Av	1	27	M 2
Gregg Pl	1	27	M 2
Gregory La	14	28	H 6
Greta Pl	1	27	N 3
Gridley Av	3	26	H 2
Grille Ct	9	30	D 9
Grimsby St	6	29	N 7
Grissom Av	14	28	H 5
Griswold Ct	1	27	M 3
Groton St	12	31	J10
Grove Av	2	26	K 2
Grove Pl	2	26	K 2
Grove St	4	27	O 3
Grymes Hill Rd	1	27	N 3
Guilford St	5	29	P 5
Guillard Av	12	31	H 9
Gulf Av	14	26	G 3
Gunton Pl	9	28	E 8
Gurdon St	14	26	K 4
Gurley Av		28	H 8
1-399	8	28	J 8
400-OUT	12	28	H 8
Guyon Av	6	28	K 8

H

STREET NAME AND HOUSE NUMBERS	ZONE NO.	MAP NO.	MAP GRID
Hafstrom St	6	28	K 8
Hagaman Pl	2	26	K 2
Hale St	7	30	C11
Hales Av	12	31	H10
Hallister St	9	30	E10
Halpin Av	12	31	G 9
Hamden Av	6	29	M 6
Hamilton Av	1	27	N 1
Hamilton St	4	27	N 4
Hamlin Pl	2	26	K 3
Hammock La	12	30	F 9
Hampton Green	12	28	F 8
Hampton Pl	9	28	E 8
Hancock St	5	29	N 6
Hank Pl	9	30	F11

STREET NAME AND HOUSE NUMBERS	ZONE NO.	MAP NO.	MAP GRID
Hannah St	1	27	O 2
Hanover Av	9	30	F 11
Hanover Av	4	27	N 4
Harbor La	3	26	J 2
Harbor Loop	3	26	H 2
Harbor Rd	3	26	H 2
Harbor View Ct	1	27	N 2
Harbor View Pl E	5	27	P 4
Harbor View Pl N	5	27	P 4
Harbor View Pl S	5	27	P 4
Harbour Ct	8	31	J 10
Hardin Av	10	27	L 3
Hardy Pl	8	31	J 9
Hardy St	4	27	N 3
Harold Av	12	31	H10
Harold St	14	28	K 5
Harris Av	14	26	K 4
Harris La	9	30	E 9
Harrison Av	2	26	K 2
Harrison Pl	10	27	L 1
Harrison St	4	27	O 3
Hart Av	10	27	M 2
Hart Blvd	1	27	M 2
Hart Loop	6	29	K 8
Hart Pl	7	30	C11
Hartford Av	10	27	M 3
Hartford St	8	31	J 9
Harvard Av	1	27	N 1
Harvest Av	10	27	L 3
Harvey Av	14	26	K 4
Harvey St	5	27	O 4
Hasbrouck Hill Rd	4	29	N 5
Hastings St	5	29	O 5
Hatfield Pl	2	26	K 2
Haughwout Av	2	26	K 2
Haven Av	6	29	M 6
Haven Esplanade	1	27	N 2
Havenwood Rd	1	27	N 2
Haverford Av	14	28	H 6
Hawley Av	9	30	F 10
Hawthorne Av	14	26	J 3
Hay St	4	27	N 4
Haynes St	9	30	F 10
Haywood St	7	30	C11
Hazel Pl	14	26	J 3
Heaney Av	3	26	H 2
Heather Ct	3	26	J 3
Heberton Av	2	26	K 2
Hecker St	7	30	C11
Heenan Av	12	31	G 9
Heffernan St	12	28	G 8
Heinz Av	8	31	J 10
Helena Rd	4	29	M 5
Helene Ct	9	30	E10
Helios Pl	9	30	E 9
Hemlock Ct	9	28	E 8
Hemlock La	9	30	D 9
Hemlock St	9	30	E 9
Hempstead Av	6	29	N 7
Henderson Av		27	L 2
1-370	1	27	M 2
371-OUT	10	27	L 2
Henderson Ct	10	27	M 2
Hendricks Av	1	27	N 2
Henning St	14	27	L 4
Henry Pl	5	29	N 6
Herbert St	9	30	F 11
Hereford St	8	28	J 8
Herkimer St	1	27	M 3
Herrick Av	9	30	D10
Hervey St	9	28	E 8
Hett Av	6	29	M 8
Heusden St	3	26	J 2
Hewitt Av	4	27	M 4
Hickory Av	5	29	O 5
Hickory Cir	12	28	F 8
Hickory Ct	9	28	E 8
High St	5	27	P 4
Highland Av	1	27	M 3
Highland La	8	31	J 10
Highland Rd	8	31	J 9
Highmount Rd	8	31	J 9
Highpoint Rd	4	29	M 5
Highview Av	1	27	N 1
Hill St	4	27	O 3
Hillbrook Ct	5	27	O 4
Hillbrook Dr	5	29	O 5
Hillcrest Av	8	31	J 9
Hillcrest Ct	5	27	N 4
Hillcrest Rd	1	27	N 3
Hillcrest St		31	J 10
1-243	8	31	J 9
244-OUT	12	31	J 10
Hillcrest Ter	5	29	N 5
Hilldale Ct	5	27	O 4
Hillis St	12	31	G10
Hillman Av	14	26	H 4
Hillridge Ct	5	27	O 4
Hillside Av	4	27	N 3
Hillside Ter	8	31	J 9
Hilltop Pl	8	31	J 9
Hilltop Rd	12	31	J 10
Hilltop Ter	4	29	M 5
Hillview La	4	27	M 5
Hillview Pl	4	29	M 5
Hillwood Ct	5	27	O 4
Hinton St	12	28	G 8
Hirsch La	14	26	H 3
Hitchcock Av	6	28	K 7
Hoda Pl	12	31	G10
Hodges Pl	14	27	L 4
Holbernt Ct	2	26	K 2
Holcomb Av	12	30	F 9
Holden Blvd	14	26	K 4
Holdridge Av	12	31	H10
Holgate St	14	26	J 4
Holiday Dr	14	26	J 3
Holiday Way	14	26	J 3
Holland Av	3	26	H 1
Holly Av	8	31	J 9
Holly Pl	6	29	L 7
Holly St	4	29	N 5
Holsman Rd	1	27	N 4
Holton Av	9	30	F 11
Home Av	5	27	P 4
Home Pl		26	J 3
1-69	2	26	J 3
70-OUT	14	26	J 3
Homer St	1	27	O 2
Homestead Av	2	26	K 2
Hooker Pl		26	J 2
1-199	2	26	J 2
200-OUT	3	26	J 2
Hooper Av	6	28	K 8
Hope Av	5	27	O 4
Hope La	5	27	P 4
Hopkins Av	6	28	K 8
Hopping Av	7	30	B11
Houseman Av	3	26	J 2
Houston La	2	26	J 3
Houston St	2	26	K 2
Howard Av	1	27	M 4
Howard Cir	1	27	N 3
Howard Ct	10	27	L 3
Howe St	10	27	L 3
Howton Av	8	28	J 8
Hoyt Av	1	27	M 2
Hudson Pl	3	26	J 2
Hudson St	4	27	O 3
Hughes Av	14	26	G 4
Huguenot Av	12	28	F 8
Huguenot Av	12	31	G10
Hull Av	6	29	M 6
Humbert St	5	29	O 5
Humbolt St (now Raily St)	12	28	F 8
Hunt La	4	29	M 5
Hunter Av	6	29	M 6
Hunter Pl	1	27	M 2
Hunter St	4	29	N 5
Hunton St	4	29	N 5
Hurlbert St	5	29	N 6
Huron Pl	1	27	M 2
Hurst St	10	26	K 2
Husson St		29	M 6
1-199	5	29	M 6
200-OUT	6	29	M 6
Hyatt St	1	27	O 1
Hygeia Pl	4	27	O 3
Hylan Blvd		30	B12
1-1969	5	27	O 4
1970-3534	6	29	M 7
3535-4225	8	31	K 9
4226-5503	12	31	G11
5504-6800	9	30	D12
6801 -OUT	7	30	C12
Hylan Pl	6	29	M 7

I

STREET NAME AND HOUSE NUMBERS	ZONE NO.	MAP NO.	MAP GRID
Ibsen Av	12	28	G 8
Ida Ct	12	31	G10
Idaho Av	9	30	E10
Idlease Pl	6	29	N 7
Igros Ct	9	30	E10
Ilion Pl	6	29	L 7
Ilyse Ct	6	28	K 8
Ilyssa Way	12	28	G 8
Ina St	6	29	M 8
Indale Av	9	30	E11
Independence Av	14	28	H 7
Industrial Loop E	9	30	D 8
Industrial Loop W	9	30	D 8
Industry Rd	14	26	F 4
Inez St	9	30	F11
Ingram Av	14	26	K 4
Innis St		26	J 2
1-134	2	26	J 2
135-OUT	3	26	J 2
Interstate Hwy 278		26	F 2
Interstate Hwy 278		27	N 4
Inwood Rd	1	27	N 4
Iona St	5	29	N 7
Ionia Av		30	F10
1-796	12	30	F10
797-OUT	9	30	F10
Iowa Pl	14	26	K 4
Irma Pl	1	27	M 3
Iron Mine Dr	4	29	M 6
Ironwood St	8	28	J 8
Iroquois St	5	29	N 7
Irving Pl	4	27	N 3
Irvington St	12	31	G11
Isabella Av	6	29	L 8
Isernia Av	6	29	M 8
Islin Pl	2	26	K 2
Islington St	8	28	J 8
Ismay St	14	28	K 5
Isora Pl	6	29	L 8
Ivy Ct	9	30	E 9

J

STREET NAME AND HOUSE NUMBERS	ZONE NO.	MAP NO.	MAP GRID
Jackson Av	5	29	O 5
Jackson St	4	27	O 2
Jacobs St	7	30	C11
Jacques Av	6	29	L 7
Jaffe St	14	26	J 3
Jaime La	12	28	G 8
James Ct	14	26	J 3
James Pl	5	27	O 4
Jansen Ct	12	31	G10
Jansen St	12	31	H10
Jardine Av	14	26	H 4
Jarvis Av	12	31	G11
Jasper St	14	28	K 5
Jean Pl	14	26	H 3
Jeanette Av	12	31	G 9
Jefferson Av	6	29	M 6
Jefferson Blvd	12	31	G 9
Jefferson St		29	M 6
1-200	4	29	M 6
201-OUT	6	29	M 6
Jeffrey Pl	7	30	C11
Jenna La	4	29	M 5
Jennifer Ct	14	28	H 5
Jennifer La	6	29	M 8
Jennifer Pl	14	26	H 4
Jerome Av	5	29	N 6
Jerome Rd	5	29	N 5
Jersey St	1	27	N 1
Jessica Ct	12	31	H 9
Jessica La	9	30	E 9
Jewett Av		26	K 2
1-593	2	26	K 2
594-OUT	14	26	K 3
Jillian Ct	10	26	K 3
Joan Pl	14	27	L 3
Joel Pl	6	28	K 7
Johanna La	9	30	F11
John St	2	26	K 2
Johnson Av	7	30	B11
Johnson Pl	4	29	N 5
Johnson St	9	30	D 8
Johnston Ter	9	30	E11
Joline Av	7	30	C11
Joline La	7	30	C12
Jones Pl	10	27	M 2
Jones St	14	26	H 4
Joseph Av	14	28	K 5
Joseph La	5	29	O 5
Josephine St	14	27	L 4
Journeay Av	12	30	F 9
Journeay St	3	26	H 2
Joyce La	7	30	C11
Joyce St	5	29	M 6
Jules Dr	14	26	H 3
Julie Ct	14	26	K 4
Jumel St	8	28	J 8
Juni Ct	14	28	J 6
Juniper Pl	6	29	M 6
Jupiter La	3	26	H 2
Justin Av	6	28	K 8

K

STREET NAME AND HOUSE NUMBERS	ZONE NO.	MAP NO.	MAP GRID
Kaltenmeier La	5	27	O 4
Kalver Pl	3	26	J 2
Karen Ct	10	26	K 3
Katan Av		31	H 9
1-479	8	31	H 9
480-OUT	12	31	H 9
Katan Loop	8	31	J 9
Kathleen Ct	7	30	C12
Kathy Ct	12	28	H 8
Kathy Pl	14	28	H 6
Kay Pl *(off Maryland Av)	5	27	O 4
Keating Pl	14	28	J 5
Keating St	9	30	F11
Keats St	8	31	J 9
Keegans La	8	31	K 9
Keeley St	5	27	P 4
Keiber Ct	14	26	K 3
Kell Av	14	26	K 4
Keller Av	9	30	F10
Kelly Blvd	14	28	J 6
Kelvin Av	6	28	K 8
Kemball Av	14	26	K 4
Kenilworth Av	12	28	G 8
Kenmore St	12	28	G 8
Kenneth Pl	9	30	E11
Kennington St	8	28	J 8
Kenny Rd	9	30	D11
Kensico St	6	28	K 7
Kensington Av	5	29	O 5
Kent Av	14	29	L 5
Kent St	6	28	K 6
Kenwood Av	12	31	G11
Keppel Av	7	30	C12
Kermit Av	5	29	N 5
Kerry La	7	30	C12
Keune Ct	4	29	M 5
King St		31	J 10
1-209	8	31	J 10
210-OUT	12	31	J 10
Kingdom Av	12	31	G10
Kinghorn St	12	31	H10
Kingsbridge Av	14	26	H 3
Kingsland St	9	30	F11
Kingsley Av	14	26	K 3
Kingsley Pl	1	27	N 2
Kinsey Pl	3	26	H 2
Kirby Ct	1	27	N 1
Kirshon Av	14	26	H 3
Kissam Av	6	29	L 8
Kissel Av		27	M 2
1-399	10	27	M 1
400-OUT	1	27	M 2
Kiswick St	6	29	M 7
Klondike Av	14	28	H 5
Knapp St	14	28	H 5
Knauth Pl	5	29	O 5
Knesel St	9	28	E 8
Knollwood Ct	3	26	H 3
Knox Pl	14	27	L 4
Knox St	9	30	F11
Koch Blvd	12	31	H10
Kraft Pl	12	31	G10
Kramer Av	9	30	E 9
Kramer Pl	2	26	K 2
Kramer St	5	29	O 5
Kreischer St	9	30	C 9
Kruser St	6	29	L 7
Kunath Av	9	30	E 8
Kyle Ct	12	28	F 8

L

STREET NAME AND HOUSE NUMBERS	ZONE NO.	MAP NO.	MAP GRID
Labau Av	1	27	M 4
Laconia Av		29	N 6
1-599	5	29	N 6
600-OUT	6	29	N 6
Ladd Av	12	28	G 8
Lafayette Av	1	27	M 1
Lafayette St	7	30	B11
LaForge Av	2	26	K 2
LaForge Pl	2	26	K 2
LaGrange Pl	2	26	K 2
LaGuardia Av	14	27	L 4
Lake Av	3	26	J 2
Lakeland Rd	14	27	L 3
Lakeside Pl	5	29	O 5
Lakeview Ter	5	29	N 5
Lakewood Rd	1	27	M 3
Lamberst La	14	26	G 3
Lambert St	14	26	H 3
Lamberts La	14	26	H 3
Lamoka Av		31	H 9
1-331	8	31	H 9
332-OUT	12	31	H 9
Lamont Av		30	E10
1-796	12	30	F10
797-OUT	9	30	E10
Lamped Loop	14	28	H 6
Lamport Blvd	5	29	O 5
Lander Av	14	26	H 3
Landis Av	5	29	O 5
Langere Pl	5	27	O 3
Lansing St	5	29	O 6
Larch Ct	9	28	E 8
Laredo Av	12	31	H 9
Larkin St	2	26	K 1
LaSalle St	3	26	J 2
Latham Pl	9	30	E 9
Lathrop Av		26	K 3
1-300	14	26	K 3
301-OUT	2	26	J 3
Latimer Av	14	28	G 5
Latourette La	14	28	J 6
Latourette St	9	30	E11
Laurel Av	4	27	N 3
Lava St	5	29	O 6
Law Pl	10	27	L 3
Lawn Av	6	28	K 7
Lawrence Av	10	27	M 2
Lawton Av	14	28	F 5
Layton Av	1	27	N 1
Leason Pl	14	28	J 6
Ledyard Pl	5	29	N 5
Lee Av	7	30	C11
Leeds St	6	29	L 8
Legate Av	12	28	G 8
Leggett Pl	14	26	H 4
Legion Pl	5	27	O 4
Lehigh St	7	30	C11
Leigh Av	14	26	H 3
Lenevar Av	9	30	E 9
Lenhart St	7	30	C11
Lennon Ct	8	28	H 8
Lenore Ct	14	26	J 3
Lenzie St	12	31	H10
Leo St	14	26	J 3
Leona St	14	26	H 4
Leonard Av		26	J 3
1-330	14	26	K 3
331-OUT	2	26	J 3
LeRoy St	14	28	G 5
Leslie Av	5	29	N 5
Lester St	14	27	L 4
Leverett Av		28	H 8
1-546	8	28	H 8
547-OUT	12	28	H 8
Leverett Ct *(off Leverett Av bet Miles Av and Greaves Av)	8	28	J 8
Levit Av	14	26	J 3
Levit Pl	14	26	J 3
Lewiston St	14	28	J 6
Lexa Pl	12	31	G10
Lexington Av	2	26	K 2
Lexington La	8	28	J 8
Leyden Av	3	26	H 2
Liberty Av		29	N 6
1-149	4	29	M 6
150-OUT	5	29	N 6
Lighthouse Av	6	28	K 7
Lightner Av	14	27	L 4
Lilac Ct	3	26	H 2
Lillian Pl	8	31	J 10
Lily Pond Av	5	29	P 5
Lincoln Av	6	29	M 7
Lincoln Pl	5	27	O 4
Lincoln St	14	27	L 4
Linda Av	5	29	P 5
Linda Ct	2	27	K 2
Linda La	12	28	G 8
Lindbergh Av	6	29	L 7
Linden Av	12	31	G11
Linden Av	3	26	J 2
Linden Pl	4	27	P 4
Linden St	10	27	M 1
Lindenwood Pl	8	31	J 9
Linton Pl	8	28	J 8
Linwood Av	5	29	O 5
Lion St	7	30	C11
Lipsett Av	12	31	G10
Lisa La	12	30	F 9
Lisa Pl	14	26	H 4
Lisbon Pl	6	29	M 6
Lisk Av	3	26	H 3
Liss St	12	31	H10
Little Clove Rd	1	27	M 4
Littlefield Av	12	31	J 10
Livermore Av		26	K 3
1-99	2	26	K 3
100-OUT	14	26	K 3
Livingston Av	14	26	K 4
Livingston Ct	10	27	M 1
Llewellyn Pl	10	26	K 2
Lloyd Ct	10	27	L 3
Lockman Av	3	26	H 2
Lockman Loop	3	26	H 2
Lockwood Pl	14	26	K 3
Locust Av	6	29	L 7
Locust Ct	9	30	E 9
Locust Pl	8	31	J 9
Logan Av	1	27	M 4
Lois Pl	1	27	M 2
Lola St *(off Quincy Av opposite Pinto St)	5	29	N 7
Lombard Ct	12	28	F 8
London Ct	6	28	K 6
London Rd	6	28	K 6
Long Pond La	4	27	O 4
Longdale St	14	26	H 3
Longfellow Av	1	27	M 4
Longview Rd		27	N 4
1-145	4	27	N 4
146-OUT	1	27	N 4
Loret Ct	10	27	L 2
Loretto St	7	30	C12
Loring Av	12	28	G 8
Lorraine Av	12	31	G 9
Lorraine Loop	9	30	E 9
Lortel Av	14	27	L 4
Louis St	4	27	N 2
Louise La	1	27	M 4
Louise St	12	31	G10
Lovelace Av	12	28	H 8
Lovell Av	14	28	J 5
Lowell St	6	28	K 6
Lower Sharrott Rd *(near Sharrotts Rd)	9	30	D 9
Lucille Av	9	30	E 9
Ludlow St	12	31	G 9
Ludwig La	3	26	H 3
Ludwig St	10	27	L 2
Luigi Ct	6	29	L 7
Luigi Pl	6	29	L 7
Luke Ct	6	28	J 8
Lukes Av	9	28	E 8
Luna Cir	12	31	H10
Lundi Ct	14	28	J 6
Lundsten Av	9	30	D 9
Lupton St	14	28	K 5
Luten Av	12	30	F10
Lyle Ct	6	28	K 8
Lyman Av	5	27	P 4
Lynch St	12	31	G11
Lyndale Av	12	31	H 9
Lyndale La	12	31	H 9
Lynhurst Av	5	27	O 3
Lynn Ct	14	26	J 3
Lynn St	6	29	L 8
Lynnhaven Pl	10	27	L 3
Lyon Pl	14	26	J 3

M

STREET NAME AND HOUSE NUMBERS	ZONE NO.	MAP NO.	MAP GRID
Mace St	6	28	K 7
Mackay Av	14	28	F 6
Macon Av	12	28	G 6
Macormac Pl	3	26	H 2
Mada Av	10	27	M 2
Madan Ct	14	26	J 3
Madera St	9	30	F11
Madigan Pl	4	27	N 4
Madison Av	14	26	J 3
Madsen Av	9	30	C11
Magnolia Av	5	29	N 6
Maguire Av	9	30	E 9
MaGuire Ct	9	30	E10
Maiden La	7	30	C11
Main St	7	30	B11
Maine Av	14	26	K 3
Major Av	5	29	O 5
Malden Pl	6	29	L 8
Mallard La	9	30	E10
Mallory Av	5	29	O 5
Mallow St	9	30	E 9
Malone Av	6	28	K 8
Malvine Av	9	30	E 9
Manchester Dr	12	30	F 9
Mandy Ct	9	30	E 9
Manee Av	9	30	E11

STREET NAME AND HOUSE NUMBERS	ZONE NO.	MAP NO.	MAP GRID
Manhattan St	7	30	C12
Manila Av	6	29	M 8
Manila Pl	6	29	M 8
Manley St	9	30	C 9
Mann Av	14	26	K 4
Manor Ct	6	28	J 7
Manor Rd		27	L 3
1-200	10	27	L 3
201-OUT	14	27	L 3
Manorville Ct	5	29	O 5
Mansion Av	8	31	K 9
Maple Av	2	26	K 1
Maple Ct	12	28	F 8
Maple Pkwy	3	26	J 2
Maple Ter	6	29	M 8
Mapleton Av	6	29	N 7
Maplewood Av	6	28	K 7
Maplewood Pl	6	29	M 7
Marble St	14	26	K 4
Marc St	14	26	J 3
Marcie La	8	31	K 9
Marcy Av	9	30	F 9
Maretzek Ct	9	30	E10
Margaret St	8	31	J 9
Margaretta Ct	14	26	K 3
Maria La	12	31	H 9
Marianne St	2	26	K 3
Marie Pl	5	29	N 5
Marie St	4	27	N 4
Marine Dr	9	30	E11
Marine Way	6	29	M 8
Mariners La	3	26	J 2
Marion Av	4	27	N 2
Marion St	10	26	K 2
Marisa Cir	9	30	E 9
Mark St	4	29	N 5
Market St	10	27	L 2
Markham Ct *(in Edwin Markham Housing)	10	27	L 1
Markham Dr *(in Edwin Markham Housing)	10	27	L 1
Markham La *(in Edwin Markham Housing)	10	27	L 1
Markham Pl	14	26	K 3
Markham Rd *(in Edwin Markham Housing)	10	27	L 1
Markham Walk *(in Edwin Markham Housing)	10	27	L 1
Marne Av	12	28	H 8
Marscher Pl	9	30	F11
Marsh Av	14	28	H 6
Marshall Av	14	29	L 5
Martha St	1	27	M 4
Martin Av	14	26	K 4
Martineau St	3	26	H 1
Martling Av		27	L 3
1-214	10	27	L 3
215-OUT	14	27	L 3
Marvin Rd	9	30	E10
Marx St	1	27	L 4
Mary St	4	27	N 4
Maryland Av	5	27	O 4
Maryland La *(off Maryland Av)	5	27	O 4
Maryland Pl *(off College Av)	14	27	L 3
Mason Av		29	M 7
1-532	5	29	N 6
533-OUT	6	29	M 7
Mason Blvd	9	30	E 9
Mason St	4	29	N 5
Massachusetts St	7	30	B12
Mathews Av	10	27	M 3
Matthew Pl	3	26	J 3
Maxim St *(now Court Pl)	6	28	K 7
Maxine La	14	26	J 3
Maxwell Av	12	31	G11
May Av	14	26	H 3
Mayberry Promenade	12	31	H10
Maybury Av	8	31	J 9
Maybury Ct	6	31	K 9
McArthur Av	12	28	G 8
McBaine Av	9	30	E 9
McClean Av	5	29	O 5
McCormack Pl	5	29	N 5
McCully Av	6	28	K 7
McDermott Av	5	29	N 6
McDivitt Av	14	28	J 5
McDonald St	14	28	K 5
McFarland Av	5	29	O 5
McGregor St	9	30	F11
McKee Av	8	31	K 9
McKinley Av	6	28	K 7
McLaughlin St	5	29	O 6
McVeigh Av	14	28	J 6
Meade Loop	9	30	D11
Meade St	9	30	D11
Meadow Av	4	27	N 4
Meadow Av		29	N 5
Meadow Ct	9	28	E 8
Meadow La	6	31	J 8
Meadow Pl	5	29	N 6
Medford Rd	4	29	M 5
Medina St	6	29	L 8
Meeker St	6	28	K 6
Meisner Av	6	28	K 6
Melba St	14	27	L 4
Melhorn Rd	14	27	L 4
Melissa St	14	26	J 3
Melrose Av	1	27	M 3
Melrose Pl	8	31	J 9
Melville St	9	30	F11
Melvin Av	14	28	F 5
Melyn Pl	3	26	J 2
Memo St	9	30	F11
Memory Ct	4	27	O 3
Memphis Av	12	31	H 9
Mendelsohn St	5	27	O 4
Mercer Pl	8	31	J 9
Mercury La	14	28	J 6
Meredith Av	14	26	F 4
Merkel Pl	6	31	L 9
Merle Pl	5	27	O 4
Merrick Av	1	29	L 5
Merrill Av	14	26	H 4
Merriman Av	14	27	L 3
Merry Mount St	14	28	H 6
Mersereau Av	3	26	H 1
Metcalfe St	4	27	N 3
Metropolitan Av	1	27	M 3
Meyer La	5	27	O 4
Michael Ct	8	28	J 8
Michelle Ct	3	26	J 2
Michelle La	6	29	M 8
Middle Loop Rd	8	28	H 8
Midland Av	6	29	M 6
Midland Rd	8	31	J 9
Midway Pl	4	29	N 5
Milbank Rd	6	29	M 8
Milburn Av	6	29	L 7
Milburn St	6	29	L 7
Milden Av	1	27	M 4
Mildred Av	14	28	G 5
Miles Av	8	28	J 8
Milford Av	1	27	M 4
Milford Dr	1	27	M 4
Mill Rd	6	29	L 8
Miller St	14	27	L 3
Mills Av	5	29	O 5
Milton Av	6	29	M 8
Mimosa La	12	28	F 8
Minerva Pl	1	27	N 1
Miniturn Av	9	30	E10
Minna St	4	29	N 5
Minthorne St	1	27	O 2
Minturn Av	9	30	E10
Mobile Av	6	28	K 7
Moffett St	12	31	G 9
Mohn Pl	1	27	M 4
Monahan Av	14	28	J 5
Monroe Av	1	27	O 2
Monroe Pl	14	28	K 5
Monsey Pl	3	26	J 3
Montauk Pl	14	26	J 4
Montell St	2	26	K 2
Monterey Av	12	28	H 8
Montgomery Av	1	27	O 2
Monticello Ter	8	31	J 9
Montreal Av	6	28	K 8
Montvale Pl	8	31	J 9
Moody Pl	10	27	M 2
Moore St	6	28	K 7
Morani St	14	26	J 4
Moreland St	6	29	M 7
Morgan La	14	26	H 4
Morley Av	6	28	K 7
Morningstar Rd	3	26	J 2
Morris Pl	8	31	J 9
Morris St	9	28	E 8
Morrison Av	10	27	L 2
Morrow St	3	26	H 2
Morse Av	14	29	L 5
Morton St	6	28	K 7
Mosel Av	4	27	N 4
Mosel Loop	4	27	N 4
Mosely Av	12	31	G10
Motley Av	14	27	L 4
Mott St	12	31	H 9
Mountainside Rd	4	29	N 5
Mountainview Av	14	27	L 4
Mulberry Av	14	28	H 5
Mulberry Cir	14	28	H 5
Muldoon Av	12	28	F 7
Muller Av	14	26	K 3
Mundy Av	10	26	K 3
Murdock Pl	3	26	J 2
Murray Hulbert Av	1	27	O 2
Murray Pl	4	27	N 3
Murray St	9	30	C11
Myle St	9	30	C10
Myrna La	12	30	F 9
Myrtle Av	10	27	L 2

N

STREET NAME AND HOUSE NUMBERS	ZONE NO.	MAP NO.	MAP GRID
Nadal Pl	14	26	H 4
Nadine St	6	28	K 7
Nahant St	8	28	J 8
Nancy Ct	6	28	J 8
Nancy La	7	30	C12
Narrows Rd N		27	N 4
1-360	5	27	O 4
361-OUT	4	27	N 4
Narrows Rd S		27	N 4
1-360	5	27	O 4
361-OUT	4	27	N 4
Nash Ct	8	31	J 9
Nashville St	7	30	C11
Nassau Pl	7	30	C11
Nassau St	1	27	N 1
Natalie Pl	14	26	J 3
Nathan Ct	9	30	E10
Natick St	6	28	K 7
Naughton Av	5	29	M 6
Nautilus Ct	5	27	P 4
Nautilus St	5	27	P 4
Navesink Pl	6	29	M 8
Neal Dow Av	14	26	K 3
Neckar Av	4	27	N 4
Nedra La	12	28	F 8
Nehring Av	14	28	H 6
Nelson Av	8	31	J 9
Neptune Pl	14	26	J 4
Neptune St	6	29	M 8
Nesmythe Ter	1	27	N 3
Netherland Av	3	26	H 2
Neutral Av	6	29	M 8
Nevada Av	6	28	K 6
New Dorp La	6	29	L 7
New Dorp Plz	6	29	L 7
New La	5	27	P 4
New St	2	26	K 2
New York Pl	14	26	K 3
Newark Av	3	26	K 2
Newberry Av	4	29	N 5
Newfolden Pl	7	30	C11
Newkirk Av	2	26	K 2
Newton St	12	31	G11
Newvale Av	6	28	J 7
Niagara St	1	27	M 4
Nicholas Av	2	26	K 1
Nicholas St	1	27	N 1
Nicolosi Dr	12	31	G11
Nicolosi Loop	12	30	G11
Nightingale St	6	29	L 6
Niles Pl	14	28	K 5
Nina Av	14	26	J 4
Nippon Av	12	30	F 9
Nixon Av	4	27	O 2
Noble Pl	10	27	L 2
Noel St	12	31	H10
Nolan Av	8	31	J 9
Nome Av	14	28	H 5
Norden St	4	29	M 5
Norma Pl	1	27	M 3
Normalee Rd	5	29	O 5
Norman Pl	9	30	F11
North Av		26	K 3
1-70	2	26	K 3
71-OUT	14	26	K 3
North Bridge St	9	30	C10
North Burgher Av	10	27	L 1
North Clove Rd	1	27	M 3
North Dr	5	27	O 4
North Gannon Av	14	26	K 4
North Mada Av	10	27	M 2
North Pine Ter	12	31	G10
North Railroad Av		29	N 6
1-800	4	29	N 6
801-OUT	6	29	M 6
North Railroad St	12	31	G10
North Randall Av	1	27	M 2
North Rhett Av	8	31	J 9
North Saint Austin's Pl	10	27	M 2
North St	2	26	K 1
North St	10	27	L 1
North Tremont Av	14	26	J 3
Northcote Av	4	27	N 4
Northcote Pl *(near Northcote Av)	4	27	N 4
Northentry Rd	4	29	M 6
Northern Blvd	1	27	M 4
Northfield Av	3	26	H 2
Northfield Ct	3	26	H 1
Northport La	14	28	H 6
Norwalk Av	14	27	L 4
Norway Av	5	29	O 5
Norwich St	14	28	K 5
Norwood Av	4	27	O 3
Norwood Ct	4	27	N 3
Nostrand Av	14	26	H 4
Notre Dame Av	8	31	H 9
Notus Av	12	31	G 9
Nubro St	9	30	F10
Nugent Av		29	N 7
1-700	5	29	O 6
701-OUT	6	29	N 7
Nugent St	6	28	K 7
Nunley Ct	4	27	N 4
Nutley Pl	10	27	M 3
Nutwood Ct	6	28	J 8

O

STREET NAME AND HOUSE NUMBERS	ZONE NO.	MAP NO.	MAP GRID
Oak Av	6	29	L 8
Oak Ct	8	31	J 9
Oak La	12	28	G 8
Oak St	5	27	O 4
Oakdale Av	4	29	M 5
Oakdale St		31	H10
1-199	8	31	J 9
200-OUT	12	31	H10
Oakland Av	10	27	L 2
Oakland Ter	4	27	N 3
Oakley Pl	6	29	L 7
Oakville St	14	28	K 5
Oakwood Av	1	27	M 2
Oban St	12	31	H10
Oberlin St	5	29	O 5
Occident Av	4	27	N 2
Ocean Av	5	29	P 5
Ocean Drive Way	12	31	H11
Ocean Rd	8	31	J 9
Ocean Ter		29	L 5
1-168	14	29	L 5
169-OUT	1	27	M 4
Oceanic Av	12	31	J10
Oceanside Av	5	29	O 6
Oceanview Av	12	31	H11
Oceanview La	1	27	M 4
Oceanview Pl	8	31	J 9
O'Connor Av	14	26	K 4
Odell Pl	9	30	F10
Oder Av	4	27	N 4
Odin St	6	29	L 7
Ogden St	12	31	H10
O'Gorman Av		28	K 8
1-399	6	28	K 8
400-OUT	8	31	K 9
Ohio Pl	14	26	K 3
Old Amboy Rd	12	31	H 9
Old Farmers La	4	27	M 5
Old Mill Rd	6	28	J 7
Old Mill Rd		29	L 8
Old Town Rd		29	N 5
1-131	4	29	N 5
132-OUT	5	29	N 5
Oldfield St	6	29	M 7
Olga Pl	5	27	O 4
Olive St	10	27	L 2
Oliver Av	9	30	E10
Oliver Pl	14	26	H 4
Olympia Blvd		29	N 7
1-920	5	29	O 6
921-OUT	6	29	N 7
Omaha St	3	26	G 1
Oneida Av	1	27	M 4
Ontario Av	1	27	M 4
Opp Ct	12	28	H 8
Opp St	12	28	H 8
Opus Ct	4	27	O 3
Orange Av	2	26	K 2
Orange St *(off Union Av)	3	26	J 2
Orchard Av	7	30	C11
Orchard La	12	31	H10
Orchard St	12	31	G 9
Orchid La	14	28	H 5
Ordell Av	2	26	K 3
Oregon Rd	5	29	N 5
Orinoco Pl	3	26	J 2
Orlando St	5	29	O 6
Ormond Pl	5	27	O 3
Ormsby Av	9	30	F11
Osage La	12	31	H10
Osborn Av	8	31	J 9
Osborne St	12	31	H10
Osgood Av		27	N 3
1-294	4	27	N 3
295-OUT	5	27	O 4
Oswald Pl	9	30	E11
Oswego St	1	27	M 4
Otis Av	6	29	L 7
Otsego Av	1	27	M 4
Outerbridge Av	9	30	E10
Oval, The	4	29	M 6
Ovas Ct	12	31	H 9
Overlook Av	4	29	M 5
Overlook Dr	4	27	N 4
Overlook Ter	5	29	O 5
Ovis Pl	6	28	K 8
Ox Ct	14	28	H 5
Oxford Pl	1	27	N 2
Oxholm Av	1	27	M 3

P

STREET NAME AND HOUSE NUMBERS	ZONE NO.	MAP NO.	MAP GRID
Pacific Av	12	31	H 9
Page Av		30	C11
1-143	9	30	C11
144-OUT	7	30	C11
Palace Ct	4	29	M 5
Palisade St	5	29	P 5
Palma Dr	4	27	N 4
Palmer Av	2	26	K 2
Pamela La	2	29	N 5
Pan St	9	30	C11
Paradise Pl	7	30	C12
Parish Av	14	28	F 5
Park Av	2	26	K 2
Park Ct	1	27	M 3
Park Dr N	14	28	H 5
Park Hill Av	4	27	O 3
Park Hill Cir	4	27	O 3
Park Hill Ct	4	27	O 3
Park Hill Dr *(off Park Hill Ct)	4	27	O 3
Park Hill La	4	27	O 3
Park La	1	27	N 3
Park Pl	1	27	N 1
Park Rd	12	31	H10
Park St	6	28	K 7
Park Ter	8	31	J 9
Parker St	7	30	C11
Parkinson Av	5	29	N 5
Parkview Loop	14	26	J 4
Parkview Pl	10	27	M 3
Parkwood Av	9	30	E10
Parsons Pl	1	27	M 3
Patten St	7	30	B11
Patterson Av		29	N 7
1 - 669	5	29	N 7
670-OUT	6	29	N 7
Patty Ct	12	31	H 9
Paulding Av	14	26	H 4
Pauw St	1	27	N 2
Pavillion Hill Ter	1	27	O 2
Pawling Av	12	30	F10
Paxton St	1	27	O 2
Payne St	14	28	H 6
Pearl St	4	27	N 3
Pearle Pl	12	31	H10
Pearsall St	5	29	O 6
Pearson St	14	28	G 5
Peck Ct	6	29	K 8
Peel Pl	6	29	L 8
Peggy La	6	29	N 7
Pelican Cir	6	29	M 8
Pelton Av	10	27	L 1
Pelton Pl	10	27	L 1
Pemberton Av	8	28	J 8
Pembrook Loop	9	30	E10
Penbroke Av	1	27	M 2
Pendale St	6	29	L 8
Pendleton Pl	1	27	N 1
Penn Av	6	29	L 7
Penn St	14	27	L 4
Penton St	9	30	E11
Percival Pl	9	30	E11
Percival St	9	30	E11
Perine Av	5	29	N 6
Perkiomen Av	12	28	H 8
Perry Av	14	26	K 4
Perry Ct	9	28	E 8
Pershing Cir	1	27	O 2
Pershing St	5	29	O 5
Perth Amboy Pl	7	30	B12
Peru St	14	29	L 5
Peter Av	6	29	L 8
Peter Ct	4	29	M 5
Peter St	14	26	J 3
Peterson St	9	30	E10
Petrus Av	12	31	H 9
Pfluger Pl	12	31	G10
Phelps Pl	1	27	N 1
Philip Av	12	31	G10
Phylis Ct	9	30	E 9
Piave Av	5	29	O 5
Pickersgill Av	5	29	O 5
Piedmont Av	5	29	O 5
Pierce St	4	27	N 4
Pierpont Pl	14	28	J 6
Pierre Pl	12	31	G11
Pike St	1	27	N 2
Pilcher St	14	28	K 5
Pine Pl	4	27	O 3
Pine St	1	27	N 2
Pine Ter	12	31	G10
Pinewood Av	6	28	K 7
Pitney Av	9	30	D10
Pitt Av	14	29	L 5
Pittsville Av	7	30	B12
Plank Rd	14	26	H 4
Platinum Av	14	28	H 6
Platt St	6	28	K 8
Plattsburg St	4	29	M 6
Plaza, The	4	29	M 6
Pleasant Ct	4	27	O 3
Pleasant Pl	4	27	O 3
Pleasant Plains Av	9	30	D11
Pleasant St	8	31	J 9
Pleasant Valley Av	4	27	N 3
Plymouth Rd	14	28	H 5
Poe Ct	7	30	C11
Poe St	7	30	C11
Poets Cir	12	28	F 8
Poi Pl	14	28	H 6
Poillon Av	12	31	G10
Poland Pl	14	27	L 4
Polk Walk	5	27	P 4
Pommer Av	4	27	N 2
Pompey Av	12	31	H 9
Pond St	9	28	E 8
Pond Way	3	26	H 2
Pontiac St	2	26	K 3
Poplar Av	9	28	E 8
Poplar La	9	30	D 9
Port Richmond Av	2	26	K 2
Portage Av	14	28	K 5
Portland Pl	1	27	M 2
Portsmouth Av	1	27	M 4
Post Av		26	K 2
1-875	10	26	K 2
876 out	2	26	K 2
Post La	3	26	H 1
Potter Av	14	27	L 3
Pouch Ter	5	29	O 5
Poultney St	6	29	M 7
Powell La	12	30	F 9
Powell St	12	30	F 9
Prague Ct	9	30	F11
Prall Av	12	30	F10
Pratt Ct	12	28	F 8
Prescott Av	6	29	L 6
President St	14	26	K 4
Presley St	8	31	J 9
Preston Av	12	31	H 9
Prices La	14	28	F 5
Primrose Pl	6	29	L 8
Prince La	9	30	E 9
Prince St	4	27	N 3
Princess Av	3	26	J 2
Princess La	3	26	J 2
Princess St	3	26	J 2
Princeton Av	6	29	L 7
Princeton La	12	28	F 8
Princewood Av	9	30	F10
Prol Pl	12	31	J10
Promenade Av	6	29	L 8
Property St	8	31	J 9
Prospect Av	1	27	M 2
Prospect Pl	6	29	L 7
Prospect St	4	27	O 2
Providence St	4	29	N 5
Public Pl *(intersection of Wright St and Canal St)	4	27	O 3

STREET NAME AND HOUSE NUMBERS	ZONE NO.	MAP NO.	MAP GRID
Pulaski Av	3	26	J 2
Pulaski St	3	26	G 2
Purcell St	10	27	L 3
Purdue Ct	14	28	H 6
Purdue St	14	28	H 6
Purdy Av	14	26	K 4
Purdy Pl	9	30	F 12
Purroy Pl	4	27	N 3
Putnam Pl	1	27	N 2
Putnam St	12	31	H 9
Putters Ct	1	27	M 3

Q

STREET NAME AND HOUSE NUMBERS	ZONE NO.	MAP NO.	MAP GRID
Queen St	14	26	K 4
Queensdale St	9	30	F 10
Quimby Av	14	26	G 4
Quincy Av	5	29	N 7
Quinlan Av	14	26	K 4
Quinn St	4	27	O 3
Quintard St	5	29	O 5

R

STREET NAME AND HOUSE NUMBERS	ZONE NO.	MAP NO.	MAP GRID
Racal Ct	14	28	H 6
Radcliff Rd	5	29	O 5
Radford St	14	28	H 5
Radigan Av	9	30	E 9
Rae Av	12	31	G10
Railroad Av		31	K 9
1-16	8	31	K 9
17-OUT	5	29	M 6
Raily Ct	12	28	F 8
Raily St	12	28	F 8
Rainbow Av	2	26	K 2
Raleigh Av	10	27	L 3
Ralph Av	12	31	G 9
Ralph Pl	4	27	N 4
Ramapo Av	9	30	E 9
Ramble Rd	8	31	J 9
Ramblewood Av	8	31	J 9
Ramona Av		30	E10
1-444	12	30	F 9
445-OUT	9	30	E10
Ramsey La	14	26	K 4
Ramsey Pl	4	27	N 3
Randall Av	1	27	M 2
Rankin St	12	31	H10
Ransom St	9	30	F10
Raritan Av		29	M 5
1-199	4	29	N 5
200-OUT	5	29	N 6
Raritan Bay	8	31	J 10
Rathbun Av		30	F10
1-752	12	31	G 9
753-OUT	9	30	F10
Ravenhurst Av	10	26	K 3
Ravenna St	12	31	H10
Rawson Pl	14	28	G 5
Ray St	12	31	H 9
Raymond Av	14	27	L 4
Raymond Pl	10	27	L 2
Reading Av	12	28	H 8
Rebecca Ct	9	30	C10
Rector St	10	27	L 2
Red Cedar La	9	30	D 9
Redgrave Av	6	28	K 8
Redmond St	4	29	M 5
Redwood Av	8	28	J 8
Redwood Loop	9	30	E 9
Regal Walk	3	26	H 3
Regan Av	10	27	M 2
Regent Cir	12	28	F 8
Regina La	12	28	G 8
Regis Dr	14	26	H 3
Reid Av	5	29	N 5
Reiss La	4	27	M 5
Remond Av	4	29	M 5
Remsen St	4	29	N 5
Rene Dr	6	28	K 8
Renee Pl	14	26	H 3
Renfrew Pl	3	26	J 2
Reno Av	6	29	L 7
Rensselaer Av		30	E10
1-796	12	30	F 9
797-OUT	9	30	F 9
Renwick Av	1	27	M 4
Reon Av	14	27	L 4
Retford Av	12	31	H 9
Retner St	5	29	O 5
Revere La	6	28	J 7
Revere St	1	27	M 3
Rewes Av	6	31	L 9
Reynaud St	5	29	O 6
Reynolds St	5	27	O 4
Rhett Av	8	31	J 9
Rhine Av	4	27	N 4
Rice Av	14	27	L 3
Richard Av	9	30	D11
Richard La	14	26	J 4
Riche Av	14	28	G 5
Richmond Av		28	H 7
1-800	2	26	K 2
801-907	3	26	J 3
908-3074	14	26	H 4
3075-OUT	12	28	H 8
Richmond Ct	3	26	H 1
Richmond Hill Rd		28	H 6
1-669	14	28	H 6
700-OUT	6	28	J 7
Richmond Pkwy	12	31	G 9
Richmond Pkwy	9	30	E 10
Richmond Pl	9	30	D11
Richmond Rd		28	K 7
1-1717	6	29	M 5
1718-OUT	6	29	K 7
Richmond Ter		26	J 2
1-1049	1	27	N 1
1050-1872	10	27	L 1
1873-2439	2	27	K 1
2440-OUT	3	26	J 2
Richmond Valley Rd	9	30	C11
Ridge Av	4	29	M 5
Ridge Ct	1	27	M 3
Ridge Loop	4	27	M 5
Ridgecrest Av	12	31	H 9
Ridgefield Av	4	27	N 4
Ridgeway Av	14	28	G 5
Ridgewood Av	12	28	H 8
Ridgewood Pl	1	27	M 2
Riedel Av	6	28	K 8
Riegelman St	2	26	K 3
Riga St	6	31	L 9
Rigby St	6	28	J 7
Riley Pl	2	26	K 2
Ring Rd	14	28	H 6
River Rd	14	26	F 4
Rivington Av	14	28	H 5
Roanoke St	14	28	K 5
Roberts Dr	6	29	M 8
Robin Ct	9	30	D 9
Robin Rd	5	29	O 5
Robinson Av	12	31	H 9
Rochelle Pl	12	31	H 9
Rochelle St	4	29	M 5
Rochelle St	6	31	L 9
Rockaway St	7	30	C12
Rockland Av		28	J 6
1-301	6	28	K 6
302-OUT	14	28	J 5
Rockne St	14	28	H 6
Rockport St	12	31	G10
Rockville Av	14	28	H 5
Rockwell Av	5	27	O 4
Rodeo La	4	27	O 4
Roderick Av	5	29	O 5
Rodman St	14	26	J 3
Roe St	10	27	L 2
Roff St	4	27	N 3
Rogers Pl	12	31	G10
Rokeby Pl	10	27	M 2
Rolling Hill Green	12	28	F 8
Roma Av	6	29	M 8
Roman Av	14	26	H 3
Roman Ct	7	30	C12
Rome Av	4	29	N 5
Romer Rd	4	29	M 5
Ronald Av	3	26	J 2
Roosevelt Av	14	26	K 4
Roosevelt Ct	14	26	K 4
Roosevelt St	4	27	N 4
Rose Av	6	29	L 7
Rose Ct	1	27	M 3
Rose La	12	30	G10
Rosebank Pl	5	27	O 4
Rosecliff Rd	3	26	H 3
Rosedale Av	12	30	F 9
Rosewood Pl	4	27	N 2
Ross Av	6	29	L 7
Ross La	12	31	H10
Rossville Av	9	28	E 8
Roswell Av	14	28	F 5
Row Pl	12	28	G 8
Rowan Av	5	29	N 7
Roxbury St	3	26	H 2
Royal Oak Rd	14	27	L 3
Rubenstein St	5	27	O 4
Rudyard St	6	29	M 7
Rugby Av	1	27	M 3
Ruggles St	12	31	G10
Rumba Pl	12	30	F 9
Rumson Rd	14	28	H 7
Rupert Av	14	28	K 5
Russek Dr	12	30	F 9
Russell St	8	31	J 10
Rustic Pl	8	31	J 9
Ruth Pl	5	29	N 5
Ruth St	14	26	K 3
Ryan Pl	12	31	H10
Rye Av	12	31	H 9

S

STREET NAME AND HOUSE NUMBERS	ZONE NO.	MAP NO.	MAP GRID
Sable Av	4	27	N 4
Sable Loop	6	28	J 8
Saccheri Ct	8	31	J 9
St. Adalbert Pl	3	26	J 2
St. Andrews Ct	6	28	J 7
St. Andrews Pl	7	30	C11
St. Andrews Rd	6	28	J 7
St. Anthony Pl	2	26	K 3
St. Austins Pl	10	27	M 2
St. George Dr	4	29	M 5
St. George Rd	6	28	J 7
St. George Rd		28	K 7
St. James Av	4	29	M 5
St. John Av	14	26	K 3
St. Johns Av	5	27	O 4
St. Josephs Av	2	26	K 2
St. Julian Pl	1	27	O 2
St. Lukes Av	9	28	E 8
St. Marks Pl	1	27	N 1
St. Mary Av	5	27	O 4
St. Patricks Pl	6	28	J 7
St. Pauls Av		27	O 2
1-198	1	27	O 2
199-OUT	4	27	O 2
St. Peter's Pl	1	27	N 1
St. Stephens Pl	6	29	L 7
Salamander Ct	9	30	D 9
Sally Ct	12	28	H 8
Sampson Av	8	28	J 8
Samuel Pl	3	26	H 2
Sand La	5	29	O 5
Sandalwood Dr	8	28	J 8
Sandborn St	12	31	H10
Sanders St	3	26	J 3
Sandgap St	12	31	H10
Sands St	4	27	O 2
Sandywood La	9	30	E 9
Sanford Pl	14	27	L 4
Sanford St	7	30	C11
Sanilac St	6	29	M 7
Satterlee St	7	30	B12
Saturn La	14	28	J 6
Saunders St	4	27	N 4
Savin Ct	4	29	N 5
Savoy St *(connects Hafstrom St with Montreal Av)	6	28	K 8
Sawyer Av	14	26	K 3
Saxon Av	14	28	H 5
Saybrook St	14	26	H 4
Scarboro Av	5	27	P 4
Scarsdale St	8	31	J 9
Scenic La	4	27	O 4
Scheffelin Av	6	28	K 6
Schley Av	8	28	J 8
Schmidts La	14	27	L 4
Schoharie St	1	27	M 4
School Rd	5	27	P 4
School St	8	31	J 9
Schubert St	5	27	O 4
Schuyler St	1	27	O 1
Scott Av	5	29	O 5
Scranton Av	12	31	H 9
Scranton St	4	29	N 5
Scribner Av	1	27	N 2
Scudder Av	9	30	E10
Sea Gate Rd	5	27	P 4
Seabreeze La	7	30	C12
Seacrest Av	12	31	J 10
Seacrest La	7	30	C12
Seafoam St	6	29	M 8
Seagate Ct	5	29	P 5
Seagate Rd	5	27	P 4
Seaside La	5	29	P 5
Seaver Av		29	M 6
1-80	6	29	M 6
81-OUT	5	29	M 6
Seaview Av		29	M 6
1-184	4	29	M 6
185-OUT	5	29	N 6
Seeley La	8	31	J 9
Seguine Av	9	30	F 11
Seguine Pl	12	31	H 9
Seidman Av	12	31	H10
Seldin Av	14	26	H 3
Selkirk St	9	28	E 8
Selvin Loop	3	26	H 3
Seneca Av	1	27	M 4
Seneca Loop	14	26	J 4
Seneca St	10	27	L 2
Serrell Av	12	31	H 9
Seth Ct	1	27	N 3
Seth Loop	5	27	P 4
Seven Gables Rd	4	27	N 4
Seward Pl	14	26	K 4
Seymour Av	2	26	K 2
Shadow La	6	28	K 7
Shadyside Av	9	30	E11
Shafter Av	8	28	J 8
Shale St	14	28	J 6
Sharon Av	1	27	M 2
Sharon La	9	30	E10
Sharpe Av	2	26	K 2
Sharreti Pl	2	26	K 2
Sharrott Av	9	30	E11
Sharrotts La	9	30	E 9
Sharrotts Rd	9	30	C 9
Shaughnessy La	5	27	O 4
Shaw Pl	2	26	K 3
Shawnee St	1	27	M 3
Sheffield St	10	27	L 2
Sheldon Av		30	F 9
1-780	12	31	G 9
781-OUT	9	30	F 9
Shelley Av	14	28	G 5
Shelterview Dr	4	27	N 3
Shenandoah Av	14	28	G 5
Shepard Av	14	28	J 5
Sheraden Av	14	26	K 4
Sheridan Av		27	N 4
1-46	4	27	N 4
47-OUT	5	29	N 5
Sheridan Ct	6	28	K 8
Sheridan Pl	12	31	G10
Sherman Av	1	27	N 1
Sherrill Av	12	28	G 8
Sherwood Av	9	30	E11
Sherwood Pl	8	31	J 9
Shiel Av	9	30	E 9
Shield Pl	1	27	M 4
Shift Pl	12	30	F 9
Shiloh St	14	28	H 5
Shirley Av	12	31	H10
Shirra Av	14	28	J 5
Shore Acres Rd	5	27	P 4
Shore Av	12	31	G11
Shore Rd	7	30	B12
Short Pl	12	31	G11
Shotwell Av	12	28	G 8
Sideview Av	14	26	H 4
Signal Hill Rd	1	27	N 3
Signs Rd	14	26	H 4
Silver Beach Dr	4	27	M 4
Silver Ct	1	27	M 3
Silver Lake Rd	1	27	M 2
Simmons La	14	28	G 5
Simmons Loop	14	28	G 5
Simonson Av	3	26	J 2
Simonson Pl	2	26	K 2
Simpson St	5	29	N 6
Sinclair Av		30	F 9
1-772	12	31	G 9
773-OUT	9	30	F 9
Singleton St	9	30	F11
Sioux St	5	29	N 7
Sky La	4	27	O 4
Skyline Dr	4	27	O 4
Slaight St	2	26	K 2
Slater Blvd	5	29	N 6
Slayton Av	14	28	J 5
Sleepy Hollow Rd	14	28	H 5
Sleight Av	7	30	C12
Sloane Av	6	28	K 6
Slosson Av	14	27	L 3
Slosson Ter	1	27	O 2
Smith Av	14	27	L 3
Smith Ct	14	26	K 4
Smith Pl	2	26	K 3
Smith St	5	27	O 4
Smith Ter	4	27	O 2
Smyrna Av	12	31	G 9
Sneden Av	12	31	G 9
Snug Harbor Rd	10	27	M 1
Sobel Ct	4	27	N 4
Sommer Av	14	26	H 4
Sommers La	14	27	L 4
Sophia La	4	29	M 5
Soren St	14	28	K 5
South Av		26	H 1
1-799	3	26	H 2
800-OUT	14	26	H 3
South Beach Av	5	29	O 5
South Bridge St	9	30	C10
South Ct *(off Cleveland Al)	5	29	O 5
South Drum St	9	30	E10
South Gannon Av	14	26	J 4
South Goff Av	9	30	E11
South Greenleaf Av	14	27	L 3
South Hawthorne Av	14	26	J 4
South Mann Av	14	26	K 4
South Railroad Av		28	K 8
1-700	5	29	N 5
701-OUT	6	29	L 7
South Railroad St	12	31	G10
South Saint Austin's Pl	10	27	M 2
South Service Rd	9	30	D11
South St	10	27	L 2
South Woodbine Av	14	26	J 4
Spar Av	9	30	E 9
Spark Pl	14	26	G 4
Sparkill Av	4	29	N 5
Spartan Av	3	26	H 2
Speedwell Av	14	26	H 4
Spencer St	14	26	F 4
Sperry Pl	12	30	F 9
Sprague Av	7	30	C11
Spratt Av	6	28	K 8
Spring St	4	29	M 5
Springfield Av	14	26	K 3
Springhill Av	1	27	M 2
Spruce La	9	30	D 9
Spruce St	6	28	K 7
Stack Dr	12	30	F 9
Stadalbert Pl	3	26	J 2
Stafford Av		30	E 9
1-718	12	31	G 9
719-OUT	9	30	E 9
Stage La	4	27	O 4
Stanley Av	1	27	M 2
Stanley Cir	8	31	H 9
Stanwich St	4	29	N 5
Star Ct	12	31	H 9
Starbuck St	4	27	N 4
Stark Ct	1	27	N 2
Starlight Rd	1	27	N 4
Starr Av	10	27	M 3
State Hwy 440	9	30	D10
	14	28	F 6
	14	26	G 4
State St	10	27	L 2
Staten Island Blvd		27	M 4
1-99	1	27	M 4
100-OUT	14	27	N 4
Staten Island Expwy		26	G 2
Staten Island Expwy		27	M 4
Station Av	9	30	D11
Stebbins Av	10	27	M 1
Stecher St	12	31	G10
Steele Av	6	29	L 7
Steers St	14	28	K 5
Steinway Av	14	28	H 5
Stephen Loop	14	28	H 5
Stepney St	14	28	J 6
Sterling Av	6	29	L 7
Stern Ct	8	31	J 9
Steuben St		27	N 4
1-300	4	27	N 4
301-OUT	5	29	O 5
Stevenson Pl	9	30	E11
Stewart Av	14	26	J 3
Stieg Av	8	28	J 8
Stobe Av	6	29	M 6
Stone La	14	28	H 6
Stone St	4	27	N 3
Stonecrest Ct	8	31	J 9
Stonegate Dr	4	29	N 5
Stoneham St	6	31	L 8
Storer Av	9	30	C 9
Stratford Av	1	27	N 3
Stratford Ct	14	28	H 6
Strauss St	5	27	O 4
Strawberry La	12	31	H11
Stroud Av	12	28	H 8
Studio La	4	27	O 4
Sturges St	14	27	L 3
Stuyvesant Av	12	31	H 9
Stuyvesant Pl	1	27	O 1
Suffolk Av	14	26	K 4
Summer St	5	27	P 4
Summerfield Pl	3	26	H 2
Summit Av	6	29	L 7
Summit Pl	12	31	G10
Summit Rd	7	30	B12
Summit St	7	30	C12
Sumner Av	14	26	J 3
Sumner Pl	1	27	N 2
Sunfield Av	12	28	G 8
Sunnyside Ter	1	27	M 4
Sunrise La *(off Woods of Arden bet Shirley Av and Osage La)	12	31	H10
Sunrise Ter	4	27	N 2
Sunset Av	14	26	K 4
Sunset Hill Dr	1	27	M 3
Sunset La	7	30	C12
Surf Av	7	30	C12
Surf Ct	7	30	D12
Surfside Plz	7	30	C12
Susan Ct	4	27	O 3
Susanna La	12	28	G 8
Sussex Green	12	30	F 9
Sutton Pl	12	30	F 9
Swaim Av	12	31	G11
Swan St	1	27	O 2
Sweetbrook Rd	12	28	H 8
Sweetwater Av	8	31	J 10
Swinnerton St	7	30	B12
Sycamore St		31	H10
1-167	8	31	J 9
168-OUT	12	31	H10
Sydney Pl	6	29	L 7
Sylva La	5	27	P 4
Sylvan Ct	7	30	C12
Sylvan Pl	3	26	H 2
Sylvaton Ter	5	27	O 3
Sylvia St	12	31	H 9

T

STREET NAME AND HOUSE NUMBERS	ZONE NO.	MAP NO.	MAP GRID
Tabb Pl	2	26	K 2
Tacoma St	4	29	N 5
Taft Av	1	27	N 1
Taft Ct	14	26	K 4
Talbot Pl	4	27	O 3
Tallman St	12	31	H10
Tanglewood Dr	8	28	J 7
Tappen Ct	4	27	O 3
Targee St	4	27	N 3
Tarlee Pl	8	31	J 9
Tarlton St	6	31	L 9
Tarring St	6	29	L 8
Tarrytown Av	6	29	L 8
Tarter Pl	4	27	O 2
Tate St	2	26	J 2
Tatro St	6	28	K 8
Taunton St	6	28	K 8
Taylor Ct	10	27	L 2
Taylor St	10	27	L 2
Teakwood Ct	8	28	J 8
Teleport Dr	11	26	G 4
Temple Ct	14	28	G 5
Tenafly Pl	12	31	G10
Tennyson Dr		31	J 10
1-344	8	31	J 10
345-OUT	12	31	J 10
Teresa Ct	2	27	K 2
Teri Ct	14	28	J 6
Terrace Av	9	30	E10
Terrace Ct	6	28	K 6
Thames Av	1	27	M 3
Thayer Pl	6	28	K 8
Theatre La	4	27	O 4
Thelma Ct	4	27	O 3
Thelma Dr	14	26	H 3
Theresa Pl	1	27	N 3
Thollen St	6	28	K 8
Thomas Pl	6	29	L 8
Thomas St	6	28	K 7
Thompson Pl	5	27	O 4
Thompson St	4	27	O 3
Thornycroft Av	12	31	H 9
Thurston St	14	26	J 4
Tiber Pl	1	27	M 4
Tiger Ct	14	26	J 3
Tilden St	1	27	N 2
Tillman St	14	27	L 4
Tilson Pl	4	27	O 4
Timber Ridge Dr	6	28	J 8
Timothy Ct	14	26	H 4
Tioga St	1	27	M 4
Titus Av	6	29	M 8
Toddy Av	14	28	H 5
Todt Hill Ct	4	29	L 6

STREET NAME AND HOUSE NUMBERS	ZONE NO.	MAP NO.	MAP GRID
Todt Hill Rd		27	L 4
1-399	14	27	L 4
400-OUT	4	29	L 5
Token St	12	28	G 8
Tom Ct	10	27	M 2
Tompkins Av		27	O 3
1-330	4	27	O 3
331-OUT	5	27	O 4
Tompkins Cir	1	27	O 2
Tompkins Ct	10	27	L 1
Tompkins Pl	4	27	O 3
Tompkins St	4	27	O 3
Tone La	5	27	O 4
Tonking Rd	6	28	K 6
Topping St	6	29	M 8
Toscany Ct	5	29	O 6
Tottenville Pl	7	30	B12
Towers La	14	28	G 5
Townley Av	14	27	L 4
Townsend Av	4	27	O 3
Trantor Pl	2	26	J 2
Travis Av	14	26	G 4
Travis Av		28	H 5
Treadwell Av	2	26	K 2
Treetz Pl	14	27	K 4
Tremont Av	14	26	J 3
Trent St	8	31	K 9
Trenton Ct	9	30	F11
Tricia Way	7	30	C12
Trinity Pl	10	27	L 2
Trossach Rd	4	27	N 3
Trout Pl	12	31	G11
Troy St	8	28	J 8
Truman St	7	30	C11
Trumbull Pl	1	27	N 2
Tryon Av	12	28	G 8
Tuckahoe Av	12	31	G10
Tudor St	8	28	J 8
Tulip Cir	12	30	F 9
Turf Ct	14	28	J 6
Turf Rd	14	28	J 6
Turner St	9	30	D 9
Tuttle St	14	26	J 3
Twin Oak Dr	4	27	M 4
Twombley Av	6	28	K 8
Tyler St	10	27	L 3
Tynan St	12	28	G 8
Tyndale St	12	31	H10
Tyron Av	12	31	G 9
Tyrrell St	7	30	B11
Tysen Ct *(bet Richmond Hill & Arthur Kill Rds, connects Center St to Clarke Av)	6	28	J 7
Tysen St	1	27	M 1
Tysens La	6	29	L 7

U

STREET NAME AND HOUSE NUMBERS	ZONE NO.	MAP NO.	MAP GRID
Uncas Av	9	30	E10
Union Av	3	26	J 2
Union Ct	3	26	J 2
Union Pl	4	27	O 3
University Pl	1	27	M 2
Upton St	4	29	N 5
Urbana St	4	29	N 5
Utah St	7	30	B11
Utica St	9	30	E11
Utter Av	14	27	L 3
Uxbridge St	14	26	K 4

V

STREET NAME AND HOUSE NUMBERS	ZONE NO.	MAP NO.	MAP GRID
Vail Av	9	30	E11
Valdemar Av	9	30	F10
Valencia Av	1	27	M 2
Valley Green Rd	12	30	F 9
Valleyview Pl	14	27	L 4
Van Allen Av	12	28	G 8
Van Brunt St	12	31	H 9
Van Buren St	1	27	M 1
Van Cortlandt Av	1	27	M 4
Van Duzer St		27	N 3
1-229	1	27	O 2
230-OUT	4	27	N 3
Van Name Av	3	26	J 2
Van Pelt Av	3	26	J 2
Van Riper St	2	26	J 2
Van St	10	27	L 1
Van Tuyl St	1	27	N 2
Van Wyck Av	9	30	F11
Vanderbilt Av	4	27	N 3
Vassar St	14	28	H 6
Vaughan St	5	27	O 4
Vedder Av		26	J 3
1-50	14	26	J 3
51-OUT	2	26	J 3
Veith Pl	9	31	G11
Veltman Av	2	26	K 3
Venice Av	4	29	N 5
Venus La	14	28	J 6
Venus Pl	12	30	F 9
Vera St	5	29	M 6
Vermont Av	5	27	O 4
Vermont Ct	14	28	K 5
Vernon Av	9	30	F10
Vespa Av	12	30	F 9
Veterans Rd E	9	30	D10
Veterans Rd W	9	30	D 9
Victoria Rd	12	30	F 9
Victory Blvd		28	F 6
1-1500	1	27	N 2
1501-OUT	14	27	L 4
Vienna Ct	5	27	O 4
Villa Av	2	26	J 2
Villa Nova St	14	28	H 6
Village La	12	31	H 9
Vincent Av	6	28	K 7
Vine St	1	27	N 1
Vineland Av	12	31	G 9
Viola Pl	14	26	J 3
Violet St	9	30	E11
Virginia Av	5	27	O 4
Virginia Pl	14	26	K 3
Vista Av	4	29	N 5
Vista Pl	5	29	O 5
Vivian St	5	29	O 6
Vogel Av	9	30	E10
Vogel La	14	26	K 4
Vogel Loop	14	26	K 4
Vogel Pl	9	30	E10
Von Braun	12	28	G 8
Vreeland St	2	26	K 2
Vulcan St	5	29	O 6

W

STREET NAME AND HOUSE NUMBERS	ZONE NO.	MAP NO.	MAP GRID
Waddell Av	9	30	D10
Wade St	14	26	K 3
Wadsworth Av	5	27	P 4
Wadsworth Rd	5	27	P 4
Wadsworth Ter	5	27	O 4
Wagner College Rd *(near Wagner College)	1	27	N 4
Wagner College St *(near Wagner College)	1	27	N 4
Wagner St	5	27	O 4
Wahler Pl	6	29	N 7
Waimer Pl	12	31	H 9
Wainwright Av	12	28	H 8
Wakefield Av	14	28	G 5
Wakefield Rd	12	31	J 10
Walbrooke Av	1	27	M 2
Walch Pl	9	30	F11
Walcott Av	14	28	K 5
Walden Av	6	29	L 6
Waldo Pl	14	27	L 4
Waldron Av	1	27	M 3
Wales Pl	10	27	M 1
Walker Ct	12	28	G 8
Walker Dr	3	26	J 2
Walker Pl	12	30	F 9
Walker St		26	J 2
1-199	2	26	K 2
150-OUT	3	26	J 2
Wall St	1	27	O 1
Wallace Av	5	29	O 5
Walloon St	3	26	J 2
Walnut Av	8	31	J 10
Walnut Pl	6	29	L 7
Walnut St	10	27	M 1
Walters Av	1	27	L 4
Wandel Av	4	27	N 4
Ward Av	4	27	N 2
Wards Point Av	7	30	B12
Wardwell Av	14	26	K 3
Waring Av	12	28	G 8
Warren St	4	27	N 3
Warwick Av	14	26	K 4
Washburn Av	3	26	H 2
Washington Av	14	28	K 5
Washington Pl	2	26	K 2
Watchogue Rd	14	26	J 3
Water St	4	27	O 3
Waterbury Av	9	30	E11
Waterford Ct	5	29	P 5
Waters Av		26	J 3
1-300	14	26	K 3
301-OUT	2	26	J 3
Waterside Pkwy	8	31	K 9
Waterside St	6	29	M 8
Waterview Loop	1	27	O 2
Watkins Av	12	28	G 8
Watson Av	14	28	G 5
Wave St	4	27	O 2
Wavecrest St	6	29	M 8
Waverly Pl	4	27	N 3
Wayne Ct *(in Edwin Markham Housing)	10	27	L 1
Wayne Pl *(in Edwin Markham Housing)	10	27	L 1
Wayne St	10	27	L 2
Wayne Ter *(in Edwin Markham Housing)	10	27	L 1
Weaver St	12	31	H10
Webster Av	1	27	N 2
Weed Av	6	29	M 8
Weiner St	9	30	D11
Weir La	7	30	C11
Wellbrook Av	14	26	K 4
Welles Ct	1	27	M 2
Wellington Ct	14	28	J 6
Wellington Green	12	30	F 9
Wemple St	3	26	H 2
Wendy Dr	12	30	G10
Wenlock St	3	26	J 2
Wentworth Av	5	29	O 6
Weser Av	4	27	N 4
West Buchanan St	1	27	N 1
West Castor Pl	9	30	F 9
West Caswell Av	14	26	J 3
West Cederview Av	6	28	J 7
West Ct *(off Cleveland Al)	5	29	O 5
West Fingerboard Rd		29	N 5
500-900	5	29	O 5
901-957 (odd)	4	29	N 5
902-958 (even)	5	29	O 5
959-OUT	4	29	N 5
West Raleigh Av	10	27	L 3
West Service Rd	14	28	F 8
West Shore Expwy		26	G 4
West Shore Expwy		30	D10
West St	10	27	L 2
West Ter	12	30	F10
Westbrook Av	3	26	J 2
Westbury Av	1	27	M 2
Westcott Blvd	14	26	K 3
Westentry Rd	4	29	M 6
Western Av	3	26	G 1
Westervelt Av	1	27	N 1
Westfield Av	9	28	E 8
Westminster Ct	4	29	M 5
Westport La	14	28	H 6
Westport St	14	28	H 6
Westwood Av	14	26	J 4
Wetmore Rd	1	27	N 4
Whalley Av	12	31	H 9
Wheeler Av	14	26	K 4
Wheeling Av	9	30	E10
Whirl La	9	30	E 9
Whitaker Pl	4	29	N 5
White Ct	12	31	H 9
White Oak La	9	30	D 9
White Pl	10	27	L 2
White Plains Av	5	27	O 4
White St	5	27	P 4
Whitehall St	6	29	L 8
Whitewood Av	10	27	M 3
Whitlock Av	4	29	L 5
Whitman Av	8	31	J 9
Whitney Av	5	29	N 5
Whitwell Pl	4	29	L 5
Wiederer Pl *(off Price St)	4	27	N 3
Wieland Av	9	30	E 9
Wilbur Pl	14	26	K 4
Wilbur St	9	30	F11
Wilcox St	3	26	J 3
Wild Av	14	28	F 5
Wilder Av	6	28	K 7
Wildwood La	7	30	C12
Wiley Pl	6	29	L 7
Willard Av	14	26	K 3
Willard Pl	14	26	K 3
William Av	8	31	J 10
William St	4	27	O 2
Willis Av	1	27	N 2
Willow Av	5	27	O 3
Willow Brook Ct	2	26	J 3
Willow Brook Pkwy	2	28	K 6
Willow Brook Rd		26	J 3
1-309	2	26	J 3
310-OUT	14	26	J 4
Willow La	6	31	J 8
Willow Pond Rd	4	29	M 5
Willow Rd E	14	26	J 3
1-160	3	26	J 2
161-OUT	14	26	J 3
Willow Rd W		26	J 3
Willow Wood La	8	28	J 8
Wills Pl	5	29	O 6
Wilson Av		31	H 9
1-299	8	31	H 9
300-OUT	12	31	H 9
Wilson St	4	29	N 5
Wilson Ter	4	27	N 4
Wilsonview Pl	4	27	N 4
Wiman Av	8	31	J 9
Wiman Pl	5	27	P 4
Winans St	9	30	D11
Winant Av	9	28	E 8
Winant La	9	30	C 9
Winant Pl	9	30	C 9
Winant St	3	26	J 2
Winchester Av	12	31	H 9
Windemere Av	6	28	K 8
Windermere Rd	5	29	O 5
Windham Loop	14	28	H 6
Winding Woods Loop	7	30	C12
Windom Av	5	29	P 5
Windsor Ct	14	27	L 4
Windsor Rd	14	27	L 4
Windy Hollow Way	4	29	M 6
Winfield Av	5	29	N 5
Winfield St	5	29	O 6
Wingham St	5	27	O 4
Winham Av	6	29	M 8
Winslow	12	31	H10
Winston St	12	28	G 8
Winter Av	1	27	N 2
Winthrop Pl	14	27	L 4
Wirt Av	9	30	E 9
Wirt La	9	30	E 9
Witteman Pl	1	27	M 4
Woehrle Av	12	28	G 8
Wolcott Av	12	31	G 9
Wolcott St	14	28	K 5
Wolkoff La	3	26	H 3
Wolverine St	6	28	K 7
Wood Av	7	30	C11
Wood Ct	9	28	E 8
Woodbine Av	14	26	J 3
Woodbridge Pl	14	26	K 3
Woodcliff Av	3	26	H 2
Woodcrest Rd	3	26	H 3
Woodcutters La	6	28	K 8
Wooddale Av		29	L 5
1-399	4	29	M 5
400-OUT	1	29	L 5
Woodhaven Av	4	29	M 5
Woodhull Av	12	30	F10
Woodland Av	8	28	J 8
Woodlawn Av	5	29	N 5
Woodrow Rd		30	E 9
1-1120	12	30	F 9
1121-OUT	9	30	E 9
Woodruff La	10	27	L 2
Woods Of Arden Rd	12	31	H10
Woodside Av		27	N 3
All except 2	4	27	N 3
2 only	1	27	N 3
Woodstock Av	1	27	N 2
Woodvale Av	9	30	E11
Woodvale Loop	9	30	E11
Woodward Av	14	26	J 4
Woolley Av	14	26	K 4
Wrenn St	9	30	F10
Wright Av	3	26	J 2
Wright St	4	27	O 3
Wygant Pl	2	26	K 2
Wyona Av	14	26	J 4

X

STREET NAME AND HOUSE NUMBERS	ZONE NO.	MAP NO.	MAP GRID
Xenia St	5	29	N 6

Y

STREET NAME AND HOUSE NUMBERS	ZONE NO.	MAP NO.	MAP GRID
Yafa Ct	14	26	J 3
Yale St	3	26	H 3
Yeomalt Av	12	31	G11
Yeshiva La	9	30	E10
Yetman Av	7	30	C11
Yona Av	14	26	J 4
York Av	1	27	N 1
York Ter	1	27	N 1
Young St	4	27	N 3
Yucca Dr	12	30	F 9
Yukon Av	14	28	H 7

Z

STREET NAME AND HOUSE NUMBERS	ZONE NO.	MAP NO.	MAP GRID
Zachary Ct	10	26	K 3
Zebra Pl	9	28	E 8
Zeck Ct	14	26	J 3
Zeni Pl	6	29	M 7
Zephyr Av	12	31	G11
Zoe St	5	29	M 6
Zwicky Av	6	29	M 7

NUMBERED STREETS

STREET NAME AND HOUSE NUMBERS	ZONE NO.	MAP NO.	MAP GRID
1st Av	14	26	J 4
1st Ct	12	31	H11
1st St (New Dorp)	6	29	L 7
1st St (Oakwood)	6	29	L 8
2nd Av	14	28	J 5
2nd Ct	12	31	H11
2nd St (New Dorp)	6	29	L 7
2nd St (Oakwood)	6	29	L 8
3rd Av	14	26	J 4
3rd Ct	12	31	H11
3rd St (New Dorp)	6	29	L 7
4th Av	14	26	K 4
4th Ct	12	31	H11
4th St (New Dorp)	6	29	L 7
7th St (New Dorp)	6	29	L 7
8th St (New Dorp)	6	29	L 7
9th St (New Dorp)	6	29	L 7
10th St (New Dorp)	6	29	L 8

The information shown in this atlas has been obtained from various authoritative sources. Nevertheless, a work of this scope may contain some inaccuracies. Any errors and omissions called to our attention will be greatly appreciated.